*Charles Sprague Sargent
and the Arnold Arboretum*

Charles Sprague Sargent in 1919

Charcoal drawing by John Singer Sargent

Charles Sprague Sargent
and the Arnold Arboretum

S. B. Sutton

Harvard University Press
Cambridge, Massachusetts
1970

Preface

About four years ago, when I learned that Professor Richard A. Howard, Director of the Arnold Arboretum, was looking for someone to investigate the early history of the Arboretum in anticipation of its one-hundredth anniversary, I offered myself as a candidate for the task. Since then, I have spent the greater part of my working hours preparing this book, in the same building where Charles Sargent once officiated, within the Arboretum.

To speak of the Arboretum in its first half century is to speak of Sargent. The Arboretum was his creation—a product of his talent as an administrator, horticulturist, and botanist. He devoted himself with passionate intensity to institution-building and to his study of trees. That he undertook this work at some expense to his personal life is revealed in the contents of the letters and stories which survive him. His correspondence is singularly lacking in emotional content; he is remembered by all—family and associates—as an introverted, stern, scholarly gentleman.

The second important figure during the early years of the Arboretum was Ernest H. Wilson, whose colorful adventures as a plant hunter in the Far East brought public acclaim to the institution.

The efforts of these men took them far beyond the boundaries of the Arboretum: Sargent tramped the North American forests; Wilson explored remote corners of China.

Though their world of great estates and horticultural pomp has nearly vanished in an urban-oriented society, their work speaks urgently as the gracious, green spaces of forests and gardens diminish.

More people have aided me in this project than I can hope to thank properly. The Arnold Arboretum staff patiently answered my relentless questions, and reminisced for me, though none of them, of course, knew Sargent or Wilson. Bernice Schubert, Carroll Wood, Professor Howard, and Gordon DeWolf commented upon the manuscript; Dr. DeWolf ran down countless bothersome details. The former Librarian of the Harvard University Herbaria, Mrs. Lazella Schwarten, and her successor, Victor Marx, traced letters and books for me. I must also thank Mrs. Mildred Pelkus, Mrs. Thomas Walsh, and Miss Sonia Adrouny for helping me through the mechanics of manuscript preparation.

Sargent's correspondence is scattered widely. I have tried to obtain copies of letters for the Arboretum library or, failing that, to read the originals and make notes. Individuals throughout the country and in Europe have been helpful, and to list them would occupy more than a page. However, I especially appreciate the assistance of Charlotte W. Stove at the American Museum of Natural History; Mrs. Ernest Jesse Palmer; Arthur O'Keefe, formerly of the Department of Parks and Recreation of the City of Boston; the late Henry F. duPont, and Augustin H. Parker, former Chairman of the Committee to Visit the Arnold Arboretum. My single disappointment in obtaining original material came when, despite the efforts of the University Librarian at the University of California, Berkeley, I was unable to see the letters which Sargent wrote to the late John Muir. I mention this incident because I know I am only one among many whose research has been hindered by the unavailability of the Muir collection.

Sargent's daughter-in-law, Mrs. Dagmar Sargent, spoke with me and was kind enough to read the manuscript. I also wish to acknowledge the cooperation of the Sargent family in permitting me to quote freely from Sargent correspon-

Preface

vi

dence, and particularly of Mrs. Russell W. Davenport and Winthrop Sargent in providing me with anecdotes and letters. I am similarly thankful to Mrs. Muriel Wilson Slate for permission to quote from the letters of her late father, Ernest Wilson; and to her husband, Dr. George Slate, for sharing his memories. The Royal Botanic Gardens, Kew, has graciously given permission to quote unpublished letters of Sir Joseph Hooker and Sir William Thiselton-Dyer. Mrs. K. A. Bunker, the late Mrs. Alfred Rehder, John Wister, Mrs. William Ellery, Mrs. Van Wyck Brooks, and Mrs. Roger Ernst all supplied me with helpful information.

Like others working in the field of botanical history, I have found the several works of Andrew Denny Rodgers III indispensable to my study. I am indebted to Miss Sheila Pim of Ireland, for permission to quote from her biography of Augustine Henry, and to Mrs. Elswyth Thane Beebe for permission to quote from Sargent letters which she published in *Mount Vernon: The Legacy*. I remember with pleasure the kindly, unhurried interview granted to me by Walter Muir Whitehill, Director of the Boston Athenaeum; his associate, David McKibbin, who is working on a biography of John Singer Sargent, generously shared his familiarity with Sargentiana. I am grateful to Hunter Dupree and to Joseph Ewan both of whom took time to read the manuscript and make detailed suggestions for its improvement. Professor Ewan, aware of my project from the beginning, graciously located several letters and bits of information for me.

S.B.S.

Jamaica Plain
February 1969

Preface

vii

Contents

Illustrations

Unless otherwise indicated, illustrations are reproduced by courtesy of the Arnold Arboretum.

Frontispiece   Charles Sprague Sargent in 1919; charcoal drawing by John Singer Sargent
   Courtesy of the Trustees of the Sargent-Murray-Gilman-Hough-House Association

Foreword

Richard A. Howard, Director, Arnold Arboretum

When the Arnold Arboretum takes note in 1972 of the centennial of its establishment, it will have had but four directors: Charles Sprague Sargent, Elmer Drew Merrill, Karl Sax, and Richard Alden Howard. Perhaps my two predecessors did, as I do, look back at the former director, consider his problems and his methods of their solution, admire his accomplishments, and perhaps even express regret at actions he took or didn't take.

Charles Sargent did not have this opportunity. He was appointed as the first director to create the Arnold Arboretum in 1873, and he served in that role until his death at the age of eighty-six in 1927. His was a unique opportunity in the history of botanical gardens, to create one in association with a great university and to guide its development for a period of fifty-five years.

In terms of modern administration Sargent was fortunate. He had authority and isolation, qualified friends for counsel, a choice of talented labor, the desire and opportunity to travel, a staff whose time and talents were undisturbed by radio or television or the speed of modern communication, private personal funds and friends who could help financially, no restrictions of precedent or programs that had to be maintained, and only the restrictions of space and climate for the types of plants he wanted to grow. Perhaps he was fortunate, too, in that no hurricane or major storm destructive to tree growth hit the Arboretum during his directorship.

When the trustees of the estate of James Arnold asked the President of Harvard to assume responsibility for one clause of his will that supported a horticultural activity, Harvard had a botanical garden in Cambridge. It was founded in 1805 and followed a traditional pattern of symmetrical arrangement of systematic beds, herbaceous borders, a central pond, and display greenhouses. George Emerson, one of Arnold's trustees, knew this garden and its emphasis on herbaceous plants and wanted for the college a comparable collection of trees. Sargent could, therefore, turn his attention only to woody plants, which required less labor and financial support. In addition, propagation greenhouses were not as costly as display houses.

Sargent had a broad directive. He was to grow "all the trees, shrubs and herbaceous plants, either indigenous or exotic, which can be raised in the open air at the said West Roxbury," and he was to "teach the knowledge of trees within the University," The location of the fledgling arboretum was to be the Bussey farm owned by Harvard in what is now Jamaica Plain. Sargent began with an inventory of the native and cultivated plants persisting there and sought to introduce others from the United States and abroad. Sargent was not a botanist, and it was Asa Gray who pointed out the pertinent similarities of plant species and of climate in eastern Asia and estern North America. Eastern Asia was to receive Sargent's primary attention. Many plants from Japan and China had already reached the New World directly or as introductions from the gardens of Europe. Although there were no other American arboreta for him to consider, Sargent knew the Asian plants in the private estate of H. H. Hunnewell in Wellesley and William S. Clark's introductions to Amherst. He acquired propagation material from these collections, and he established an exchange of material with Kew and other gardens of Europe through

Foreword

personal visits and by correspondence. Eventually Sargent was to visit Asia himself. Still later he employed E. H. Wilson, whose collections in Asia enhanced the reputation of the Arnold Arboretum as a center of plant introduction and distribution.

Sargent displayed early an awareness of the value of dried botanical specimens as verification that plants had been seen in specific geographic areas at specific times. These were documentation, more reliable than the written word and more valuable than the drawing or photograph. Moreover, they could be studied at leisure, because they would last indefinitely. Sargent desired that there be in the resource collection of the Arnold Arboretum herbarium specimens of both native and cultivated plants. He was as interested in the plants of the tropics as in those of temperate regions as objects of study for the benefit of all mankind.

A herbarium and a living collection could be studied best with a knowledge of what had been published. Sargent began a collection of books for the Arnold Arboretum and housed it in his own home. When little institution money was available, he purchased them with his own funds. Dollar values are relative to the times, but books he purchased for less than a hundred dollars would today sell for thousands. His choice was cosmopolitan within the fields of science pertinent to botany and horticulture.

The original Arnold bequest was $103,800, of which only the income could be used. Even then a portion was to be capitalized annually. Thus Sargent received about $3,000 a year to pay salaries and wages, build greenhouses and an administration building, create roads, and supply protection for the collections. He dipped into his own funds liberally and secured gifts from his personal friends. Never in his administration did the Arboretum operate within the income from the endowment. Annual gifts to make up the deficit varied from $2,000 to $45,000 and averaged $26,500 over a period of twenty years, a sum still considered as generous support today. He arranged for the city of Boston to take over the land and to construct and maintain the roads and paths.

Foreword

The families of Hunnewell and Ames were continually generous and gave regular support to Sargent and his Arboretum. Eighteen separate major bequests from personal friends of Sargent came to the Arboretum during his administration to further the work he was doing by increasing the endowment.

The Arnold Arboretum has never been a large organization, compared to most scientific establishments. During Sargent's administration the staff was pathetically small, yet these individuals earned a wide and lasting reputation for their contribution to knowledge. Sargent had on his staff an excellent plant propagator and a working superintendent. Early employees shared responsibilities for the library and herbarium or served as illustrators and curators. Part-time workers mounted herbarium specimens received from the collectors, who were subsidized. Yet with only the nucleus of a staff the living collections were developed and a herbarium and library accumulated.

Sargent wrote a report of the first fifty years of the Arnold Arboretum in 1922, five years before his death. He reported that between five and six thousand species and varieties of trees and shrubs belonging to 87 families and 325 genera were grown at the Arnold Arboretum. He reported the complete failure of any plants from the southern hemisphere to prove hardy in the Arnold Arboretum, but he listed 1,932 taxa he believed had first been introduced into cultivation in the United States under the auspices of the Arnold Arboretum. A total of 778 were initial introductions into cultivation anywhere. Sargent told of the accomplishments during these years which developed the living collections, the herbarium, the library, several publications, a collection of photographs, a program of education, an increase in the endowment, a program of travel and exploration. He then listed these five objectives for the future:

1. The collection of more information about the trees in many parts of the world. He cited the need for specimens and introductions from Kamtschatka, China,

Foreword

xiv

Indochina (Tonkin, Annam, and Siam), the Altai Mountains of Siberia and the regions south of that range. He said, "The work which it [the Arboretum] has accomplished in its first fifty years in North America and the Japanese Empire should be extended over the rest of the world"; and he commented, "The exploration of the tropical forests of the world will require perhaps a century and a large expenditure of money to accomplish. It is work that this Arboretum should begin and steadily push forward."

2. The Arboretum requires a properly equipped department for the study of the diseases of trees in this country and in other parts of the world.

3. The Arboretum requires a department in which the study of insects dangerous to trees and the methods for their control can be carried on.

4. The Arboretum needs a department for the breeding of new races of plants.

5. A rose garden and a rock garden planned comprehensively would add much to the horticultural value of the Arboretum and bring many visitors to it.

Sargent concluded, "Only a larger endowment is needed to make possible these Arboretum activities and extensions."

Sargent died in 1927, having had a tenure in office longer than any subsequent director can expect, since Harvard, as trustee, has now established a retirement age for its appointees. After Sargent's death a fund drive raised over a million dollars in endowment in his memory. A brochure published for that drive listed the Arboretum's accomplishments as scientific, economic, and cultural. Sargent established a pattern of development so sound that subsequent directors have deviated only slightly from his guidelines. The grounds have increased in size from 250 acres to nearly 400 acres, including the Case Estates in Weston. Some plants Sargent introduced and listed have not proven hardy, but they have been replaced by newer introductions so that the total holdings in hardy plants number about 6,500. The

Foreword

library has grown from 43,500 items to 76,000. The herbarium has increased from 280,000 specimens to 909,000, with valuable representation of plants from the Pacific tropics and the American tropics, as well as of plants under cultivation elsewhere around the world. Travel and exploration by the staff or supported by funds from the Arboretum continue, mostly in the tropics. The areas of interest to Sargent are inaccessible in modern times for political reasons. Educational programs for the public are well known, augmented now by the possibilities of radio and television. More of the staff teach classes at Harvard and guide graduate students. The publications Sargent began continue to flourish. The *Journal of the Arnold Arboretum* is now in its fifty-first volume, and the *Bulletin of Popular Information,* no longer free, has been renamed *Arnoldia* and is now sixtynine years old.

Sargent reported an endowment and other funds of nearly one million dollars. Although these now exceed seven million, the Arboretum could not exist today on the income from the endowment alone, and friends are still needed to supply annual gifts.

The problems of vandalism to the plantings and to the grounds, which Sargent reported so frequently, continue to vex his successors. Modern machinery for the care of the collections has replaced the scythe and much hand labor. Hay is no longer cut and stacked, but more areas of grass are cut fine and left as a mulch to be supplemented with chipped brush and commercial fertilizers.

Sargent's five goals have been modified, but not necessarily for lack of funds. The study of insects and plant diseases has been developed by vigorous programs of the state and federal government. Plant breeding has become a function of the Departments of Forestry and Agriculture but is included in the research programs of many Arboretum staff members. The rose garden has proven impractical in the Boston climate, and the rock garden never developed because of the costs of maintenance.

In Sargent's will he expressed confidence in the future. A

Foreword

xvi

sum of $10,000 was to be invested to accumulate interest for one hundred years. Then half of the fund could be used, but the other half was to be built up again for a century. The Directors of the Arnold Arboretum who will use these funds in 2028 and 2128 have not been born, but their legacy from Charles Sargent continues to grow. Few men have achieved such immortality.

Foreword

Part One. Beginnings

1

The Importance of Being Sargent

Charles Sprague Sargent was born, on an April Saturday in 1841, into a household which pointed with pride to such prominent names as Saltonstall, Brooks, Winthrop, Everett, Gray, Ward, and Hunnewell hung like ornaments on its genealogical tree. The family credited Epes Sargent, a Gloucester merchant, shipowner and son of William, who arrived in the New World from England some time before 1675, with being its American-born ancestor. The second Epes commissioned Paul Revere to engrave bookplates with a coat of arms—three frolicking dolphins within a baroque frame and a fourth without—which successive Sargents all used. The infant Charles Sprague Sargent, four generations removed from the venerable original Epes, belonged to that branch of the family begotten by Epes' son Daniel.[1] Today questions of ancestry are merely a passing curiosity; but in nineteenth-century Boston, membership in one of the elite families was a guarantee of social acceptability and a passport to power and influence. Physically too, Charles had an advantage, for Sargents were generally "large, robust, and long-lived, with a singular absence of such chronic disease as tuberculosis."[2]

Charles' father, Ignatius, was a Boston merchant and banker. In traditional New England fashion, he received his business education in the counting house of Thomas Handasyd Perkins, considered by many to have been the greatest of Boston's merchant princes. For a while, in association with Peter Chardon Brooks, Jr., under the firm name of Sargent & Brooks, Ignatius conducted business as a merchant at waterfront headquarters at No. 50 Commercial Wharf. In 1830 he was selected a director of the Globe Bank; he eventually relinquished his interest in Sargent & Brooks and became president of the bank in 1842. Like the financial giants of the century, he scented profits in the operation of railroads and invested in the Boston and Albany Railroad, of which he was a long-time director, as well as in the Connecticut River Railroad, and progressively added to his already substantial share of the Sargent family fortune.

Ignatius married twice; his first wife, Sarah Charlotte Gray, died two years after the birth of their only child, a girl. His second wife, Henrietta, Sarah's elder sister, bore him three children, among whom Charles was the youngest and second son. The Gray sisters were daughters of a Salem merchant, Samuel Gray, and Mary Brooks, the sister of the Reverend Cotton Brown Brooks and Peter Chardon Brooks, who was rumored to be the richest man in New England.

When Charles was born, the family lived at No. 2 Joy Street on Boston's Beacon Hill in a "Greek Revival" town house which Ignatius had purchased so that he might be near his good friend, Col. Thomas H. Perkins, Jr., the son of his old mentor, who lived at No. 1. During the summer the Sargents removed to their country place in Medford until 1847 when, again in pursuit of Col. Perkins' company, they summered in the fashionable Boston suburb of Brookline and, after 1852, finally established year-round residence there. By the time Ignatius had moved his family out to Brookline, there were only two children at home. Sarah Ellery, his daughter by the first marriage, had married an acceptably distant cousin, and the couple lived in Philadelphia. Before that, in 1844, the elder boy, young Ignatius, had died within three days of his eighth birthday, a tragedy which touched his stern father but which little Charles could scarcely comprehend.

The second son bore the impressive name of Charles

Sprague Sargent VI even though he was the first "Charles Sprague" of the Sargent family. He was named after one Charles Sprague who, while conscientiously performing his duties as cashier at the Globe Bank, earned a local reputation as a poet and even won occasional recognition in some of the refined literary reviews. If Ignatius had any hopes that his son would have a poetic nature, however, he was to be sorely disappointed, for it was from his father that Charles would inherit his character, and he would resemble the poet Sprague in name only.

In later years Charles Sargent remembered his father as a taciturn, tenacious, and stern gentleman who disguised a tender heart with a silent, formidable exterior. His business acumen cannot be doubted, for he was financially successful, and respected by his colleagues. He reigned as undisputed head of his family, but domestic interests were secondary to his business activities. To readers of Boston biographies Ignatius Sargent would not be a novelty, trained as he was in the great counting houses, adept in business affairs and severe, dignified, and shy of temperament. Long after he died, James Bowditch recalled his individual style:

> He left his Boston office daily in ample time to take the 2:30 P.M. steam train for home, and to look over the afternoon paper before the train started. He invariably occupied the same seat on the left-hand side of the car, well up toward the front.
>
> Some bright schoolboy conceived the idea of capturing this seat in advance of the old gentleman's arrival.
>
> Accordingly, one afternoon six gay youngsters occupied the coveted seat together with the two others back and front adjoining . . .
>
> When the old gentleman came he of course took in the situation at a glance. He said nothing, but gave the bunch one withering look and sat down beyond. Whether the boys expected an explosion or not I never knew, but Mr. Sargent took no further notice of them whatever . . .

The Importance of Being Sargent

The joke was never again indulged in and all parties concerned doubtless were on the whole satisfied. It was well played on both sides.[3]

And yet, Ignatius Sargent was a man who took pains to print a letter to his son, "Charlie," almost five at the time, saying, "You are a good little boy and I love you very much. If you continue to improve in your writing I shall give you one of these days a pretty little desk with pens, paper, ink, seals, knife, and everything useful."[4] He appeared in a photograph taken in 1855 looking very businesslike indeed, with the corners of his narrow mouth drawn down in a slight frown, a strong chin beneath a stronger nose (the Sargent trademark), and furrows between his dark eyebrows. He cut a handsome figure, for large, dark, soft eyes mellowed his somber expression.

Along with his sister Henrietta, older by three years, Charlie spent the early years of his life on the Brookline estate which Ignatius quaintly dubbed "Holm Lea" (inland island pasture). After the purchase of the original plot in 1845, the Sargents gradually added to the estate until it spread out over about one hundred and thirty acres and was the largest private estate so close to the heart of Boston. Here, with characteristic thoroughness, Ignatius indulged his interest in horticulture, transforming the rolling terrain into handsome parkland and gardens.

The Sargent family had all the ingredients required for the making of a "good" Boston family. In various branches of the family tree one finds a Chief Justice of the Supreme Court of Massachusetts (Nathaniel Peaslee Sargent, d. 1791); a political writer and sergeant-at-arms in the House of Representatives at Washington (Nathan Sargent, d. 1875); a sprinkling of successful merchants including, of course, Ignatius Sargent; the wife of the founder of Universalism in America (Judith Sargent, whose second husband was the Reverend John Murray, d. 1815); its own Unitarian Reverend John Turner Sargent (d. 1877), whose wife Mary was the moving spirit of the Radical Club of

Beginnings

6

Boston; a founder of the American Academy of Dramatic Art (Franklin Haven Sargent, d. 1923); and the painter John Singer Sargent (d. 1925).* Other Sargents, such as Horace Binney Sargent (d. 1908), who wasted his fortune in unsound financial speculations and rode a sleigh pulled by reindeer, nearly became black sheep,[5] but for the most part they were a family of sound accomplishments. The tradition continues. Francis W. Sargent, elected Lieutenant Governor of Massachusetts in 1966 and succeeding John Volpe as Governor in 1969 traces his American beginnings back to the Gloucester Epes.

Sargents bore strong physical resemblance to one another. Charles and John Singer Sargent, though only third cousins once removed, posing together in a 1921 photograph, look enough alike to be brothers. Evidently the Sargent bearing went back to remote English ancestors, for one piece of Sargentiana has become a family legend. An American lady who was a guest at dinner in London was in conversation with a strange gentleman. He turned to her and said, "Madam, you much resemble a person I know." "I was about to make the same remark as to yourself," she parried. "I am a Sargent," he said; "So am I," replied the lady.[6] American Sargents, beginning with Epes, preserved their grave countenances for posterity by sitting for noted artists, and were all the portraits assembled, the collection would include several Copleys, a Gilbert Stuart, oils and sketches by John Singer Sargent, Henry Sargent—the other painter in the family—John Trumbell and St. Memins.

Among the Sargents of his generation Ignatius was the silent, stern businessman, whose character is popularly associated with Boston masculinity. Ignatius was no word-waster. That there is practically no information available concerning either of his wives is not surprising since Boston women seem to have distinguished themselves first by being

---

* Nor is it surprising to find that the Sargents had their own genealogist. Mrs. Emma Worcester Sargent, wife of Winthrop Sargent, whose mother was also a Sargent, was the author of *Epes Sargent of Gloucester and His Descendants.*

The Importance of Being Sargent

daughters of Boston fathers, and second by being wives of Boston husbands. Assuming that her New England breeding prevailed, Henrietta Gray Sargent, Charles' mother, maintained a household according to her husband's pleasures, took responsibility for rearing the children under her husband's direction, and was for all the world an obedient wife, gracious hostess, and affectionate mother.

Young Charles began his life with Boston winters and Brookline summers, finally passing all year long at Holm Lea. Unfortunately there is little information about how he spent his childhood, for as an adult he seldom talked about his youth. He did not, it is said, show any unusual or significant early interest in plants, nor was he in any other way extraordinary. After Sargent's death in 1927, his longtime associate E. H. Wilson, the botanical explorer, admitted ruefully, "I have virtually no information about his early life. On one occasion, being in a reminiscent mood, he drove me around and pointed out the house on Joy Street, Boston, in which he was born. Passing the Arlington Street side of the Public Garden, he remarked that there he used to put on his skates, and that opposite the Harvard Club he frequently fished for smelts through the ice." [7]

There is no record of his early schooling, but it must have been about 1851 that he entered the Epes Sargent Dixwell School for boys, which had just opened in Boylston Place. It was another case of keeping things in the family, for the founder of the school was yet another Sargent, who made a name for himself in education as headmaster of Boston Latin School, founder of his private school, and cofounder of the Cambridge Industrial School. If Charles' school performance paralleled his Harvard record, he was far from being a scholarly child. Adhering to tradition, however, he entered Harvard College in the fall of 1858 along with half a dozen other boys from the Dixwell school.

Sargent's college education was classical, including two years each of Latin and Greek, a year each of French, Spanish, and Italian; chemistry, astronomy, physics, metaphysics, and four courses in rhetoric, which apparently were of no

Beginnings

8

use in making him an able public speaker. What is surprising, in retrospect, is that he was one of the very few students in his class who did not elect to study botany, which was then combined with zoology as the Natural History course; the class was taught by Professor Asa Gray, who was already

Charles Sprague Sargent, ca. 1862

recognized as an important figure in American botany although not a particularly stimulating lecturer. In 1859, while Sargent was in college, Darwin's *Origin of Species* appeared, and Gray became its American protagonist, rocking scientific and religious foundations. Though Harvard scientists debated Darwinism hotly, most undergraduates were only vaguely aware of the issue and were detached from the furor.

For the most part, the University atmosphere was stodgy. There was as much emphasis on a young man's deportment

The Importance of Being Sargent

9

as on his academic progress. The college administrators and, hence, the faculty, made little effort to encourage original thinking. The students learned lessons by heart and parroted them back in written or oral recitations. In these circumstances the diligent student succeeded, but not necessarily the intelligent one. Sargent's record reveals a consistent lack of application although his manners were exemplary. Considering the number of actions which the college officially viewed as misbehavior and the youthful temptations to transgress, it is remarkable that he earned only two reprimands over four years—one for noise during recitations and the second for repeated absences or tardiness at prayers. Scholastically, however, his troubles began in his freshman year, when he was required to study Greek over Christmas vacation and later received warning that he was in danger of failing his final examinations. His record was so poor that halfway through his sophomore year President Felton advised his father to remove him from the class until September. Presumably Ignatius dealt effectively with his son, for Sargent finished his studies with no further warnings.[8]

Sargent graduated in 1862, eighty-eighth in a class of ninety. In a photograph taken with his classmates, he appears as a startlingly handsome but gloomy young man. There is no apparent explanation for his scholastic record. Since his career proved him capable of diligence and intellectual excellence, one can only guess that he was profoundly uninterested in his formal education.

During Sargent's junior year, the Confederate States rebelled against the federal government and, as they said at Harvard, "the country and the sons of Harvard were in arms." Sargent, along with forty per cent of his classmates, enlisted in November of 1862; he received the rank of First Lieutenant and was assigned to the Second Louisiana Infantry. It was a move he was not forced to make, for later when conscription began on July 8, 1863, some well-known Boston sons chose to pay the $300 alternative to military duty without suffering loss of face. Sargent was given duty as aide-de-camp on General Nathaniel P. Banks' staff at the

Beginnings

headquarters of the Department of the Gulf at New Orleans. (Horace Binney Sargent had served as Banks' ADC in 1860.) He saw field service in the Teche Campaign, the Louisiana Red River Campaign, the seige and capture of Port Hudson, and the campaign which secured the capture of Mobile. During the Teche and Red River campaigns, General Banks' forces spent most of their time in retreat. In any event, in July 1864 Sargent attained the rank of Captain, and by March he was a brevet Major, a reward for his "faithful and meritorious Service" during the campaign against Mobile. His military career ended on August 2, 1865, when he was honorably discharged. Of this interlude there is little else to be said. A family intimate who later had occasion to comment observed that "the letters he wrote to his family during his army life gave little evidence that his imagination was stirred by the events in which he was taking part, and curiously enough in view of his later career, there was little description of what was to him a new and strange country."[9] It was many years later that he tramped the Gulf states collecting plants.

During the next three years Sargent traveled in Europe. Whether this was strictly a pleasure trip and part of a gentleman's education, or whether he was also learning something about banking is a mystery. One would like to know whether he visited gardens and developed his interest in horticulture during this period. Sargent himself, however, dated the beginning of his study of trees after his return to Boston in 1868.

Sargent was twenty-seven when he came back from Europe to the family estate in Brookline. Behind him lay an uninspired performance at Harvard, a dutiful, but unremarkable, military service, and some three years of foreign journeys. This did not add up to a very promising future and gave no indication of the direction he would take. At an age when his contemporaries were committed to professions, Sargent had made no choice of a career. As the only surviving son, and one who in later years proved to have inherited his father's mercantile instincts if not his love for com-

The Importance of Being Sargent

11

merce, it would have been reasonable to expect him to find a place in one of the Boston business firms. Instead he took on the management of Holm Lea, thus making an inauspicious beginning to his career as a horticulturist.

The practice of horticulture on a grand scale was a prevailing passion among the wealthy in the nineteenth century. In an epoch when wealth was still identified with land ownership, the privileged rich, who were still more or less concentrated in the East, built themselves palatial homes surrounded by elaborate gardens and glass houses to shelter exotic plants, all immodestly calculated to arouse envy and admiration among their acquaintances. From Boston to Newport, from the banks of the Hudson to Philadelphia and Delaware, were acres of elegant—sometimes pretentious—private parks and gardens. Within the wide boundaries of the Sargent family, in fact, there were two other horticulturists, Henry Winthrop Sargent and Horatio Hollis Hunnewell, who marked the imagination of young Charles.

Henry Sargent was Ignatius' first cousin, and it is to him that Charles later admitted his debt of inspiration. Born in Boston in 1810, Henry was educated at Harvard. He studied law but never practiced. For a short while he was a banker in New York, but he had little heart for high finance, so at the age of thirty-one he went into semi-retirement and devoted his time to horticulture while keeping one eye on his investments. He purchased a country place, which he called "Wodenethe" (Saxon for "woody promontory"), on a plateau above Fishkill Landing on the Hudson River in New York State, directly across the river from the estate of Andrew Jackson Downing, the "father of American landscape gardening." Downing was just then on the eve of fame, for in 1841 he published *A Treatise on the Theory and Practice of Landscape Gardening,* a book which was not only very popular but which was also to have enduring effects on American landscapes. Downing, a fastidious man with a penchant for the English Gothic, criticized the rigid formality of gardens popular in continental Europe, which

Beginnings

12

threatened to captivate the American imagination; he yearned for "tasteful simplicity" in American landscape design, and championed the English, or "natural" style as described by Repton and Loudon.

> By Landscape Gardening [Downing wrote], we understand not only an imitation, in the grounds of a country residence, of the agreeable forms of nature, but *an expressive, harmonious, and refined imitation*. In Landscape Gardening, we should aim to separate the accidental and extraneous in nature, and to preserve only the spirit, or essence. This subtle essence lies, we believe, in the expression more or less pervading every attractive portion of nature. And it is by eliciting, preserving, or heightening this expression, that we may give our landscape gardens a higher charm, than even the polish of art can bestow.[10]

Downing became Henry Sargent's close friend and advised him in the planning of Wodenethe. The site of the twenty-two acre estate, while potentially exquisite, was heavily wooded with trees, which obscured the river. Sargent claimed that most of the landscaping was done with an axe: the judicious removal of existing trees to open up river vistas while excluding the neighboring houses from sight and allowing spindly forest trees space for shapely growth.[11] Downing was evidently well pleased with the results, for in 1849 he referred to the estate as "a bijou full of interest for the lover of rural beauty."[12]

With both his own interests and Downing's in mind, Henry Sargent traveled in Europe, North Africa, and the Near East from 1847 to 1849, filling long letters with commentaries on the English, French, and Italian gardens and parks that Downing had not yet seen for himself. Sargent had a good eye, and his words expressed with wit and warmth his pleasure in the exploration of the Old World horticultural splendors, though he thought only the promontory of Belle Agio at Lake Como could compete with the

The Importance of Being Sargent

13

beauties of the Hudson. He returned to Wodenethe with a refreshed spirit, an enthusiasm for conifers, and new plants for his gardens. Among them, for example, was the weeping *Pinus ponderosa*, which he admired for the first time in England.[13]

Downing and Sargent shared an affectionate friendship as well as their common interest in horticulture. Downing dedicated his 1850 volume, *Architecture of Country Houses*, to Sargent. Sargent felt great sorrow at Downing's premature death in the disastrous fire of the *Henry Clay* steamboat in 1852. Apart from his sense of personal loss, Sargent missed the influence his friend had wielded in landscaping affairs and took the pessimistic view that rural tastes—after a brief show of improvement—were taking a downhill course. Attempting to perpetuate Downing's principles, Sargent wrote a supplement to the sixth edition of *Landscape Gardening* in 1859, which he introduced with the worrisome remark that "There has been no one since Mr. Downing's death who has exactly filled the niche he occupied in the public estimation";[14] and it was some years before the landscape architect Frederick Law Olmsted exerted anything like the influence Downing had commanded. Meanwhile, however, Henry Sargent continued the cultivation of his estate and acquired such a remarkable collection of conifers that anyone in the United States who was seriously concerned with planting such trees owed it to himself to inspect Wodenethe. As for the owner, he delighted in showing off his accomplishments.

Much as he loved the Hudson River, Henry Sargent was Bostonian born and bred, and he paid frequent visits to family and friends in Massachusetts. While calling on his Brookline relatives he often visited Horatio Hollis Hunnewell. Hunnewell had married Isabella Welles, Henry's first cousin. Hunnewell, who was the same age as Sargent, possessed an enviable talent for making money. In 1825, at the age of 15, his family sent him to Paris to learn banking in a family financial establishment, and within ten years he

Beginnings

14

became a partner in the company. His successful career as a financier seemed assured until the 1837 financial crisis destroyed his prospects. Two years later Hunnewell returned to Boston and, shrewdly investing his reduced capital in railroads and real estate, rapidly recuperated a sizeable fortune. He had a taste for country life and devoted more and more of his energies to his estate in West Needham (later named Wellesley, in honor of his wife's family).

Encouraged by Henry Sargent, Hunnewell spent five years hard at work on an Italian garden—its terraces bordering a small lake—which reminded one of a miniature version of Sargent's description of Belle Agio at Como. Only, the topiary work would have irritated Downing. Through Sargent, too, Hunnewell developed a liking for rhododendrons and after 1856 began importing them in large numbers for his arboretum. Once again bearing in mind the interests of his cousin at Fishkill Landing, it is not surprising that Hunnewell purchased additional property which he set aside for a pinetum, aiming to "plant in it every conifer, native and foreign, that will be found sufficiently hardy to thrive in our cold New England climate." [15] While Hunnewell carried out his work independently, the source of his inspiration was clear, and he executed his plans to Sargent's obvious satisfaction and admiration. When Sargent wrote the supplement to Downing's *Landscape Gardening,* he gave eloquent praise to the Hunnewell place as an example of how an area of essentially flat, arid land could be transformed—by the spade—into an attractive parkland.

Neither Henry Sargent nor Hunnewell pursued his hobby half way. Their wealth permitted them time to indulge their interests and means to achieve their aims, but many men would have been satisfied with less thorough results. They both had excellent layman's knowledge of plants, but while Sargent's association with Downing left him particularly sensitive to the problems of landscape gardening, Hunnewell dabbled in things scientific, patiently experimenting with his plants, concerning himself with their hardiness and

The Importance of Being Sargent

15

proper classification, and now and then consulting the Harvard botanist, Asa Gray, whom he met socially or saw at the university botanic garden.

Wodenethe and the Hunnewell estate conformed to Downing's idea of tasteful simplicity and went a step beyond,

Henry Winthrop Sargent, 1870

displaying collections of unusual completeness planted in a manner both pleasing and educative. Ignatius Sargent's horticultural efforts were pale in contrast to those of Henry Sargent and Hunnewell, but Ignatius was first of all a banks-and-railroads man. On the other hand, he had a magnificent piece of land in a neighborhood that Downing had praised: "a kind of landscape garden, and there is nothing in America, of the sort, so inexpressibly charming as the lanes which lead from one cottage, or villa, to another." [16] It was not till Charles finally took matters in hand, however, that Holm Lea fulfilled its horticultural potential.

Beginnings

Horticulture, as distinct from agricultural research or botany, was scarcely a profession at the time. It was, rather, a rich man's hobby. While people like Hunnewell or Henry Sargent grew ornamental plants, applying a combination of elementary botany, intuition, and loving care, they remained gifted amateurs and did not mistake their diversion for a profession. The study of agricultural problems was beginning to attract government funds and, consequently, men. There were, of course, tradesmen who dealt profitably in seeds and plants. Men like Asa Gray and George Engelmann, famous as botanists, had studied medicine before turning to botany. The professional horticulturist, as we understand the term today, did not exist; the closest approximations were the landscape architects, such as Frederick Law Olmsted, and they were few in number. As for the hired gardener, his approach to his work was seldom scientific. Unless Charles Sargent had some inkling of his future association with Harvard, which is doubtful, it is difficult to see what he had in mind in selecting to make a study of horticulture and trees. It seems unlikely that he adopted this course with foresight. It is more likely that he was not enthusiastic about a financial career, in fact had very little idea what to do with himself, and so lapsed into managing his father's estate pending a more permanent decision. Perhaps he was influenced by Hunnewell, Henry Sargent, or Ignatius. They may well have sensed the need for the kind of work young Sargent eventually would undertake and encouraged his interest from the beginning, but what anyone could hope to achieve with a private estate was very limited.

Holm Lea is gone now. After Charles Sargent's death in 1927, it was sold off in lots. Perhaps the city could not tolerate so vast a private estate so near its heart. What was once a horticultural showplace is now the site of expensive, tasteful, conventional, suburban homes.

Ignatius Sargent purchased the first part of the estate, four adjoining plots, in 1845. While removed from Boston's

The Importance of Being Sargent

busy center, the Brookline neighborhood was by no means a wilderness. Downing described the area poetically:

> No animals are allowed to run at large, and the open gates, with tempting vistas and glimpses under the pendant boughs, give it quite an Arcadian air of rural freedom and enjoyment. These lanes are clothed with a profusion of trees and wild shrubbery, often almost to the carriage tracks, and curve and wind about, in a manner quite bewildering to the stranger who attempts to thread them alone; and there are more hints here for the lover of the picturesque in lanes, than we ever saw assembled together in so small a compass.[17]

Eventually other major plots were added to the original purchases, including the Thomas Lee place of about 20 acres. The Norfolk County records show nineteen transactions between 1845 and 1873, when the estate was completed. The Lee land, especially, was a splendid purchase, for as Downing had pointed out, Mr. Lee nurtured a collection of rhododendrons and kalmias and a set of good trees. From the beginning, the Sargents developed Holm Lea in keeping with the surrounding atmosphere of pleasing, calculated disorder. No formal flower beds, no topiary gardens, no geometric schemes. As the years went by, Holm Lea became a realization of Downing's ideal—nature, under control, allowed to follow its own inclinations—a rambling simplicity that appealed to the sober Boston banker and his son.

In this setting, Sargent began his career. He had no pertinent educational background, no proper instructors, and no practice in his chosen "profession." He had, however, good instincts where horticulture was concerned and showed signs of a capacity for enthusiastic labor. Perhaps because there is a meager amount of information concerning Sargent's childhood and adolescence, he seems to leap forward from listless boyhood into sudden maturity. One longs to invent a nature-loving child, or to unearth the tale of a young man pining over the loss of some dark-haired

Beginnings

18

beauty, but all available evidence contradicts such romantic fantasies.

Within the four years following his return from Europe, the course of Sargent's future, professional and personal, took shape. While carrying out improvements at Holm Lea, he learned to know his neighbors—a wealthy, powerful group—and they, for their part, conceived respect for his ability. Good relations with his neighbors were to pay extra dividends in the years to come. From his tutors, Henry Sargent and Hunnewell, he learned the theories of landscape gardening handed down from the English school through Downing. Familiar from childhood visits, the Sargent pinetum and Hunnewell's rhododendrons suddenly caught his fancy. He learned to call plants by their Latin names and to distinguish differences between closely related specimens. In his quiet way, he must have studied hard and absorbed a great deal of information, for when he began his career at Harvard in 1872 he was filled with vigorous ideas.

Even as a young man Sargent seldom revealed his feelings. Throughout his life, his restraint was such that people often suspected that he had no feelings at all, that his stoic exterior concealed an emotional vacuum. These were his shortsighted acquaintances, or those who gradually reconsidered their opinions when they witnessed him performing some unexpected gesture of kindness or displaying his perfectly healthy temper. Even if he was "colder roast Boston" than some, Sargent did not puzzle most Bostonians; to many outsiders, however, he was inscrutable. To John Muir, the famous naturalist—whose own passions were constantly near the boiling point—he was positively infuriating, but the two were close friends. He was an enigma to the Harvard botanist Asa Gray, who liked him and thought well of his executive talents but never dreamed that his research work would amount to anything extraordinary.

He had an eye for women. To the end of his life his family teased him about his preference for the company of beautiful ladies, and even in his old age he showed a flattering deference and sparkle in their presence. As a young man he exhibited taste in selecting a wife. From a social point of view he was a good match for any girl: he came from one of the best Boston families, his fortune was secure, he was properly educated and traveled, and he had recently accepted an important post at Harvard. If he was a bit sober for a young man, he was purposeful.

Andrew Robeson could only approve of his daughter's future husband. Robeson, too, was a good name, of Scottish origin. In the New World, this branch of the family earned its fortune in New England cotton mills. The Andrew Robesons had been living in Rhode Island, first at Newport and later at Tiverton. Plump, attractive Mary Allen—one could more easily be both in those days—was twenty, twelve years Sargent's junior, when they married in 1873. She was a complete lady, in full possession of the social graces befitting the mistress of an elegant home, decorously quiet in her gaiety. She liked parties and pretty clothes, and had a weakness for rich foods; fortunately, the fashions suited her voluptuous figure.

The courtship must have been a proper and decorous affair. The handsome Sargent looked romantic enough, and perhaps his serious ways impressed Mary Robeson. If he was not a cavalier lover, he offered the kind of comfortable security which few sensible women could, or their fathers would, ignore. Whatever the motivations may have been, they were wed in Boston at the Emmanual Church by Reverend Dr. Vinton on the Wednesday before Thanksgiving. Asa Gray, who was at the wedding breakfast, liked the bride and observed that, as in most marriages, she was *"brighter than he."* [18]

Perhaps she was not "brighter," but she supplied to his household and his life the ingredients they lacked. Where he was shy, she was outgoing; where he held his feelings at bay, she lavished affection and concern; where he was gruff, she was gentle. In her way, she carried the emotional burden for both of them. But like his father before him, Sargent was more involved in his work than in his family. He traveled

Beginnings

often, staying away from home for weeks or even months at a time. Occasionally Mary went with him, but more often indifferent health or domestic duties required her presence at Holm Lea; besides, she did not care much for the rough living of field trips.

He began his work early in the morning and continued as late as possible. Whether he was in the house or not, he was its unquestioned master, and his wife respected his every wish. She saw to it that he was not bothered by details, which she knew could render him fearsomely grouchy. For his part, he was probably more tender with her than with any other person. But even for a nineteenth-century woman who did not question her place in the home, he was a difficult man, and a woman with fewer inner resources than Mary Sargent would likely have despaired and lost her warmth. As the years passed she became increasingly religious, perhaps an indulgence of her sentimental nature. Yet God never took precedence over Charles Sargent.

The Importance of Being Sargent

2

The Shadow of Asa Gray

Cambridge and Boston lie near each other separated only by the waters of the Charles River. Generally speaking, out-of-staters think of Boston and Cambridge as the same place or, at least, take few pains to distinguish between them. It is an almost justifiable mistake since, aside from their geographic proximity, the two cities are historical brothers. Traditionally, Boston is the commercial and social center of the area, while Cambridge, through Harvard, provides intellectual spark. Sargent's first stay at Harvard, as a student, had been more in the way of performing a tribal rite than in fulfilling an educational need. In 1873, when he returned, this time bearing a title and a Corporation appointment as Director of the Botanic Garden of Harvard University, he had to make a modest entrance, for by then Harvard had become the focal point of botanical study in the United States, and Asa Gray, from whom Sargent took over the Garden, was the acknowledged lion among American botanists. Sargent, aside from his social qualifications, was a nobody.

Gray was nearing his sixty-second birthday and had so many duties and projects underway that he could complete none of them without assistants to lighten his burdens.[1] An energetic man, his diverse interests sometimes distracted him from strict application to his research. But what he had already accomplished was enormous. Gray had been born in New York State, the son of a tanner, and had been educated in medicine. He took an interest in nature and turned to botanizing for pleasure while still a medical student. Eventually his pastime overtook his profession, and he gave up medicine altogether, first to teach natural sciences at the Utica Gymnasium, and finally, in 1833, to work as junior assistant to Dr. John Torrey in New York. Torrey, himself a chemist and doctor-turned-botanist, was rapidly gaining distinction as the country's leading plant systematist. He was swamped with work, for he was being asked to identify specimens from many sources including government-sponsored exploring expeditions to the West Coast. The Torrey-Gray collaboration could hardly have been more mutually beneficial; Gray could study botany exclusively from the large collections which were sent to Torrey; he learned quickly from Torrey and in return gave invaluable aid in the determination of specimens. He was a prodigious worker and stimulating company for his mentor.

But Torrey could pay little, and his funds were soon exhausted. Had Gray possessed Sargent's wealth, the next few years would have been easier for him. He had no problem finding work to do, but he barely squeezed out a living for all his labors. A chance to accompany Charles Wilkes on an expedition to the Pacific Ocean and South Seas region had to be passed up because the journey was bogged down for many months with administrative complications, and Gray could not afford, either professionally or financially, to hold out longer. Reluctantly, he accepted an appointment as Professor of Botany at the University of Michigan in 1838. His first mission was a trip to Europe to purchase books for the University library. Ultimately, although he conscientiously fulfilled the assignment, the real value of the journey lay in the opportunities he found for meeting and exchanging ideas with the great European botanists of the day—the Hookers, George Bentham, Joseph Decaisne, the de Candolles, Robert Brown, and others. There was an uneventful encounter with Charles Darwin; but Darwin had not yet articulated his theory of evolution, and neither man sus-

The Shadow of Asa Gray

pected how the future would link their studies. Gray had a splendid trip. He studied material in the Old World herbaria with zeal and delighted the Europeans with his quick grasp of botanical matter. Throughout his travels he secured friendships which would bring him pleasure for years to come and would benefit the natural sciences.

When Gray returned to the United States, the University of Michigan was in a muddle and no longer prepared to take him on. Again laboring under insecure circumstances and mostly on the strength of his own leftover funds, he relieved the overworked Torrey of the task of recruiting and organizing botanists for the *Flora of North America*. Simultaneously he became a regular contributor to the *American Journal of Science*—he later became an associate editor—and did some field work. Once again, however, his money began to dwindle. So when Harvard acted favorably on his application, offering him an appointment as the Fisher Professor of Natural History and head of the Botanic Garden, in 1842, he was genuinely pleased to accept it. For Harvard the selection was a shrewd one because Gray had the fastest-growing reputation as a botanist in the country, and the University saw a chance to improve its unremarkable position in a field that was beginning to attract considerable attention. The results far exceeded expectations.

While he performed double duty at Harvard as supervisor of the Botanic Garden and Professor of Natural History, Gray used spare moments to continue work on the North American *Flora*, especially his own study of the complicated sunflower family, the Compositae. Between projects he worked in the active scientific clubs of Boston and Cambridge and before long was well known among the local intelligentsia. He married Jane Loring, who came from a prominent Boston family—her father was a member of the Harvard Corporation—and settled into his Cambridge environment. In 1851, the Grays traveled to Europe, and Gray met Darwin for the second time over lunch at Kew.

Although it is Darwin who is remembered for the theory, there were other scientists, notably Alfred Russel Wallace,

Beginnings

24

whose investigations led them simultaneously to similar conclusions. Gray himself had been struggling with the standard concept of immutable species. In 1855 he made his third European journey and again encountered the man who before had made so little impression upon him. Darwin was no botanist, but he knew plants well enough to be intelligently curious about their geographic distribution, a topic which also intrigued Gray, whose information about the American flora supported Darwin's budding theory. Moreover, Gray knew that his good friend Joseph Hooker sympathized with views that Darwin only hinted at in their conversations; the full force of the evolution theory was still secret. When Gray went back to Harvard, he kept up a correspondence with Darwin, at first answering botanical queries without realizing how Darwin used his information. In 1857, however, Darwin finally unveiled his ideas to Gray. Gray could not swallow Darwinism whole; there were points where the two friends did not agree. But Gray recognized that Darwin had gone a long way to solve his puzzlement about species by giving theoretical credibility to his idea that a single species might appear in different forms.

Meanwhile the figure of Louis Agassiz loomed large in Gray's life. The Swiss-born Agassiz, a geologist and zoologist, had been at Harvard since 1846. With his continental manners and flair for public speaking, he captured a following and was an imposing force in the American scientific community. At first he and Gray were friends, but as their intellectual differences began to surface, the friendship cooled to superficial cordiality until the humiliated Agassiz was embittered. Agassiz's assertion that "A species is a thought of the Creator" and his background of German idealism conflicted with Gray's empirical methods, and, about a year before Darwin's *Origin* appeared in print, the two clashed in a series of debates and articles in which Gray defended inductive reasoning. Agassiz spoke better on his feet, but Gray's theories were cogent and he wrote with graceful precision. As the struggle wore on in the Cambridge Scientific Club and the American Academy, Gray

The Shadow of Asa Gray

finally introducted Darwin's findings in support of his argument, although he cautiously refrained from total commitment to all the implications. Although Gray's disagreement was properly with Agassiz, the publication of Darwin's book enlarged the scale of the debate. So in the spring of 1860, the two men grappled with Darwin's theories. Gray, as Darwin's intimate, felt responsible for giving his thesis a fair hearing in America and courageously set out to explain evolution and natural selection as objectively as he could to a breathless audience.

Even before Darwinism won wide approval, the ground seemed to crumble beneath Agassiz's argument. Although Agassiz never lost his faithful and often generous admirers, his more thoughtful colleagues fell away and his prestige declined. Gray was applauded as Darwin's champion. His position was sometimes misunderstood, however, for he never became reconciled to Darwin's agnosticism.

The strains of the Agassiz debate and the Darwin question, which involved Gray for several years, and the disruptive influences of the Civil War, robbed him of precious research time. While he performed a valuable task for science in general, his work at the Garden and in the herbarium suffered. As Torrey aged, more and more of the routine work of identification fell to Gray. No matter how rapidly he dealt with the piles of dried specimens on his tables, new ones replaced them. Overshadowing other considerations was the guilty knowledge that the *Flora of North America* was unfinished. In December 1871, Gray laid his woes plainly before Harvard President Charles Eliot:

> With the present academic year I shall have completed thirty years of service in the professorial chair to which I was called in the spring of 1842. The Garden, which had been under no professorial care for years, and which has since had a long and hard struggle for existence, the conservatories, the herbarium and its library, both steadily increasing, and now the lecture-room, laboratory, etc., make up an establishment which has grown by de-

Beginnings

26

grees into one which requires much time, care, and anxiety to administer, and for which I have now done the main part of what could be expected of me or any one man. The experience of the last and present year clearly shows me that the work of instruction, steadily increasing in its demands . . . weighted more and more with the load of administration, is more than I can carry on . . . I suppose that either the duties of instruction or of administration, beyond that of the herbarium, must be entirely surrendered. If I can be spared, and if what I could do for the herbarium could be reckoned an equivalent for rent of the house I reside in, I should crave to resign both the charge of the Garden and of the professorship. There is reason to think that the time is at hand when changes such as are here suggested may be propitiously made.

When I came here, in 1842, I was carrying on and publishing a most important original work, the "Flora of North America." I have worked on it from time to time, but I have never been able to publish any more of it. And now what was done has all to be done again, and carried if possible to a completion; and there is no one else to do it if I do not.[2]

Gray's plea did not fall on deaf ears. President Eliot was an old friend, and the University could not overlook the request of a scientific giant. In fact, within the thirty years of Gray's tenure, both the Harvard botanical resources and the science itself had increased in scope. The more refined botany became, the less feasible it was that any one man could cope with all of it. Gray therefore needed and was given help. Between 1872 and 1874 Harvard appointed four men to the botanical staff: Sereno Watson worked with Gray in the herbarium and was designated its Curator in 1874; George Lincoln Goodale, a plant physiologist, assumed Gray's teaching task—and, being a good lecturer, proved more entertaining and popular than Gray; William Gilson Farlow, once Gray's assistant, did phytopathological

The Shadow of Asa Gray

research at the Bussey Institution and finally became Professor of Cryptogamic Botany in 1879; Charles Sprague Sargent took over the new Arnold Arboretum and the Garden. Each man was a specialist, and Gray needed them all.

Although he entered botany in middle life, Watson had determined the collections made between 1867 and 1870 by Clarence King's U. S. geological exploration of the fortieth parallel north latitude. Goodale was a graduate of Harvard Medical School, but like others, had shifted over to botany, and taught natural sciences at Bowdoin. Farlow, another medical doctor, had learned his botany first with Gray and then had spent two years at Strasbourg studying with Anton de Bary, the outstanding authority on lower plants. Each of these men brought educational background and experience to Harvard. Sargent, however, had been supervisor of his father's estate and was little more than a glorified gardener.

Given the nature of his academic credentials, there is a mystery surrounding Sargent's appointment. Gray apparently did not have a hand in the selection, for shortly after he wrote President Eliot about his projected retirement, he mentioned to Joseph Hooker that he was looking for a candidate to direct the garden, and asked for suggestions, but did not receive any.[3] Subsequently he approved of Eliot's nomination, Professor William Henry Brewer, a Yale botanist, but Brewer refused to leave New Haven.[4] One may well ask how Sargent entered the picture. Certainly there were other men in the country with more to recommend them. Sargent's appointments came in rapid installments. In May 1872, he became Professor of Horticulture at the Bussey Institution, a position created only a year before for the historian Francis Parkman. For years, when he was not embroiled in history, Parkman gardened with fervor and success on his Brookline estate. He had experience in plant breeding and growing and delighted at the prospect of teaching his hobby as part of Eliot's effort to inject the new Bussey establishment with life. But, nearly blind and suffering bad health, he could do only token justice to his

Beginnings

28

task and decided to resign. It is conceivable that he recommended his successor, for he knew Sargent, and Holm Lea, as a neighbor.

In June, the Harvard Corporation (according to Gray's view, at a loss to find a man to take on the project) named Sargent Curator of the new arboretum; in November 1873, he was promoted to Director of the Arnold Arboretum and also named Director of the Botanic Garden in Cambridge. There is a story somewhere in this sequence; but with only circumstantial evidence, it is difficult to be sure what it is. It is, for example, fair to speculate that H. H. Hunnewell was a power behind the scenes. He and Gray had been friendly acquaintances for years. They played whist together now and then and crossed each other's paths at various club functions. Hunnewell's interest in horticulture brought him to the Botanic Garden for visits, so he knew Gray's quarters; as a member of the Committee to Visit the Harvard Botanic Garden he was aware of Gray's problems. Like many influential Bostonians, Hunnewell kept himself informed about Harvard, and he was a personal friend of President Eliot's. In 1871, he financed—at first, anonymously—the badly needed addition of a lecture room and laboratory to the botanical buildings in Cambridge to the extent of $10,000.[5] Any institution that relies heavily on private endowments takes care to please its benefactors—especially its rich benefactors—and Harvard was no exception. If Hunnewell acted to sponsor Sargent, the University would have been disposed in his favor. Furthermore, Sargent's wealth and social position would doubtless be an advantage in securing financial support for horticultural work.

The man responsible for the founding of the Arnold Arboretum appears only briefly in the pages of this history, for only in his death did he affect that institution. James Arnold, born in 1781 in Providence, Rhode Island, went to New Bedford, then New England's whaling center, as a young man and found employment as a clerk in the office of

The Shadow of Asa Gray

29

William Rotch, Jr., merchant. Arnold married Rotch's daughter Sarah in 1807 and worked his way into a partnership in the firm. Arnold's will indicates that he had a lucrative career, for he left an estate valued at about one million dollars. How much of this fortune may be attributed to Arnold's proper wiliness or industry is not certain, but he was surely an acute businessman. Some part of his wealth came from heavy investment in Michigan timberland, a risk which paid off handsomely. In 1820 he purchased some eleven acres in New Bedford and surrounded his home with an English style garden which he opened to the public on Sundays. Downing—who seems to have seen every garden in those days—singled out Arnold's residence from among all the New Bedford homesteads and pronounced it "a charming spot" and a "very interesting and instructive suburban seat."[6] Arnold apparently developed the garden as a matter of course and preferred spending his idle hours studying classical literature. It was Sarah Arnold who was responsible for the garden.[7]

When Arnold died in December 1863, he did not leave a legacy to Harvard outright. He placed in trust with George B. Emerson, John James Dixwell, and Francis E. Parker, one and one-quarter of the twenty-four parts of his residuary estate "to be by them applied for the promotion of Agricultural, or Horticultural improvements, or other Philosophical, or Philanthropic purposes at their discretion, and to provide for the continuance of this Trust."[8] In proportion to the total estate it was not a large sum; the "Poor and Needy in New Bedford"—only the "deserving" ones—received a quarter share more. By the time the money was transferred to Harvard, the endowment amounted to $103,847.57.

As their actions eventually proved, the trustees were conscientious and mindful of Arnold's wishes. Two of them, Emerson and Dixwell, were tree lovers; Parker, the third executor, was the legal mind in the group. Emerson, related to Arnold's wife by marriage, apparently was a close friend of Arnold's. A mathematician and educator, he was also a part-time botanist and author of *Trees and Shrubs Growing*

Beginnings

30

Naturally in the Forests of Massachusetts, which went through five editions.[9] Back in 1842, when the Harvard Corporation puzzled over appointments, it was Emerson's voice, favoring Gray, which convinced the University officers and carried the day. Dixwell's mother was a Sargent, directly descended from Epes; Dixwell was, in fact, the brother of Epes Sargent Dixwell, whose school Charles Sargent attended as an adolescent. It is doubtful, however, that Arnold knew of any connection between his trustees and the man who would make the Arnold name famous. Dixwell, a prosperous Boston merchant-banker, raised trees on his Jamaica Plain estate for a hobby. According to Sargent, between 1860 and 1870 this collection "was one of the most important and interesting in New England."[10] Dixwell was also acquainted with Gray. Emerson, however, took the initiative in dealing with the Arnold will, for in him were combined an interest in living plants and an admiration for botany.

Gray was in Egypt when he received second-hand news of the legacy. Seizing a chance for something he had always dreamed of, on February 20, 1869, he wrote Dr. Andrew Preston Peabody, then Harvard's Acting President in Eliot's absence:

> It is known to the Corporation of the University that I have, from time to time, pressed the recommendation that the grounds around the Observatory, having the advantage of being contiguous to the Botanic Garden, with some extensions (which could lately have been had without very great cost) should be utilized for the purpose of an arboretum, if every means for its support were to be had.[11]

Gray's letter took Peabody and the Corporation by surprise and caused some embarrassment for, as yet, they had not been approached by the Arnold trustees. Peabody hurriedly wrote Emerson, who confirmed, on March 31, Gray's information. Emerson indicated his sympathy with Gray's idea

The Shadow of Asa Gray

31

of a Cambridge arboretum but he expressed crucial reservations.

> My dear friend, Dr. Gray, is correctly informed in regard to several things about Mr. Arnold's will. He did leave . . . a large bequest, probably about two thirds of what it is reported to be. This was originally intended for an arboretum. But Mr. Arnold, to leave us at liberty, extended the limits of the bequest. We have hoped that an arboretum might be formed by it. But, if the greater part of the money would have to be expended for land at houselot prices, I would be very unwilling to give it in that direction. So far as I am concerned, I mean, if possible, to have an arboretum—and for Harvard College: and, if land can be found near the College or procurable at a reasonable price, the arboretum will be more likely to be in Cambridge as an appendage to the Botanic Garden, than anywhere else. Indeed my original idea, in recommending such a bequest to my dear friend and brother, was the hope that the management of the whole garden by Dr. Gray might be facilitated by this bequest.[12]

Like many legal affairs, this one dragged on; the trustees themselves disagreed over the location of the arboretum, although they were of one accord that the fund should be used for that purpose. The Observatory idea having been abandoned early, Gray suggested another possibility in 1870. Henry Longfellow, the poet, had an interest in protecting the view from his house across the Charles River against the horrifying possibility of a slaughterhouse and consulted Gray about it. Gray, in turn, remarked in a letter to President Eliot,

> Mr. Longfellow met me yesterday with a plan in his head that you ought to know about. He proposes to be one of 12 or more to buy a large bit of Brighton Meadows for $12,000 and present it to the College—I suppose land directly opposite his house! I told him that if the land

Beginnings

32

he proposed to acquire would serve as an arboretum, I thought the likelihood of his finding partners in the purchase would be largely increased. After inquiring what an *arboretum* might be and why I thought so, he said he would go and see Mr. Emerson.[13]

As far as Gray was concerned, Brighton Meadows might not be Cambridge, but it was close enough to be an acceptable compromise. Longfellow, however, managed single-handedly without Emerson or the promise of an arboretum and bought up a seventy-acre plot along the river, which he presented to Harvard in July without making any stipulations concerning the use of the land as an arboretum. Part of the Harvard Stadium now stands on that site.

In the eyes of the University and at least one of the trustees, Cambridge and adjacent areas proved inhospitable to their plan. Without blessings from Gray, serious consideration fell upon property already owned by Harvard in the Jamaica Plain–Forest Hills section of West Roxbury, six miles from the Botanic Garden. When Benjamin Bussey died in 1842, he left Harvard 394 acres of land for use as a school of agriculture and horticulture; his granddaughter, Mrs. Thomas Motley, was given a life interest in the estate. Many plans were suggested, but nothing was done with the land until 1869, when Eliot became Harvard's president, and at his encouragement, Mrs. Motley released about seven acres for building purposes. With the cooperation of the Lawrence Scientific School in Cambridge, an ambitious program of agricultural instruction was conceived, including both botany and zoology, and work began on the construction of a stone building for the Bussey Institution. Meanwhile the remaining 387 acres remained in limbo.[14]

Precisely how the final decision on the arboretum was reached is not clear. Eliot asked advice from Emerson at the time the Bussey Institution was begun. Bussey land looked like an expedient solution to the problem of locating the arboretum. Emerson, though inclined to support Gray's wishes, thought the cost of available land in Cambridge

The Shadow of Asa Gray

33

prohibitive. Gray, increasingly cross with the situation, yearned for retirement. On December 27, 1871, he wrote to Hooker complaining, "I am laboring to have the thing annexed to the Botanic Garden here—administered as one concern, and to have somebody got to take charge of tree-raising & planting . . . and to superintend the whole garden &c.—here." [15] Gray had waited to submit his request for resignation until December 1871 but felt he could not step aside until the garden-arboretum problem was solved. On February 27, 1872, he wrote Hooker again, bemoaning the fact that Emerson, who had shown so much initial enthusiasm and efficiency, was getting old and, worse yet, was on the point of embarking for Europe to visit arboreta and "see *what he shall see,*" [16] leaving the matter to dangle until fall. Gray had little faith in either Dixwell or Parker. Then, quite unexpectedly, a settlement was reached at the end of March.

The minutes of the meetings of the Harvard Corporation are most discreet. The notes for March 18, 1872, state that President Eliot "read a memorandum of a proposed contract between George B. Emerson, John J. Dixwell and Francis E. Parker . . . whereupon it was voted that the President be authorized to sign a contract in conformity with the terms of the memorandum." Alongside this notation is a marginal afterthought: "Memorandum of a proposed contract for an Arboretum at the Bussey Inst'n." [17] The arrangement rested on the conclusion that Bussey's and Arnold's interests could both be served on Bussey property. Having gained the approval of Mrs. Motley, the trustees and the University determined to put the arboretum out in Jamaica Plain. The indenture was executed March 29, 1872.

In essence, the trustees agreed to transfer the Arnold fund to Harvard with the understanding that it would be used in the development and support of an arboretum to be established on 137 acres of Bussey property when it became available, in April 1874. The Arnold legacy was to be held by Harvard as a "separate and distinct" fund; only one-third of the net income was to be used until the accumu-

Beginnings

34

lated capital amounted to $150,000. Thereafter the University would be allowed to spend 95 per cent of the net income, while continuing to add the remaining 5 per cent to the principal. According to Sargent, one-third of the net income left less than $3,000 per year available for establishing the arboretum. Outlining the work of the arboretum, the agreement read:

The said party of the second part [Harvard] shall devote the remainder of the said net income in every year to the establishment and support of an Arboretum, to be called the *Arnold Arboretum,* which shall contain, as far as is practicable, all the trees, shrubs, and herbaceous plants, either indigenous or exotic, which can be raised in the open air at the said West Roxbury, all of which shall be raised or collected as fast as is practicable, and each specimen thereof shall be distinctly labeled, and to have the support of a professor, to be called the Arnold Professor, who shall have the care and management of the said Arboretum . . . who shall teach the knowledge of trees in the University . . . and shall give such other instruction as may be naturally, directly, and usefully connected therewith.[18]

This was a great deal to ask of $3,000 a year. Fifty years later Sargent mused that "the prospect of being able to establish a useful institution would not have been encouraging if the men interested in it had had at that time as much knowledge as hope and enthusiasm. For it is safe to say that not one of them had an idea of what an Arboretum might be, or what it was going to cost in time and money to carry out the provisions of the indenture." [19]

Gray was not in the least contented with the results of three years' haggling. In the first place, the arboretum would be located out in Jamaica Plain; in the second place— and this seems to have bothered Gray most—the Arnold fund was tied up in such a way that neither he nor the herbarium could benefit from it, and so he did not feel sufficient

The Shadow of Asa Gray

financial security to warrant his resignation of the Fisher professorship. His pique and disappointment are shown in a letter to Hooker, who had been following the story sympathetically: "Well,—as to our prospective arboretum, I have got it off my mind . . . Our University Corporation allowed the trustees of Arnold's bequest to get the better of them, and impose conditions & restrictions that reduce my interest in it to o." [20] It was in a despondent mood that he left with his wife for a summer tour of the United States, which he enjoyed despite his ruffled humor.

Gray's financial relief came, unexpectedly, through Sargent. Although as Professor of Horticulture and Curator of the Arboretum Sargent was officially located at the Bussey-Arboretum complex, he began to spend a good deal of time at Cambridge in the fall, when Gray returned. Partly he was in search of plant materials from the Garden and partly he wanted to learn as much as he could from Gray. Sargent realized the pressure of the load which Gray bore and took steps to alleviate the condition. He probably was willing to finance Gray out of his own pocket except that his display of generosity would have created an embarrassing situation for both men. Without Gray's knowledge, he arranged for his father and Hunnewell to provide $500 each a year on the condition that Gray would resign and give full time to completing the *Flora of North America*. With so little else to go on one can only speculate on a causal relationship between the financing of Gray's retirement and Sargent's subsequent appointment as Director of the Botanic Garden and of the Arboretum. Although he relinquished the burdens of his professorship, as he had originally requested in his letter to President Eliot, Gray spent the rest of his life in the house at the Garden, retaining his title and acting as director of the Herbarium and the nucleus of all Harvard's botanical activities. His position as America's foremost botanist was unassailable. As his biographer, A. Hunter Dupree, points out, the year 1873 was a turning point in Gray's life, for along with alterations at Harvard, John Torrey and Louis Agassiz both died. [21]

Beginnings

36

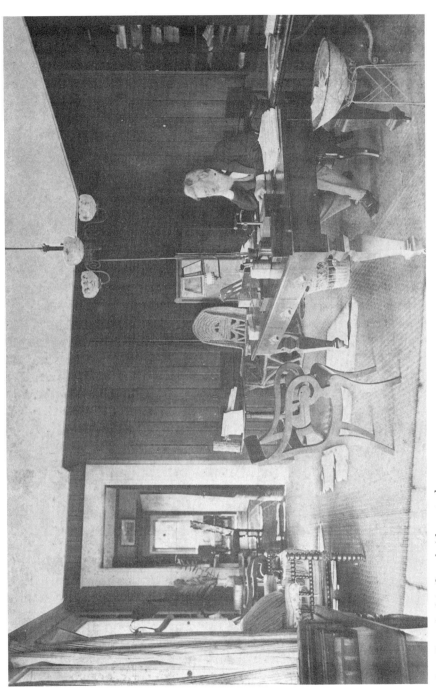

Asa Gray in his Cambridge study

The Shadow of Asa Gray

There can be no doubt that the outstanding event in the intellectual world of the middle of the century was the publication of Darwin's theories. It would be difficult to overstate its impact not only on the natural sciences but, ultimately, as it moved out of the confines of scholarly journals and academic debates, on nearly every activity of man and on his values. In 1873, the year of Sargent's Harvard appointment, Darwinism still battled its opponents, for it had by no means won unconditional approval. The outspoken antagonists were those who found the theories of natural selection and evolution offensive to orthodox religion or those who had thought one way for so long that they were unable to imagine alternatives. Predictably, scientists understood and absorbed the doctrine quicker. No small share of gratitude is due the courage of Gray in tackling a giant like Agassiz in defense of Darwin.

Revolutionary though it was, Darwinism did not undo the work of botany, nor did it cause sudden or shocking changes in botanical techniques. In fact, it gave theoretical support to the system of classification that botanists had been using for half a century. Darwinism acted in a subtle manner, suggesting areas needful of thorough investigation. The theory of evolution made the study of fossils and lower plants pertinent to the entire vegetable world. Consideration of the variability and adaptability of species involved greater morphological precision than had heretofore been practiced by most botanists. The geographical distribution of species became an essential question. Experiments with living material in the garden were more urgent than ever before. But none of this was really new to botanists of the stature of the Hookers, Bentham, Engelmann, or Gray. Gray, for example, while a taxonomist, commanded a wide botanical vocabulary. He was a first-rate morphologist; he wrote about lower plants; he made an important contribution to plant geography by describing similarities between the floras of Japan and eastern North America. The short list gives little idea of the range of his interests and experiments.

Beginnings

Darwin's importance to these men was that he supported their scientific method with theory and made order among the various branches of research by correlating loose ends. Until the latter part of the nineteenth century, the great botanists were nearly all taxonomists, albeit versatile in other botanical disciplines. For over a century, in Europe as well as in America, a few men bore more than their share of the burden of botanical responsibility while the quantity of plant materials they handled increased. That these men were primarily systematists is not surprising. The elementary problems of naming a specimen and of understanding its relation to other members of the plant kingdom awaited solution before more detailed study could have any meaning. Up to the end of the eighteenth century the systematization of the plant world rested upon the Linnean system, a simplistic process involving the counting of male and female plant parts and organizing accordingly. Antoine Laurent de Jussieu, in 1789, and Augustin Pyramus de Candolle, in 1813—both long before Darwin—revolutionized botany by replacing the "artificial" order of Linnaeus with a "natural" system (but keeping his Latin binomials) which expressed plant relationships in terms of morphological similarities. In a broad sense, the great botanical minds of the nineteenth century were engaged in the refinement of this natural order for which Darwin's work provided a hypothetical reference.

As the natural system became more sophisticated, as world-wide botanical exploration intensified, as instruments and techniques were developed, as communication through publication improved, no individual could cope with the massive amount of data which accumulated, or questions which arose, about a plant. Thus, in the latter half of the century, botany began to diversify, partly owing to the influence of Darwinism. Where there was once one Asa Gray there were, by 1874, four specialists. Watson the taxonomist, Goodale the physiologist, and Farlow the specialist in cryptogamic botany. They were all scientists. Sargent,

The Shadow of Asa Gray

39

however, as the horticulturist found himself in the potentially awkward situation of being a nonscientist, for horticulture was not considered a proper science at the time. As long as there had been gardens, there had been horticulturists. Anyone who could grow a rosebush or a row of radishes could call himself a horticulturist if he wanted to. In different periods of history, gardens had been more or less elaborate affairs, demanding special skills and practical knowledge of the planter, and advances were made in methods of cultivation, plant breeding, and so forth. But the progress in horticulture was largely independent of botany. The horticulturist had limited interests in botanical theory because the botanist worked mainly with wild plants, regardless of their ornamental or economic value. Of course, if a botanist collected a new decorative or tasty plant, the horticulturist was an eager procurer.

When scientists began to take a serious look at cultivated plants, they turned their attention to agricultural crops, particularly grains. Americans were still a rural people, and farming was the nation's biggest business. Like any other businessman, the farmer set out to make a profit and was eager to know how to improve the quantity and quality of his products. In the United States, the first agricultural college was provided for in the Michigan state constitution in 1850; by 1880 there were more than forty agricultural schools in thirty-four states.[22] After 1850 both state and federal governments played increasingly encouraging roles in agricultural investigation; the biggest single piece of federal legislation was the Morrill Act, which Lincoln signed in 1862, allotting federal endowments to so-called industrial colleges, agriculture being categorized as an industry. The same Congress legislated an independent federal agricultural bureau, from which the U. S. Department of Agriculture evolved. The burst of activity promoted farming to agriculture and set the stage for modern agricultural methods and production problems.

The nineteenth-century concept of horticulture embraced the cultivation of fruit trees and vegetables as well as

Beginnings

ornamental plants. Education in this third area was over-looked on the institutional level for several years. Agri-culture and, by extension, "practical" horticulture were aided by the government in the public interest, but orna-mental horticulture was a private concern. In name, at least, the professorship of horticulture at Harvard's Bussey Institution, which Parkman and then Sargent held, was the first official recognition of horticulture, as distinct from botany or agriculture, by an American university or college. Neither Sargent nor Parkman accomplished much in this position, however, so Cornell University and Michigan Agricultural deserve the real credit for putting horticulture, including ornamental horticulture, on a solid academic basis around 1887, a quarter of a century behind agriculture.

Meanwhile, persons concerned with ornamental plants had little opportunity to examine living specimens unless they had access to a private collection. This was likely to be an unsatisfactory classroom since the gardeners and owners rarely paid attention to taxonomists, and plants went by common names, inaccurate or outdated Latin names, ar-bitrary commercial names, or no names at all. More and more people wanted information about decorative plants. American society adored and simulated the English Vic-torian mania for serious gardening. But the available books were out of date, and the scientific publications were too specialized and filled with weeds. The botanist could tell what the plant was, the nurseryman might tell how to grow it or why it was dying; but neither one alone filled the de-mand for practical plus simple scientific information. This is where the horticulturist—hereafter distinguished from the agriculturist—filled a gap. In a similar manner the botanic garden, as a living collection grown with the specific intention of teaching botany, served both science and the public.

To John Bartram goes the distinction of having planted the first botanic garden in the United States. But this was a private garden casually planted with specimens that he had collected on various travels, and it was only in 1891 when

The Shadow of Asa Gray

it was purchased by the City of Philadelphia that it became a public ground. Of a more public and thoughtful nature was the Elgin Botanic Garden in New York City, established in 1801 by Dr. David Hosack and, in part, aimed at systematic illustration of the "natural orders" according to both Linnaeus and de Jussieu. Rockefeller Center now stands on part of that site. The first institutionally supervised botanic garden was Harvard's, which was founded about 1805 by the combined subscriptions and initiative of Boston citizens and William D. Peck, a professor of natural history. The Garden (always referred to in University publications with an upper case "G") comprised some seven acres, upon which were constructed eventually a residence, the herbarium and library, and a greenhouse or conservatory; despite its small size the Garden was pleasant and helpful, and the more curious Boston society gardeners profited from occasional visits. By the time Sargent became Director—he was the first to bear the title—the Garden had been in existence for more than sixty years and had suffered through many ups and downs, mostly downs. After Peck's death in 1822, the responsibility for the Garden went to Thomas Nuttall, an enterprising naturalist who was indifferent to the Garden and who was often away on collecting trips. The University had trouble raising funds for upkeep of the Garden or the salary of a man to run it. Between Nuttall's departure in 1834 and Gray's arrival eight years later, there was no one to look after the Garden properly. Even Gray was handicapped. As far as he was concerned, the Garden was secondary to his other Harvard duties and his research. He planned to establish a collection of North American plants which could be used on an exchange basis with European gardens. It was a noble idea, but Gray never could spare enough time to turn it into a sustained reality. Though he sometimes used the Garden for research, he placed his confidence in the dried plants of the herbarium, thereby overlooking, by default, the possibilities of using the Garden for popular education or, as might well have been a consequence, as a public relations effort to attract donations.

Beginnings

42

Gray cannot fairly be criticized for inattention to the Garden, for he not only had other and more important obligations, but the constant shortage of funds helped snuff out any grand ideas he might have had.

When Sargent took over the Garden, it was part of the best-known botanical complex in the country, but it suffered by comparison with the herbarium, library, and laboratories which it surrounded. Unlike Gray, Sargent was free to devote full attention to it, at least for a few years, and his financial connections were powerful. He began by making a number of dramatic improvements. Although the Garden was congested, there were only some 2,000 species represented in the plantings. In a large-scale weeding campaign, Sargent discarded nonessential duplicate plants and replaced them with different species, reaching an estimated total of 9,000 by 1879.[23] He rearranged the hardy collections from a haphazard scattering to a planned grouping of plants by the same sequence that was used in the herbarium so that students and visitors could readily contrast a plant with its close relatives. Furthermore, insofar as was practical, every plant was labeled and identified by its Latin name and habitat and sometimes by a common name. The new arrangement increased the usefulness of the Garden to both the student and the casual public because the labels and groupings in themselves answered the questions most people have about plants. As the young director immodestly put it, he had "brought order out of Chaos."[24]

Within the seven years that Sargent acted as Director of the Garden, drainage systems were improved, the soil was enriched, a rock garden was built on a former waste area, and the greenhouses were repaired and remodeled. Using some of Gray's connections and establishing more of his own, Sargent built up a volume of exchange which, by 1879, he claimed exceeded even that of the Royal Botanic Gardens at Kew. Needless to say, the improvements cost money, but Sargent could happily report in 1879, when he resigned as Director, that the Garden's unexpended income had increased from $3,237.33 to $3,365.94 (that is, he had

The Shadow of Asa Gray

made the alterations without diminishing the fund) and so justify Harvard's having selected him.[25] The expenses, totaling some $14,000, had been covered by increased contributions; Sargent confided in Hooker that over half of that sum came from his own purse or the pockets of his friends—and here again one suspects the munificence of Hunnewell. There is no way of knowing how heavily Sargent taxed himself. He received a salary of $1,000 a year for the Garden (plus $1,000 as Bussey Professor and $1,500 from the Arnold Arboretum) but may have spent as much as he earned. He was not shy in soliciting support from his friends, nor did he seem to mind bearing expenses personally. What bothered Sargent, as indicated in comments he later made about the Arboretum, was his suspicion that the University officials were naive enough to believe that a garden could be maintained, even adequately, on so little capital. To twist the suspicion in another direction, however, one cannot help but wonder if the University feigned an innocent role, assuming that it could rely on Sargent's ingenuity and bank account to fill the financial gaps.

From the moment Sargent came to Cambridge, he sprang to life. He changed from the listless undergraduate to a man of dedicated, purposeful curiosity. He showed the same kind of energy and eagerness in horticulture that Gray had exhibited more than thirty years before in taxonomy. He was not another Gray. He lacked the older man's nimble intellect, but he compensated by serious determination, stubbornness, and an ability to carry out his projects to their conclusions. From the beginning he was awed by Gray, who instructed him in fundamental botany as he would have done a new student. His other colleagues, like Goodale, whom he looked down on as one of the "mere physiologists,"[26] did not impress him much; Watson was a quiet man, and Sargent saw little of Farlow. In one sense, the first few years at Harvard were difficult for Sargent because of his ill-defined position within the botanical hierarchy. The fact that he contributed his own money to the Garden gave him certain leverage within the University but put strains on his relations with his colleagues. The important thing, however, was that he got along well with Gray, for he showed a well-bred respect for his age and reputation. Both Gray and his wife liked Sargent and admired his serious attitude. "It is most pleasant and hopeful," Gray wrote Alphonse de Candolle, "when, as in the present instance, a young man of means and best social position chooses to devote his time and energies to practical scientific ends, rather than to business or pleasure." [27] Gray found Sargent a "real gentleman" in his behavior, but sensed that he was no diplomat. [28] Sargent's independent, single-minded ways rubbed some of his colleagues the wrong way and irritated certain University officers. President Eliot, though grudgingly grateful for the improvements over at the Garden, disliked its Director, partly because he had little control over his activities especially in questions relating to the Arboretum. Sargent disdained popularity as long as he could proceed in his chosen direction. Gray also had a streak of arrogance—perhaps justified by his commanding position—and not only collected adversaries like Agassiz but also inspired great resentment among botanists who were jealous of his authority. Sargent's instinctive aloofness, accentuated by his social caste, prevented him from making quick friendships with associates, although later, when he felt secure in his position, he professed to respect them all, Goodale included.

Sargent made the daily trip from Brookline to Cambridge by carriage, leaving Holm Lea early in the morning. During the day he was either in the Garden or the herbarium, spending hours with Gray, consulting on plans and going through the piles of herbarium specimens learning plants and taxonomy. Gray's initial reaction was that Sargent was a man "who has a vast deal to learn" [29] but he was soon praising his "real perseverance." [30] Even though he was more than thirty years younger, Sargent needed stamina to keep up with the master, for Gray was a man with a legendary memory and the reputation of being able to deter-

The Shadow of Asa Gray

mine a specimen at a glance. Not only did he give Sargent the benefit of his experience, but he also provided him with introductions to other botanists.

In any science isolated research is meaningless. Individuals may make progress in a specific area, but unless the new knowledge is shared through publication or more direct means, nothing is accomplished. As far as American botany is concerned, first Torrey and later Gray, principally through their work on the *Flora of North America*, did much to correlate the work of geographically scattered botanists. Gray corresponded with many European botanists and kept abreast of their activities. Considering the absence of telephones and airplanes, not to mention that typewriters were not in common use before the 1890's, the daily mail itself must have been a considerable chore.

Gray's unique position at the heart of things was an enormous advantage to a neophyte like Sargent. Introductions from Gray commanded respect, and he gave them liberally. Shortly after Sargent had been named Director of the Arboretum, and after his wedding, he decided to make a combined business-honeymoon trip to Europe. The newlyweds spent most of their time in Britain and France, where the Director inspected botanic gardens for ideas and negotiated exchange programs. To Sargent, the high point of the trip was his visit to the Royal Botanic Garden in Edinburgh, which he thought the best he had ever seen, surpassing even the great gardens at Kew. His judgment showed imagination, for he visited Edinburgh in January, possibly the worst time of the year to see any European garden, especially one in Scotland's gloomy winter climate. He filled enthusiastic journal-like letters to Hunnewell with horticultural intelligence and conceived dreams for the new arboretum. Nothing he saw in Europe satisfied him, and he grew confident that with the aid of the favorable New England climate he could do much better.[31]

Mary Sargent learned quickly that she could not compete with her husband's profession. While he was in the herbarium or a botanic garden, she sometimes passed her hours more sociably with acquaintances in London or Paris, or she slipped off to browse in shops. She had to take care not to become overtired; for some time at the end of January or February of 1874, she knew that she was pregnant. The Sargents went together to call on Gray's old friend, Joseph Hooker, director of the gardens at Kew. Hooker, who had been alerted by Gray, was delighted and hospitable and encouraged Sargent in his plans for the Garden and the Arboretum. Mrs. Sargent's failure to come up to his expectations was perhaps due to her shyness and great anxiety to please. Subsequent meetings would improve Hooker's evaluation of her. The scholarly, amusing, beetle-browed Hooker got on famously with Sargent. Sargent also liked Hooker's son-in-law, William Thiselton-Dyer, who would succeed Hooker as Director of the gardens. President Eliot, also vacationing abroad, encountered the Sargents and spent a day with them at Kew discussing Sargent's ambitions for an arboretum. In Geneva for a short stop, the Sargents met Alphonse de Candolle, the Swiss botanist and the son of the famous author of *Prodromus*, Augustin Pyramus de Candolle. In Paris there was the Jardin des Plantes to visit, and at the herbarium, Sargent met Joseph Decaisne, a French botanist. In each case, Gray's letters worked magic. The Sargents explored the French countryside for nurseries and gardens. Between professional calls, they greatly enjoyed visits to musuems and art galleries.

Sargent had a fine trip and wrote thankfully to Gray, "I cannot tell you how much I have enjoyed my trip and how much of the pleasure I owe to your letters of introduction, which have everywhere given me a delightful welcome and which have allowed me to see many things that otherwise would have been shut to me." [32] Sargent returned to Brookline in early April of 1874, brimming with schemes and inspiration.

Gray's American friends also proved a great help to Sargent. Foremost among them was Dr. George Engelmann, whose reputation in America was second only to Gray's. Unlike Gray, Goodale, and many others, Engelmann actually

The Shadow of Asa Gray

practiced medicine to make a living; botany was strictly a hobby with him, but so excellent was his work that he soon made a name for himself among botanists. Engelmann was born and educated in Germany, and while he possessed a German aptitude for thorough, accurate scientific investigation, he had a gentle un-Teutonic sense of humor which made him an endearing person. Upon completing his studies in German universities and in Paris, he traveled to the United States to look after family property in Illinois. Gray drew Engelmann into his circle in the 1840's and the two were close friends for years. Aside from the pleasure of friendship, they were of mutual assistance because Engelmann settled in St. Louis, the gateway to America's undeveloped West. There was hardly a collector of any importance who did not stop off to see him en route to or from the wilderness. He had a fine private herbarium and became the authority on American conifers. Sargent quickly developed affection for Engelmann, took his chidings with good humor, and learned nearly as much from him as he did from Gray.

Sargent made other contacts—W. M. Canby, Charles Christopher Parry, Cyrus Guernsey Pringle, George Thurber, E. L. Greene, John G. Lemmon, T. S. Brandegee, and others —all part of the botanical network and all of whom would contribute to his plan to make the Arnold Arboretum a great scientific institution.

The trustees and the University came to terms, the Director was selected, and the land lay fallow in Jamaica Plain. But Sargent remained working on the Garden in Cambridge, pulling it into shape, while ruminating plans for the Arboretum. He asked questions, studied, and observed, but on the whole kept very close-mouthed about his ideas. For five years the development of the Arboretum was strictly makeshift and any major work looked hopeless. Sargent had his hands tied by the shortage of funds, so he worked cautiously and thoughtfully, using the sources he had found through the Garden as best he could to build up a nursery reserve for

Beginnings

48

Jamaica Plain. Although his time was concentrated in Cambridge, his mind was on the Arboretum, for the seven-acre Garden was only a small undertaking. He was anxious to get on with the real work.

The Shadow of Asa Gray

3

Sargent on His Own

Fifty years after the founding of the Arnold Arboretum, when it was a simple matter to confess to youthful inadequacies, Sargent magnanimously reflected that he had been as ignorant about building an arboretum as Arnold's trustees and Harvard officials had been. At the time he was doing the job, however, he masked his doubts under a display of self-confidence. He wrote later, "[I] found [myself] with a worn-out farm, partly covered with natural plantations of native trees nearly ruined by excessive pasturage, to be developed into a scientific garden with less than three thousand dollars a year available for the purpose. [I] was without equipment or the support and encouragement of the general public which then knew nothing about an Arboretum and what it was expected to accomplish." [1] He traveled, studied, and observed to remedy his lack of knowledge, but finding a solution to the financial problems was more difficult. Had he faced a question of raising a sum of twenty thousand or even fifty thousand dollars, Sargent might have been able to manage it alone. Fortunately, however, he had vision enough to realize he must arrange long-range financial security for the Arboretum. So for the first few years of his appointment as Director, he confined his activities to forming a nursery with the use of the Bussey Institution greenhouses and taking care of preliminary problems such as thinning out the natural forests and providing better drainage. His major interest in the Bussey Institution was in the use of their facilities; he did nothing that resembled "professing" in his capacity of Professor of Horticulture and was at loggerheads with the Bussey staff in conflict-of-interest situations.

Early in his administration, Sargent revealed his intention to protect the territorial integrity of the Arboretum and to establish home rule in Jamaica Plain; to this end he feared no one. In 1875, one incident provoked him so much that he carried his appeal right over President Eliot's head to the Corporation.

The Professor of Chemistry at the Bussey Institute [F. H. Storer], while engaged in grading and laying out ... has passed beyond the limits of the grounds attached to the Institute, and has entered on the Arboretum. He has continued a deep pit several feet over the boundary line, thereby threatening the life of a valuable Elm tree, and interfering with my plans of immediate planting ... When I discovered what was going on I called Professor Storer's attention to the fact that he was passing beyond the limits ... when I was informed that the work was being done by direction of the President of the University. I at once notified Mr. Eliot of what had taken place, and have used every argument in my power to induce him to have the soil returned and the grounds put in the condition in which Prof. Storer found them. Not succeeding in this, and the danger to the row of trees being imminent, no course but to appeal to your Board is left to me.
... If any officer of the University can, without my knowledge, interfere in any way with the Arboretum, or order any work within its limits, I cannot consent to be held responsible for the care of your property.[2]

There is no record that the Corporation took any specific action on this complaint save to refer it to a committee. Sargent's interpretation of mine and thine did not conform with the University authorities' original idea of close cooperation between the two Jamaica Plain establishments. He fought hard for a separate listing of the Arboretum in the Annual Reports of the President and Treasurer instead of allowing it to appear as a subdepartment of the Bussey Institution. In the long run he achieved his measure of sovereignty and, quite understandably, won Eliot's dislike.

In May 1877, the Corporation voted to discontinue Sargent's Professorship of Horticulture at the Bussey, a decision which—whether by design or default—might have reduced the number of obvious opportunities for argument. When Sargent discovered he was also losing a thousand dollars a year, financially secure as he was, he protested vehemently, claiming he had no knowledge of the various sources of his income. In a compromising mood, the Corporation changed its vote and agreed to extend Sargent's Bussey salary another three years, adding $1,000 per annum on the condition that it be applied to the collection and care of books and dried specimens for the Arboretum.

While engaged in the early phases of planting and politics, Sargent came by a piece of uncommonly good luck. At about the time he became Director of the Arboretum, the City of Boston was making plans to lay out a park system. The man hired for the task was Frederick Law Olmsted, one of the most talented people ever to be engaged in the profession of landscape design. Olmsted practiced what Downing preached, with excellent results. In partnership with one of Downing's former protégés, Calvert Vaux, Olmsted had entered and won a competition for designing a park in New York City. That was in 1858; twenty years later Central Park was still not in a condition satisfactory to Olmsted, and the story of the frustrations of those years is complicated enough to fill its own volume, for politicians, newspapers, and prying citizens created havoc for Olmsted and Vaux. Nevertheless, the park was eventually completed with the integrity of the original plan left intact. Olmsted, sometimes alone and sometimes in collaboration with Vaux, executed parks for Brooklyn, Washington, D.C., and Philadelphia and consulted on countless projects. The partnership dissolved

Beginnings

amicably in 1872, about a year before Olmsted became involved with the Boston parks.

When the City of Boston began thinking about parks, Olmsted was the conspicuous candidate for the job. The Boston authorities may have had more on their hands than they bargained for, for Olmsted conceived his plans on a grand scale, with an eye to the future. He had worked in cities before and was experienced in the special problems related to landscape design in an urban environment. Olmsted envisioned for Boston not a park or several parks but a contiguous park system running from the center of the city (the old Boston Common) nearly seven miles to Franklin Park. The proposed Arnold Arboretum fell in the path of this scheme. After some discussion with his close friend Gray, and consultations with Sargent, he had a notion which, if put into operation, would be of mutual benefit to Harvard and to the City: the City should have restricted use of the Arboretum as a public park in exchange for performing maintenance services.

Sargent immediately perceived that such an alliance would open up possibilities for developing the Arboretum in a manner that he could only dream about before. That Olmsted would prepare the design was almost too good to be true, for Sargent greatly admired his work. Others did not share Sargent's enthusiasm, however; no sooner did rumors leak out than both the University—notably in the person of President Eliot—and local politicians began raising objections. But proceeding on the theory that actions were more effective than words, Olmsted prepared to lay out a plan for the Arboretum and offered to draw up the design free of charge. He needed a preliminary survey and contour map of the grounds, and he would have to charge incidental office expenses; altogether the cost would be around two thousand dollars. Modest though the sum was, it was far more than Sargent's operating budget could afford. Sargent did not even bother to take the matter to the University. In October 1877 he wrote Olmsted: "I started yesterday a subscription among some of the neighbors to raise the two thousand dol-

Sargent on His Own

53

lars for a plan of the Arboretum. My appeal has already met with such good success that the whole sum is as good as secured." [3] He could hardly have done better. Overnight he found eleven persons willing to part with at least $100 each; the value of their moral support was even greater than money. It was no accident that Sargent listed their names in his report to the President for that year, for they were all men of influence. John L. ("Jack") Gardner, John C. Phillips, William Amory, T. Jefferson Coolidge, George Emerson, and Amos A. Lawrence together made up $800. For the balance, Sargent could thank his family: his father, Henry Sargent, H. H. Hunnewell, and—if one agrees to stretch the family boundaries that far—William R. Robeson, an in-law. The Director added the last two hundred dollars himself. He was so elated with the response to his appeal that he wrote Hooker gleefully: "This I consider the greatest piece of good fortune that could possibly have happened to us as there is no one in whom I have so much confidence as in Olmsted in such matters, and the fact that his name is connected with the Arboretum will give it no small éclat with the American public. So on the whole I am very much pleased and well satisfied at the confidence that has been shown in my management as is shown by the subscription." [4]

By 1878, both men were impatient to have plans drawn, especially Sargent, who had by then been in charge for over five years with no permanent plantings to show for his labors. But Olmsted's emotional equilibrium had been upset by the latest battle with New York politicians over Central Park. For the sake of his nerves, he suggested taking a trip to Europe where he could, at the same time, look over foreign arboreta. Sargent favored the trip, noting pungently that "[t]here is so much to be learned there about this sort of work, especially what to avoid." [5] Olmsted spent the first three and a half months of the year abroad and returned refreshed. The lapse of activity, however, gave Sargent time to work up misgivings as he assessed the situation. He told Hooker,

Beginnings

54

The more I think of it the more I am appaled [*sic*] with the magnitude of the work and its great difficulty, which you can well imagine, and of my inability & want of fitness to undertake and make the most of it. Still there is no one to whom I can delegate the work, & I must do the best I can. Olmsted of course will render immense assistance in the way of taste and engineering, but the arrangement of plants so that they will tell as clearly as possible the story they are meant to illustrate I must do.[6]

Getting down to the actual work restored Sargent's confidence. During the summer of 1878, Olmsted lived in Cambridge and went over preliminary plans with Sargent and Gray.[7] Tactfully Sargent drew Gray into the early stages in hopes of healing any wounded feelings that may have lingered from the days when Gray felt his role in the Arboretum "reduced to zero." Sargent also guessed that if Gray could be won over to the idea of cooperating with the City, he would be useful in gaining President Eliot's sympathy.

No doubt one of the finest presidents in Harvard's history, Charles Eliot possessed an enlightened, puritanical character. Tall, erect, and dignified, he guided the University toward his goal of a modern educational institution. Like Sargent, his family and character were generated in New England. Asking him to agree to allow the City to operate the Arboretum as a park, restrictions or not, was almost like asking Congress to let Imperial Russia administer Alaska as a playground. The proposal necessarily meant that the University would surrender a certain amount of jurisdiction over Arboretum affairs, a prospect which did not appeal to Eliot at all. At the same time, he could not come up with a better solution. To do him justice, it is only fair to point out that he did not oppose the recommendations of Sargent and Olmsted outright. But he dragged his feet on the question and became increasingly annoyed by Sargent's proddings. Words concealed the central issue. Eliot raised nagging objections without discussing the fact that the University—

Sargent on His Own

55

and he—would suffer a loss of administrative power if the scheme went into effect. Not to be intimidated, Sargent and Olmsted explained their outlined plans, demonstrating how the Arboretum, and therefore Harvard, would benefit from the services which the City would render in return for use of the Arboretum as a park. Eliot reacted sullenly and persisted in his negative opinion.

In mid-September of 1878, Sargent took six weeks out for his first collecting trip in the far west with John C. Phillips, a fellow Harvardian (class of '58) and business associate through the Boston and Albany Railroad. They spent most of the time in central Nevada and the California Sierra Nevada range, where Sargent did a "grand amount of botanizing," and gathered quantities of seed of western species for trial in the Arboretum.[8] Upon his return he received a letter from Eliot, including a few cranky remarks on the subject of the Arboretum:

> The accumulation of the Arboretum Fund will be completed by March 1, 1879, so that it is time that the constitution and methods of the department should be carefully considered. I confess that I more & more dislike the idea of a partnership with the City. If a cemetery can protect its grounds, why not an arboretum? A paling, two or three workmen's houses at proper points, & the admission of the public on foot during fixed hours on condition of the City's providing police as at the Boston Natural History Society, rather commend themselves to my judgment. The public would not want to come in more than eight months out of twelve. Drive-ways we could not have on this scheme (or but a single short one); but are they desirable on the whole in so small an area?[9]

One can imagine Sargent's reaction to Eliot's analogy between the Arboretum and a cemetery. Eliot may have been stubborn, but he had a worthy adversary in Sargent who, in turn, had a strong ally in Olmsted. Gray's hand in the preliminary reports, coupled with the evidence from the sub-

Beginnings

scription drive that Sargent could muster powerful support among Bostonians, had a mollifying effect on the President. By 1879 he grudgingly consented to the arrangement and agreed to negotiate with City authorities. While he was working with Olmsted, bolstered as he was by future prospects, Sargent began to lose interest in the Botanic Garden. Although he had done much to improve it, it was too small; moreover, in Cambridge, he felt unpleasant restraints on his ambition. Early in 1879 he started talking about moving the Garden, herbarium, laboratories, and botanical staff to the Bussey Institution, which bordered the Arboretum. Goodale, who was as ambitious as Sargent, did not care for the idea at all and muttered threats about leaving Harvard if this scheme bore fruit. Gray, who had developed the Harvard botanical operation almost singlehandedly, was aghast at the notion and would not hear of it. When he realized that Sargent's proposal was serious, he interfered. Sargent saw he had overstepped his bounds and retreated in a gentlemanly fashion, and Gray, as a sort of compensation, gave his unqualified approval to the Arboretum scheme, helping to appease Eliot. A further outcome of Gray's diplomatic efforts to maintain order in Cambridge was the pacification of Goodale: at Gray's urging Sargent agreed to resign as Director of the Garden a year earlier than he had originally planned. Goodale would get the Garden and the $1,000 per year that went with it. Hooker, who received blow by blow descriptions of Cambridge academic intrigues from both Gray and Sargent, received Sargent's mixed feelings on the compromise:

As you know I am free of the Garden on the 1st of September [1879]. I am glad to be rid of it and to get really down at the Arboretum, which good or bad must be my life work, and where there will be always more to do than I can ever hope to accomplish. I am sorry to give up the pleasant & *instructive* daily intercourse with Gray, but that can not be helped; and I am still sorry about what I am confident will be the future of the Garden.[10]

Sargent on His Own

Sargent's mistrust of Goodale was thorough, for he wrote another friend:

> [Giving up the Garden] is not a voluntary action on my part. I am glad to be relieved of the care & labor of running it, and have always intended to get rid of it as soon as a proper person for Director could be found. But that time has not come and the Garden goes into improper and unfit hands, and all my work of the past six years will, I feel, be soon lost. Nor is the way in which the change has been brought about agreeable, placing as it does an associate [Goodale] in a contemptible position.[11]

From another point of view, however, the changes were not untimely for Sargent after all since the income from the Arnold Fund became available in March of the same year, and the Corporation appointed him Arnold Professor of Arboriculture, with a salary derived wholly from the fund which, with the completion of the designated accumulation, now yielded around $8,000 per year.

The way was thus cleared for Sargent to devote his full energies to the Arboretum and for the University to enter serious negotiations with the City of Boston. Sargent's difficulties with Eliot were negligible compared with the blockades thrown up by the City Council. As early as 1878, Boston's board of Park Commissioners, acting on the advice of Olmsted, accepted the plan of incorporating the Arboretum into the City park system and recommended that the City Council undertake to implement such an agreement with Harvard. At the outset of the considerations, however, there was a stumbling block. Olmsted's design for the Arboretum included forty-eight acres of land, comprising an area eventually to be used for a public highway, which were not owned by the University and which it could not purchase because of the restrictions on the Arnold Fund. The Commissioners suggested that the City should buy the land. This expense, on top of the cost of putting in the roads and pathways of Olmsted's

Beginnings

58

plan, plus the long-range outlay for policing the grounds, aroused dissent among the lawmakers. It was December 30, 1882, before the agreement between Harvard and the City was finally signed. During the interim of more than four years between the Park Commissioners' initial recommendation and decisive action by the City Council, red tape unraveled in disproportionate lengths.

By March 1879, the City Council had considered the first report and turned it back to the Park Commissioners, simultaneously granting them the authority to open negotiations with the University. The Commissioners, in turn, held discussions with Harvard officials and in November reported back to the Council that "it would be for the interest of the City to take the tract of land dedicated to the use of the Arnold Arboretum for a nominal sum, and lease to the College for a nominal sum, such portions as may not be necessary for driveways etc." [12] Following Olmsted's proposals, the Commissioners observed that for the best arrangement of the Arboretum the City should contribute the additional forty-eight acres to the property which they estimated could be bought for around twenty thousand dollars. The petition concluded by asking the Council "to authorize the Mayor to petition the legislature for such additional legislation as will enable them to execute such a lease." The Council did so, and in March 1880 the General Court of Massachusetts granted the necessary permission. Though this had been a tedious process, it went more or less smoothly.

The Council then began a lengthy debate on the subject. When it finally came to a vote at the October 13, 1881, session, the order necessary to secure the Arboretum for the City failed to receive the two-thirds vote it needed; only 36 votes of a total of 59 were received. The proponents of the Arboretum scheme within the Council, backed by a sympathetic press, were unwilling to regard this as a final vote and succeeded in appointing a Special Committee on the Arnold Arboretum.

Sargent's good humor fluctuated with the course of the

Sargent on His Own

59

debate. He and Olmsted appeared tirelessly before committees, and he was continually writing newspaper articles, speaking with influential persons, and in every way pushing the legislators toward positive action. He had to work largely on his own because President Eliot, while no longer opposing the plan, behaved indifferently, leaving him to wage his own battle. Fortunately Sargent was also occupied with work for the federal government on the forest trees of North America—of which more will be said later—so he did not have a good deal of time in which to brood. But after the disappointment of the October vote, with a crucial debate approaching before the end of the year, he began to have doubts and felt the need for dramatic action; there are times, he knew, when nothing is more spectacular than a show of financial power. To that end he and his allies drew up a petition, obtaining 1,305 signatures of the most influential names in Boston. In November, while the document was still in circulation, the City Council's special committee submitted its findings in the form of a majority report favoring the adoption of the Arboretum plan. There was as well a strongly worded minority opinion.

The majority report included findings based on studies made by the committee that the entire cost of purchasing the extra land, constructing roadways, and providing a water supply need not exceed $200,000; a further $10,000 per year would pay for maintenance and police protection. William Whitmore and Horace Clapp wrote a dissenting view to the effect that any action on the part of the Council would be a waste of the taxpayers' good money. The least one can say for these two men is that they were consistent and fought the Arboretum proposal all the way, even when the tide of public and political opinion turned against them. The document came up for floor debate on December 1, with Whitmore and Clapp leading the opposition and prolonging the argument in a desperate last effort to stall, if not defeat, a conclusive vote. Their attempt, however, was undercut by the petition before the Council. Clapp launched a brutal personal attack on Sargent:

Beginnings

This comes to us in the form of an order to spend $60,000 for an arboretum, or in other words a school for the study of the culture of trees. I have been trying to find out where this originated. It surely did not originate with the City of Boston as represented by its government; and we have been told in the committee that it did not originate with Harvard College. To my mind it must be either a phantasy of the Park Commissioners, or a scheme of individuals perhaps for personal glorification or public notoriety. My theory is the latter, and I am free to confess that I believe this scheme originated in the mind of one individual; that he is anxious to try an experiment which has never been tried but once before, taking his evidence, and then it was an ignominious failure ... I think he is weaving a net with the aid of an ignorant public to ensnare himself, and I think he is trying to get the City Government within this net.[13]

Whitmore stated his objection to spending money on an arboretum that would be there whether the City entered the transaction or not. He had no preference for roadways over footpaths, he claimed, so let Harvard pay for the footpaths and end the business there. He apparently did not believe Sargent's assertion that "[l]eft to itself the Arboretum can never hope to be open to the public, except in a limited and unsatisfactory manner."[14] Meanwhile, Sargent had become so irritated by the political haggling that, in a moment of bitterness he had recommended to Eliot that "unless the City is prepared to take definite action in the matter, some method for carrying out the provisions of Mr. Arnold's bequest should be devised without reference to the enjoyment or use of the Arboretum by the public."[15]

The petition, however, accomplished its goals. The *Herald* of December 1, 1881, claimed reverently that

The petition to the city council in favor of the Arnold Arboretum is probably the most influential ever received by that body. It includes almost all the large taxpayers

Sargent on His Own

of Boston, and represents property to the amount of at least $200,000,000. Picking out 42 names of business firms and individuals, almost at random, they are to be good for over $100,000,000. The entire wool trade is represented, also all the principal bankers, the dry goods trade, shoe and leather trade, and, indeed, about all the principal business houses of the city. Nearly all the prominent citizens are there, including ex-mayors and ex-Governors, and prominent clergymen, both Protestant and Catholic, and over 70 leading physicians. The petition would be a prize to a collector of autographs.[16]

The show of confidence was a triumph for Sargent, especially since it obviously got the better of some of the reluctant councilmen. A Mr. Smith confessed, in all honesty, that "[t]he only thing that would convince me that I ought to vote for this scheme is this petition. I find the names of a good many men there that I know to be honorable and highminded, but I don't believe when they signed this petition they knew what they were signing, or what the City of Boston was to get."[17] Smith cast his skepticism aside and voted with the "yeas."

Thanks to the petition, Sargent and Olmsted marshaled more defenders than they needed to carry the vote. They found instant champions among the councilmen; newspapers which had generally been quietly sympathetic rushed to shout unqualified support, pointing out that the City could acquire for a nominal sum a parkland area valued at over a million dollars. The arguments of Whitmore and Clapp rang hollow, and, at last, on December 27, 1881, the City Council authorized the Park Commissioners to take over the Arboretum land and lease it back to the University. It took another year to work out details between the Park Commissioners and the University, but the battle was won.

All matters having been settled by the end of 1882, an agreement was signed on December 30 by the City of Boston, represented by the Park Commission, and the President and Fellows of Harvard College, the reluctant Eliot holding

Beginnings

62

the Harvard pen. In essence, the agreement stipulated that Harvard transfer one hundred twenty acres to the City. These joined what finally turned out to be about forty-five acres (which the City purchased for $47,024.23), and the whole was leased back to Harvard, except for the proposed driveway and parkway areas indicated on the plan, at the rate of one dollar a year, for one thousand years, on a tax-free basis with a renewable lease. The City contracted to construct the driveways indicated in Olmsted's design and to bear the responsibility for repairing and maintaining them. The indenture set a ceiling of $75,000 on road construction costs.[18] The City would also provide police protection for the Arboretum. For its part, the City gained the land now occupied by the Arborway along the Arboretum's east boundary for highway use; above all, it got a new park which would be open to the public "at all reasonable times"; reasonable times were established as daily from sunrise to sunset. The public, of course, was expected to behave itself with decorum, subject to the discipline of the police. There was also some guarantee that Olmsted's plan would be permanent, for additional roadways or buildings could not be constructed without the common consent of the Park Commissioners and the University.

Sargent had good cause to celebrate on New Year's Eve of 1882. After more than nine years as Director of the Arboretum, the way was finally clear for him to make something out of it. The negotiations had eaten into time, but they had produced a number of benefits. During the political troubles, Sargent brought public opinion over to his side. People who had never heard of an arboretum before, much less seen one, became unexpectedly concerned about trees. The name of Charles Sprague Sargent commanded new respect in the eyes of Bostonians, who were impressed by his authority and tenacity. While the Sargent name was of no small value in itself, it cannot alone account for the strong support of the petition. A less resolute man would have had mediocre results. As it was, a modern-day Madison Avenue advertising executive would be hard put to improve on the

Sargent-Olmsted public relations tactics. With patience and clarity they undertook to educate the public, originally ignorant of the meaning of the word, as to what an arboretum was and how it could benefit them; they made them *want* one; they made the Arboretum into a *cause célèbre.*

While the Arboretum struggled through infancy, Sargent attended to numerous problems aside from the primary one of pushing the Arboretum legislation through the City's political grinder. The Cambridge Garden went to Goodale in September 1879 in the shuffle to placate the restless botanical staff. Sargent's one-man campaign to transplant Harvard botany to Jamaica Plain failed, but if the Arboretum was to be isolated from the Cambridge unit, it would need reference material. In 1879, he wrote George Engelmann, "it will be necessary for me to form a special Herbarium for the Arnold Arboretum which as you know is situated 6 miles from that at Cambridge and too far for references. I propose to confine it (for many years at any rate) to trees & shrubs of 1st North America, 2nd the whole temperate zone." [19] Within the year he moved his private stock of specimens from the Cambridge herbarium out to an unoccupied house at his Holm Lea estate, for as yet there was nowhere to put them at the Arboretum. In 1880, he had less than 1,000 mounted specimens, compared, for example, with Gray's more than 200,000 in 1865. Along with the herbarium, Sargent formed a small library stocked with his personal collection of books. Gray was not particularly pleased with the arrangement; he preferred everything to be kept within the Cambridge circle. But he could not offer a logical alternative since one could hardly expect Sargent to travel back and forth between Cambridge and Jamaica Plain every time he wanted to look at a specimen. Sargent asked John Robinson, a Salem man with a good knowledge of trees, to be in charge of the herbarium and collect specimens in New England.

As the Arboretum moved, at first slowly and then faster, from idea to reality, Sargent gathered a staff. That he se-

Beginnings

64

cured a handful of exceptional men was a combination of good luck and his ability to recognize talent when he saw it. His first bona fide staff member, Jackson Dawson, joined him in 1874. One botanist characterized Dawson as "capable almost of resurrecting a dead stick and certainly of coaxing into vigorous growth a twig found in the pocket of a shooting-jacket weeks after this had been laid aside." [20] When Sargent replaced Parkman at the Bussey Institution, he discovered Dawson working in the greenhouses. Dawson supplied him with plants for the Cambridge Garden and the Arboretum. Two years later, Sargent contrived to hire him as superintendent of the Arboretum.[21] There Dawson practiced his particular wizardry: grafting, coaxing seeds to sprout, encouraging stubborn cuttings. One spectator of his art in later years likened him to a "wizened, midsummer elf." [22] He was absolute master in the nursery area, lord of the small greenhouse, frames, and seedlings. He made himself at home there in comfortable, unchallenged disorder, hanging animal skins to dry, and keeping bits of brandy around for cold days.

Dawson stayed with the Arboretum until his death in 1916, but Robinson was only there for two years. In 1882 Sargent asked Charles Edward Faxon, a naturalist and botanical artist, to take over Robinson's duties and prepare a large number of drawings. Faxon was a man with a sophisticated education, versed in many languages, and trained as a civil engineer. A lover of nature and well tutored in natural sciences, he chose botany as a profession instead of engineering and was an instructor at the Bussey Institution from 1879 to 1884. Back in the 1860's he had made fine and accurate illustrations for Daniel Cady Eaton's *Ferns of North America*. Botanical drawing requires talents beyond those of the ordinary illustrator. Precision alone does not necessarily make a good drawing, for the beauty and value lie in the clarity of presentation and arrangement. Faxon, combining knowledge of plants with his ability to do refined art work, made an outstanding botanical artist. In fact, as they were published in later years, Sargent's volumes received

as much applause for Faxon's drawings as for the author's text.[23]
Dawson and Faxon were Sargent's professional staff in 1882. He did not even have a proper secretary. Wealthy, unemployed Francis Skinner, Jack Gardner's brother-in-law and an old schoolmate of Sargent's, volunteered to serve as an amanuensis—despite what Sargent considered bad penmanship—or to answer some of the routine incoming mail on behalf of the Director,[24] but he worked strictly at his own convenience, presumably when not better occupied. Similarly, Andrew Robeson, one of Sargent's brothers-in-law, occasionally lent a hand as a cartographer. Only Dawson and Faxon, however, were full-time, regular staff. They were typical of the men Sargent had at the Arboretum in later years. Ernest Wilson, Alfred Rehder, William Judd, and John Jack, for example, had little in common with each other except ability. They worked many years under Sargent's direction, sometimes in his shadow, other times sufficiently exposed to establish individual reputations. The Director, gruff and despotic, was less an inspiration than a source of energy, and he was scrupulously fair in distributing credit. For Sargent, after all, was his father's son. He administered the Arboretum as though it were a business venture, only instead of calculating his profits in capital gains, he counted trees, herbarium specimens, publications, and scientific research. Gray, genuinely impressed with the way Sargent had managed the Harvard-Boston agreement, remarked thoughtfully—and probably a bit wistfully—that Sargent "has developed not only a power of doing work, but of getting work done for him by other people, and so can accomplish something." [25]

Sargent's complaint that the Arboretum land was a "worn-out farm" was only partially justified according to Professor Hugh Raup, who made a detailed study of the early uses of the property. Raup points out that although most of the original forest was cleared from the land before 1700, "the actual plowing and cultivation of the land were not extensive."

Beginnings

The oft-repeated expression that the Arboretum has been grown upon "worn-out" farm is true . . . only in the sense that the soils of the area have lost some of the qualities originally given to them by the long-standing primeval forest; and that they have been compacted and the distribution of the elements in their layers modified. But they do not seem to have been unduly subjected to surface washing nor to a depletion in mineral salts.[26]

Sargent, who had not bothered to dig for historic details, only knew that in 1873 he saw undrained meadows, a marsh area, and thickets—in short, the consequences of decades of neglect. The bulk of the land, the old Bussey Farm, had not been touched since 1842, when Bussey died. On the other hand, there were promising features: the terrain was varied and rolling, there was a natural brook, and there was Hemlock Hill, a splendid stand of hemlocks, at the base of which, by the brook, people of archaic cultures once had a camp ground. According to one nineteenth-century Jamaica Plain historian, this part of the Bussey property had once been employed as parkland.

During Mr. Bussey's life, and for years after, the public enjoyed the freedom of these charming grounds. There were lovely wood paths, carefully kept, in all directions. Here was a rustic bridge spanning the jocund brook; there a willow-bordered pond, the home of gold and silver fish. This path wound back and forth to the summit of Hemlock Mountain, where was an arbor with seats for resting, surrounded by majestic trees, where lovely vistas of the distant hills and nearer valley could be enjoyed. On the gray rocks yonder were nature's moss-clad seats, where one listened to the endless whispering of the leaves, the prattle of the happy brook below, and the ever-changing songs of birds.[27]

If this was true, there remained little evidence of such poetic charms by the time Sargent took over. Hooker saw the land

Sargent on His Own

in 1877, during his only visit to America, and marked it down in his journals as a "magnificent piece of ground." [28] No doubt he envied the hills, for Kew, with its gentler climate, lies flat. Sargent had ambitious ideas about the one hundred and sixty-five acres. He set them forth officially in a letter to the Park Commissioners in 1879, separating the functions of the Arboretum into four categories: museum of living plants, scientific station, school of forestry and arboriculture, and popular educator. In the Arboretum he determined to grow "every tree and shrub capable of withstanding the climate of Massachusetts." [29] (He made no mention of the herbaceous plants mentioned in the original indenture.) Though the Massachusetts weather conditions effectively narrowed the field, Sargent planned to have thousands of species. Following Olmsted's sketches for roadways, Sargent explained:

> It is proposed to group the trees in their natural sequence along the principal drive. Each species, represented, if possible, by half-a-dozen specimens, will be planted in immediate connection with its varieties, making with its allies, native and foreign, loose generic groups in which each individual will find sufficient space for full development, and through which the visitor can freely pass. Each of these groups will rest on the main avenue so that a visitor driving through the Arboretum will be able to obtain a general idea of the arborescent vegetation of the north temperate zone without even leaving his carriage. It is hoped that such an arrangement, while avoiding the stiff and formal lines of the conventional botanic garden, will facilitate the comprehensive study of the collections, both in their scientific and picturesque aspects.[30]

Imagine a zoo where the animals are organized in sequence according to their presumed evolutionary rank, and the effectiveness of the plan is at once apparent. This is a pattern found in textbooks but not in the field. For the student

Beginnings

or scientist such an arrangement enables the easy study of closely related specimens; to a casual visitor it suggests logical contrasts rather than random comparisons. This was not an idea that originated with Sargent. In the 1780's de Jussieu put his plants in tubs and moved them about to express his emerging scheme of classification. The best European arboreta, including Kew, planted related species together, although genera did not necessarily follow any pattern. The more common practice of putting specimens in locations where the growing conditions were favorable (ecological grouping) presented problems to the botany student. As Hooker wrote Sargent, "The grouping of species has thrown a vast light on their character. An ungrouped arboretum is a perfect snare as well as a snarl. I defy any one to carry a character in his head from a plant of one species to another of the same elsewhere, if you have to pass its allies en route." [31] Sargent also wanted a supplementary shrub collection, for species which did not have tree relatives, set aside particularly for the use of gardeners and landscape designers. Certain better naturally wooded areas were to be thinned out but otherwise left alone.

Unlike a park, which is strictly a pleasure ground, the Arboretum was educational. Given the functional planting scheme, it would have been possible to lapse into a contrived, self-conscious landscape design or into an unimaginative one; there was not another arboretum in the United States to serve as a model. With the emphasis on education, the Arboretum could easily have failed in its secondary role as a park for pleasure had it not been for Olmsted's artistry and Sargent's good taste. In contrast with his inability to appreciate music—all the Holm Lea Sargents were notoriously tone deaf—he loved painting and drawing and was partial to boldness and simplicity in art. His tastes in landscaping, like those of Downing and Olmsted, ran to the simple and natural. While the effect was romantic, the philosophy was decidedly unromantic, for Sargent observed that, left to itself, nature was inclined to produce unsightly tangles of vegetation and allow stronger plants to choke out their weaker rivals and extract all nourishment from the soil. Man, while often nature's thoughtless enemy, was more properly cast as its benefactor. Sargent had no love for changing natural forms, for making things what they were not. Carving an elephant out of a shrubby plant was as ridiculous to him as pasting leaves on an elephant. He believed, however, that acting within the framework of natural forms, man could improve the function and appearance of nature.

It was in this spirit that the Arboretum was created. In the early years, before the conclusion of the agreement with the City, Sargent's work was all preparatory to the day when the settlement would be made. It is hard to imagine what he would have done if the politicians had rejected the scheme. The work would not have gone to waste, for it was essential to an arboretum under any circumstances. But Sargent was so dead set on the Olmsted plan that he did not provide for defeat. Dawson worked busily setting out trees in the Bussey nurseries, propagating seeds and cuttings. Sargent had the woodlands cleared and revitalized with young, healthy trees to replace older members of the same species. The postponement of permanent planting, however, delayed the real work of the Arboretum sufficiently to cause Sargent many hours of anxiety. In the meantime, with Robinson and Faxon, he tended to the herbarium and library at Holm Lea.

Once Sargent had his victory, changes began to appear on the landscape. By July 1883, six months after the agreement was signed, the City started work on the driveways, and even Sargent, who would have been the first to complain of delays, admitted that it progressed steadily. By late 1884, with much of the roadwork complete, Sargent began new consultations with Olmsted to refine their plans. Perhaps the long wait had been a good thing after all, for in the interim, Sargent had learned a great deal about American trees. Moreover, his ideas for the Arboretum were more sophisticated and realistic than they had been before. He abandoned a project, proposed in 1879, for devoting twenty or thirty acres to experimental forestry. In February 1885, just before the permanent plantings were put in, he wrote Olmsted:

> One function of the Arboretum is to serve as a museum of living trees. Other museums of living trees have been attempted, as you know, in various European countries. They have, it seems to me, all failed to accomplish the object they were intended to accomplish in attempting too much and too little. They have attempted too much in endeavoring to crowd into an inadequate space more trees than the space could hold; and too little in sacrificing all artistic effects to mere scientific details of botanical arrangement. All museums in these days of superabundant material or rather such portions of museums as are intended to educate the public by means of object teaching must consist of *selections* rather than complete collections... The best and most instructive museum[s]... must in the future be those in which the greatest judgment and skill is shown in the selection of the objects displayed. Selections and not accumulations will in the future I believe be the right policy of all museum management... Even if we believe it desirable to display in our museum all such [ligneous] forms we shall be unable to do it.[32]

Sargent had compromised his plan to plant "every tree and shrub capable of withstanding the climate of Massachusetts." Now he was more concerned with achieving balance. Where once he would have planted everything that would grow, he now made a wide choice of North American trees and a smaller selection of outstanding foreign trees to illustrate tree growth in the temperate zone.

Despite the fact that the City's work on roadways came to a temporary standstill in December 1885—much to Sargent's annoyance—enough headway had been made to begin putting in trees the following spring. Large numbers of conifers, ashes, elms, catalpas, birches, hickories, hop-hornbeams, and beeches were transferred from the overflowing nursery beds and planted in number. By August the Director reported seventy thousand trees and shrubs in place. Sargent remarked with confidence that "trees have never been planted with better promise of undisturbed old age."[33] The ground was prepared to receive the following spring's offering of oaks, walnuts, and chestnuts. When these were put in, Sargent directed fifty thousand shrubs to be planted among them.[34] One of Sargent's contemporaries, obviously wise by experience, wrote:

> Unfortunately, of all art processes, that of landscape making is the slowest in its consummation . . . [The landscape-gardener's] imagination must grasp the available materials and estimate their potentialities, and then, taking a bold leap into the future, he must form in his mind a picture of the ultimate scene to be unfolded, and must dispose his materials so as to develop this ideal through slow natural processes . . . In other artistic activity, realization follows close upon the heels of conception, but the finished picture of the maker of landscapes will not become an actuality for years; indeed, a century may pass before the artist's thought attains its full expression.[35]

In this context, it is easy to understand why the process of designing and planting taxed Sargent's imagination as much as Olmsted's. It is only in considering the scale, in space and time, of the Arboretum undertaking, that one can begin to grasp the quality of the man who devoted his adult lifetime to its perfection. An American elm (*Ulmus americana*), which might eventually grow as tall as 120 feet, reaches only around 30 feet after its first ten years. The white oak (*Quercus alba*) averages 90 feet in height at maturity but scarcely achieves 15 feet in ten years. The Eastern white pine (*Pinus strobus*) grows at about a foot a year, though one day it may be more than 100 feet tall.[36] Even though trees assume their mature proportions and adorn the landscape long before they reach their growth

Beginnings

72

limits, starting an arboretum is no job for a man who longs to see a finished product.

Almost fifteen years had passed since Sargent became Director of the Arboretum. In April of 1887, when the oaks were being planted, he reached his forty-sixth birthday. While one hundred and twenty thousand selected and artfully placed young plants gave him ample reason to believe that his efforts had been worthwhile, the Arboretum still left a lot to the imagination. The planting and construction were incomplete, and the small trees in their fresh holes would take years to achieve their adult stateliness. But there was no compromise in the general plan. Despite the opposition of politicians, the contrariness of Harvard's president, and the skepticism of Gray, the Arboretum came into being as Sargent and Olmsted conceived it.

Sargent on His Own

Part Two. The Arboretum and Beyond

4

In the Nation's Forests

One would think that with all the headaches and preparations for the Arboretum Sargent would have had enough to
do. But as the Cambridge Botanic Garden was too small for
his energies during the 1870's, so the Arboretum did not
contain them in the 1880's. During the summer of 1880, he
stormed the North American forests on a government mission. As it turned out, this was the first of several efforts
Sargent made to arouse the American conscience to take
measures to protect forested areas. Sargent viewed his role
as a public servant in the same fashion that the British
imperialists assumed the "white man's burden." Just as he
believed that nature could benefit from human guidance, he
believed that men had to be protected from their own abuses
by careful instruction.

Sargent claimed that his interest in forests and their
preservation was "almost entirely" due to having read
George Perkins Marsh's *Man and Nature*,[1] which first appeared in 1864. Marsh, a Vermont lawyer, manufacturer,
politician—he sat in the House of Representatives during
the 1840's—and diplomat, was a man of Renaissance temperament who cultivated several interests, including the
natural sciences. His book presented a devastating account
of the real and theoretical consequences of man's absent-
minded disrespect for nature's delicate balance. Rachel
Carson's *The Silent Spring* is no more dramatic than was

Marsh's observation that "the destructive agency of man becomes more and more energetic and unsparing as he advances in civilization, until the impoverishment, with which his exhaustion of the natural resources is threatening him, at last awakens him to the necessity of preserving what is left, if not of restoring what has been wantonly wasted." [2] Marsh sometimes gave more credit to forests than they were due, as when he discussed trees as a protection against malaria, interceptors of the "miasmatic effluvia of swampy soils"; [3] however, considering how little was known about malaria at the time, he hit surprisingly close to the mark. In Europe, where forests had been at man's mercy for centuries, experts were frantically trying to restore them. In America, although plenty of damage had already been done, it was not too late to adopt measures to prevent further abuse and make needed repairs. For a short period after it was published, Marsh's book attracted considerable attention and much praise from those people who had some idea about the problems, but shortly thereafter it dropped into obscurity. [4]

The story of the destruction of American timberlands is well known. Beginning with the East Coast settlers of Colonial times, who freely chopped trees for fuel, lodging, and shipbuilding—the latter program with the encouragement of His Majesty's Government—and on to the pioneers who moved west, seeing the forests as vast green seas to be conquered, clearing the land for crops as they went, American forests fell before the axe. Perhaps no one could really believe that in this enormous land mass the forests could be exhausted. Yet by the end of the eighteenth century the Navy realized the possibility that the East Coast timber supply for shipbuilding could be, in theory anyway, depleted. Acting upon the Navy's request, Congress, in 1799, appropriated $200,000 for the purchase of growing timber or lands suitable for growing it. The government purchased Grover's Island and Blackbeard's Island off the Georgia coast during the following years and made subsequent purchases under the act. These were the first federal reserves, marking the government's initial adventures in silviculture.[5]

Anxious for an expert analysis of the country's timber supply, in 1848, the Smithsonian Institution, still in its infancy, invited Asa Gray to prepare a report on forest trees. Gray soon abandoned the task, however, when he discovered that it involved the accumulation of too much practical data outside his personal interests.[6] Forestry matters received offhand treatment in national Census bulletins until 1870 when the Census Bureau asked William H. Brewer, the Yale botanist, to put together the section on forests. Brewer's program was less ambitious than the one the Smithsonian had proposed for Gray, but he went part way in a survey of the taxonomic distribution of woodlands and discussed the areas where forests were, or were not, being felled or destroyed by fire. Perhaps Brewer's most significant contribution was an attempt to distinguish forested areas from the general heading of "unimproved" land where they had, in the past, been lumped together with prairies and marshlands to give a meaningless total. Yet the 1870 Census excluded land not in farms from this distinction, thus limiting the value of its findings. There was a pessimistic undercurrent to the report, but it contained little conclusive evidence since it was compiled largely from systematic literature and second-hand oral reports.[7]

The government attempted to persuade settlers to maintain the forests on their new properties but, more interested in encouraging settlement at any cost, took no steps to provide for the protection of natural resources on the land which it gave away to the pioneers.[8] The railways, too, destroyed parts of the forests as they moved westward. In 1873 Congress made a naive attempt to stem the tide of timber destruction by passing the Timber Culture Act. By this law, 160 acres of public lands were awarded to any settler who would devote 40 of them to the cultivation of trees. The act, lacking the conviction of enforcement, ultimately did more harm than good, for it was a boon to speculators and sawmill

In the Nation's Forest

owners who, masquerading as settlers, acquired forest land, cut down the trees for profit, and abandoned the area. The year 1873 was not altogether bad for the forests, however. In August, Dr. Franklin B. Hough, a physician interested in conservation, presented a paper on forest problems before the American Association for the Advancement of Science at Portland, Maine. Like Sargent, Hough had read Marsh and responded to the sense of urgency. So moved was the convention that it appointed a committee, including Dr. Hough, George B. Emerson, Gray, and Brewer, to promote federal and state forestry commissions. A year later, the committee issued a report which evolved into a recommendation to Congress. In 1876, giving in to mounting pressures, Congress authorized the establishment of a Division of Forestry within the Department of Agriculture. Hough was named the first Agent of the Division.

In 1877 Hough made the first of three reports to the Department of Agriculture. He noted philosophically, "It has been observed in all countries and at all periods, that trees furnishing products demanded by commerce, or standing in the way of cultivation, become an object of inconsiderate waste."[9] Although Hough's findings were not based on original field investigation, his appeal for government participation in forest interests made an impression. Carl Schurz, then Secretary of the Interior, was sympathetic to forestry problems and favored Hough's views in principle. His department handled the census, and he was anxious to get some original documentation into the 1880 report to provide a firmer basis for the recommendation of legislation. Gray, as a Regent of the Smithsonian, was asked to suggest a man to conduct the census investigation and he named Sargent. Francis Walker, Superintendent of the Census Office, made the formal application for Sargent's services.

Sargent hesitated in accepting the position. Before 1879, his work in forestry had been done principally in Massachusetts, mostly through the Massachusetts Society for Promoting Agriculture.[10] He did not underestimate for a

The Arboretum and Beyond

minute the size of the job he was being asked to do. He knew from books and herbarium specimens, and especially from his own collecting trips, how many trees he must see and how great an area he must travel. He also had to consider his responsibilities to the Arboretum, which was then at the mercy of the politicians. After mulling over the invitation from Washington, the pragmatic Sargent wrote Hooker:

> I have almost determined to accept the direction of so much of the next U. S. Census as relates to Forests, their distribution, value, & so on . . . although the labor will be enormous, I think that in the interest of the Arboretum I should accept it. It will give me great facilities for travel at Government expense to every part of the continent and will enable me to greatly enrich the Arboretum in every way, besides doing much needed work in showing the great wealth and value of our forests, and the dangers with which their destruction will threaten us.[11]

Despite misgivings Sargent agreed to the project and went to Washington in mid-November to discuss details with the officials. The nature of the investigation on which they agreed resembled that which had been proposed by the Smithsonian to Gray in 1848: the Census report should combine systematic, geographical, and economic information based on new observations and tests.

About two weeks after his trip to Washington, Sargent wrote Engelmann in St. Louis to enlist his aid.

> I have been busy organizing the various and most difficult inquiries which have to be made in connection with this work. I am going to publish at once a catalogue of our trees, with reference to best descriptions and figures, geographical range, as I know it (and how little I know except in a general way!) economic value and uses. This catalogue I shall distribute widely with the request that recipients will furnish me with any information about

In the Nation's Forest

trees of their neighborhoods they happen to know about. I hope in this way to get a good deal of information about various points of which at present no one seems to know anything.

In this connection I am going to have the wood of all the trees tested for strength, but giving qualities . . . Shall we go to Oregon together next summer?

. . . You had better make up your mind to receiving in the future about 100 questions per week.[12]

Engelmann was a knowledgeable botanist whose special familiarity with conifers would be valuable, as would his location in St. Louis and his long acquaintance with western collections. Sargent was not entirely selfish in his motives, however. Engelmann, at seventy, had fallen into such a profound state of mental depression that all his friends worried about him. Around Christmas 1878, his son had nearly died from blood poisoning, and Engelmann had abandoned his botanical studies to nurse him back to health. Then, early in 1879, his wife Dora, her own health eroded by the strain of the son's illness, died. Anxiety, sadness, and age afflicted Engelmann, and he despaired of resuming his botany. Sargent prescribed a good field trip to revive his friend's spirits, but Engelmann needed considerable coaxing before he would venture so far. Still, he was amused by Sargent's excitement and intrigued by the project. He wrote Sargent:

Why you seem to be all upset or ready to upset us? and such a hasty scribbling! Why it is worse than mine, and —well never mind, I think I have at last deciphered all.

You have a great task before you and will have to work hard to bring out something creditable, but you can and will do it. I may be able to help you some in my quiet way, but then, that [w]on't count much. Nor can you rely much on others, you must see for yourself, and how you will get over the whole country in a few months is more than I can tell you.[13]

The Arboretum and Beyond

Then, to make matters worse, Engelmann fell off a ladder and hurt his knee—a stunt for which Sargent affectionately reprimanded him.[14]

True to form, Sargent was already operating at top speed. Unwilling to wait for a summer field trip, he prepared in January 1880 to finish out affairs in Washington, discuss matters with Engelmann in St. Louis, and then go south to look at the trees. He hoped Engelmann would join him, but the latter begged off, claiming that his knee had not mended, and, anyway, there would be nothing to see "but nature in hybernation!"[15] Sargent was not discouraged and kept to his plan. During his visit in St. Louis he extracted a conditional promise from Engelmann to join the summer expedition. Sargent proceeded south, where he found that nature was not in *complete* hibernation, for in Charlestown, Missouri, he saw a scarlet maple in bloom and made a point of telling Engelmann about it.[16]

Sargent hastened home in mid-February to find his wife in some danger because of a prolonged pregnancy. He had expected to return just in time for the birth of their fourth child, but when he discovered that the baby would not arrive on schedule he became concerned, distracted, and very much the nervous husband. He had to wait until March 7 for the birth of Charles, Jr. As he told Engelmann, "this, while it lasts, is anything but a pleasant episode in a man's life, however agreeable the results."[17] Once assured that both mother and son were thriving, he was off again, this time to catch the early spring in North Carolina.[18]

Between trips and preparations for the major effort in the summer, Sargent mapped out the work of the Census report, sending queries to correspondents in all parts of the country and soliciting their aid in information and collecting. George W. Letterman, a botanist from Missouri, agreed to work the forests west of the Lower Mississippi, a region he knew well. Cyrus G. Pringle, one of the great collectors of his day, would examine both the northeastern forests and those in Arizona and southern California. Robert Douglas, an English-born, Michigan nurseryman specializing in forest

In the Nation's Forest

trees, would go into the Dakota Black Hills. Sereno Watson said he could work on the northern Rocky Mountain region during the summer. A. H. Curtiss promised to help in Georgia and Florida. Charles Mohr of the Department of Agriculture was enlisted to do the Gulf states. G. M. Dawson, John Macoun, and Robert Bell, members of the Geological Survey of Canada, would furnish statistics on that country's forests. Michael Bebb, a specialist in the willow genus (*Salix*), offered his experience. These were only some of the men to whom Sargent applied for botanical aid, and they would supply only a portion of the work to be done. There were maps to be drawn and statistics to be compiled. This became the work of Andrew Robeson. Stephen Sharples, a Cambridge chemist, tested the strength of various woods and he, in turn, had the assistance of the U.S. Army.

Sargent, as the head of this small battalion of investigators, bore the title of "Expert and Special Agent of the Tenth Census of the United States." He took his assignment seriously, issuing demands, orders, and questions on specially printed stationery. Much as Gray had tried over the years to coordinate the work of the *Flora of North America,* so Sargent was now the coordinator of the forest study. To be sure, the latter was a relatively modest enterprise, and Sargent had the blessings of government funds to finance travel and assistance, an advantage which he was the first to acknowledge.[19] Even so, the published report represented a remarkable amount of work for such a short time, and this was largely due to Sargent's energy and administrative efficiency. He himself was exacting and tireless and he expected the same of his colleagues. When he was not off on a field trip, he bombarded them with letters, sometimes twice a day, filled with questions or requests for more material, often much to their distress, for nearly all had other obligations. The tone of his letters, except to close friends like Letterman or Engelmann, was imperious, but he got results.

Sargent's first task, as he had told Engelmann, was the publication of a catalogue of North American forest trees.

The Arboretum and Beyond

This was printed in 1880 with deliberate haste, at government expense, and circulated among various correspondents for their comments. It pretended to be nothing more than a hurried production, gleaned mostly from the available literature such as Michaux's and Nuttall's respective sylvas * of North America and Brewer's 1870 Census report, but Sargent did not want to waste time in the early stages. The *Catalogue* listed only 135 genera and 342 species, compared with the final report, which named 158 genera and 412 species. Information regarding geographical distribution was incomplete, and notations on habit were vague. But by selective circulation the little book had its desired effect. Sargent directed that it be printed on only one side of the page so that the corresponding blank page could be used for additions or corrections, and he asked that copies be returned to him for incorporation into the final report.

While Sargent assembled the *Catalogue* during the spring of 1880, Engelmann was back in St. Louis, debating with himself whether or not he should go along on the summer trip. Sargent, confident that Engelmann would succumb to the plan, mapped out what threatened to be a strenuous journey if it went according to schedule; knowing Sargent, Engelmann thought it would. Luckily, Sargent was not the only person worried about Engelmann's well-being. Charles Christopher Parry, the collector, was a longtime friend, and he too urged Engelmann to get into the field. In March, Mr. and Mrs. Parry visited Engelmann in St. Louis. Parry said he wanted to spend the summer botanizing in the West and suggested the possibility of joining Sargent's party. The plan appealed to Engelmann, who knew he could trust Parry to look after him if need be. He finally agreed to go. Since Parry was heading east anyway, it was settled that he would meet with Sargent to make final arrangements for the trip. Although Sargent had not counted on Parry, he was happy to have him along since he assured Engelmann's company.

* A sylva or silva is a description of the trees of a certain area.

In the Nation's Forest

Sargent, with Francis Skinner in tow as a volunteer aide-de-camp, set out from Brookline in the middle of June, via Kansas City, for his own trek through Colorado. He spent a couple of days longer than planned, and the schedule suffered a little, but he and Skinner finally met up with Engelmann and Parry in Ogden, Utah. From there they set out for Oregon via San Francisco. Accounts of the journey did not reach Gray back east for nearly eight weeks, when he received word from both Sargent and Engelmann. Engelmann's letter sparkled with an enthusiastic account of their journey from San Francisco:

By steamer [we went] to Portland and without stopping through the Sound to Victoria and then up Frazer River, where we made the first regular mountain ascent, near [F]ort Hope at the angle which the river makes coming from the north and turning west. We were right among the snows and were gratified in finding several alpine Conifers, among others *Abies amabilis* which is really distinct from *grandis* . . .

Back through the Sound to Portland. Up to the Cascades and the Dalles, where Sargent alone ascended an Indian trail to Douglas' [David Douglas, the Scottish botanical explorer of Douglas fir fame] original locality, where *amabilis* is splendid.

· · ·

And here we are ready to leave tomorrow for the South —Coast Range, Cascades and then Shasta.

· · ·

Parry left us a week ago to go with Suksdorf to Mt. Adams. I persist and believe the active life, great (for me great) exertion being a beneficial influence on my health—but find the greatest impediment is my knee which has not got entirely over the effects of the fall 8 months ago.[20]

Sargent's version of the trip paralleled Engelmann's. He was proud of his ascent to Douglas' site, which he described

The Arboretum and Beyond

as "A terribly hard climb, owing to fallen timber; but I was well rewarded finding there two trees besides many others which Douglas must have overlooked." The collecting had been good, and many conifers had been "flowering." As for Engelmann, Sargent reported that he was "splendid, with a spirit & courage big enough for a much stronger body. Still he keeps up wonderfully & even got up to Frazer river Mt. but with many groans. He thoroughly enjoyed it; and once rested I really think he was better for the hard two days work & the night under the stars." [21] Several years later, given an occasion to pay tribute to Engelmann, Sargent made particular reference to that journey:

> Dr. Engelmann was then rather infirm, crippled with rheumatism, and very stout. His energy, courage, and endurance were a surprise and delight to us. He never hesitated to try to get up the steepest mountains or to take long drives and rides. Generally he was badly used up at the end of a hard day, and would lie upon the ground in evident pain for an hour or two after supper, but he would rally and go to work to put up his plants of the day's collecting, working conscientiously over them for hours, sometimes when the rest of us were asleep.
>
> . . . I look back upon that journey as the most interesting and profitable one I have ever made, and its success was due to Dr. Engelmann's energy, judgment, and common sense.[22]

Parry wrote a week later, after he had already parted company with Sargent and Engelmann, that he had had his fill of rushing about and was glad to be working at his own pace. Engelmann, he said, seemed "quite lively but does not enjoy the hurry & push of Sargent. I think as soon as *he completes* the most important investigations in the *Conifers* he will take his own 'slow & sure' gait. Sargent is anxious to get round to San Francisco by 1st. Sept. & thence by some southern route home by Oct." [23]

But Engelmann, though grumbling about the haste, stuck

In the Nation's Forest

with Sargent and Skinner through southern California. In Monterey, the three bearded travelers posed for a photograph, now well known to students of botanical history, in which Sargent sits benignly clasping a cone-laden branch and Engelmann glowers fiercely. They proceeded to southeastern Arizona, nearly at the Mexican boundary, and then returned to San Francisco at the beginning of October.[24] Engelmann intended to visit his cousin, see the California vineyards, and do a bit of traveling on his own, so Sargent and Skinner boarded a train for home. They ran into a big storm in Wyoming which pursued them to Ohio, cutting them off from connections. But the trip was finally delayed by only twelve hours, and Sargent was at home on October 18. Reporting back to Engelmann on the return trip he joked, "At home I found all my belongings, old and young, in the most perfect health and everything going on as quietly as if I had never been away. We ought to have had more time in Arizona! Why did you hurry me so?"[25]

Engelmann allowed his correspondence to languish for a time and did not write Gray until January 1881:

> How it was possible not to write you in 6 months can only be accounted for by the terrible strain Sargent's restlessness and energy put us under. [H]e perhaps told you himself that he rarely took or allowed us more than "5 minutes" for anything; but he begins to feel the consequences—says himself that he is "demoralized" about the things left undone, the too great hurry and the unsatisfactory outcome. But I am afraid, indeed I knew it, you and Hooker would have been worse travelling companions [referring to Hooker's American visit in 1877 and his western field trip with Gray, which Engelmann did not join]—the "5 minutes" of Sargent would have been reduced to 2 or 3, I fear.
>
> Well, with all that, we had a glorious time; all the little inconveniences, troubles and mishaps are forgotten long since.[26]

The Arboretum and Beyond

Sargent did realize when he got home that it would have been better if they had been able to take their time along the way, but he had known this all along and had chosen to sacrifice accuracy for speed. In less than four months, they had roamed thousands of miles and done an enormous amount of work. To obtain the type of information Sargent wanted to include in the Census report, it had been the most expedient method, for there was danger in getting bogged down in details, of delaying the report, and, consequently, of diminishing its value. Now, at least, he knew which areas needed more investigation, either by him or someone else; Arizona and California, especially, needed more work. He hoped to be able to induce Watson, who had spent the summer in the Montana region, to go south in the winter.

True to his warning, Sargent started sending Engelmann his "100 questions," and Engelmann tried hard to answer. The main work ahead of Sargent was compiling and evaluating data which came to him from his several investigators throughout the country, directing the business of making maps, running tests, and preparing a text. Although the 612-page document, including several maps and tables, did not appear in print until 1884, Sargent had it ready for the press by July 1, 1883. Considering his involvement in the Arboretum negotiations and in forming a special wood collection for the American Museum of Natural History in New York at the same time, the completion of the Census report was a grand achievement.

The *Report on the Forests of North America* was Sargent's first major publication, and it was instantly acclaimed in scientific and government circles. Nothing quite so extensive had been published before on the North American forests, for not only did the report consider the distribution of species of forest trees but it also presented analyses of various economic uses of forests and their products. This approach was a vast improvement over Brewer's 1870 Census work which, while attempting to locate forested areas, made no effort to analyze the contents of the woodlands.[27]

In the Nation's Forest

The 412 species named in the *Report* were accompanied by taxonomic and bibliographic references, details on habit, distribution maps and charts, notes on popular uses and, in significant cases, tables showing the specific gravity of woods, fuel value, and behavior under transverse strain or compression. Complementary to the systematic investigation of trees and the statistical tables on the properties of their woods, Sargent added a section giving the current and potential uses of forest products, tabulating everything from railroad ties to shoe pegs. He tackled the problem of fire and other causes of forest destruction, giving details on areas where depletion was already a cause for alarm.

The great merit of the *Report* was the relevance of its contents. The investigation was fresh, having been conducted by Sargent and his assistants in the field and laboratory. Here, at last, was an up-to-date reference which could be used in support of legislative proposals. The report appeared at a time when there was mounting interest in forest protection. What the conservationists and legislators needed was some authority on which to base their recommendations, for no argument could be launched convincingly without the support of pertinent data. Sargent's report became the bible on forests for the next several years.

Although he had ample opportunity to do so, Sargent did not use the text of the *Report* as a podium or editorial column. He neither debated issues nor suggested courses of action; rather, by arranging information in an orderly fashion, he hoped that the facts would speak for themselves and stimulate remedial action. Personally, Sargent was politically conservative and considered government participation in any form as inefficient meddling. Nearly every objection he had to American policies over the years rested on a conviction that government was overextending itself. As he became familiar with the conditions of the forest, however, he reluctantly concluded that government intervention might be necessary in this instance. In an exchange with Hooker he expressed his opinions on the subject.

The Arboretum and Beyond

With us, more than in any other country, it is desirable to leave things to look after themselves so far as Government is concerned. The fewer government officials we can have & the less machinery of that sort the better; still without government interference, Federal or State, I don't see how our mountain forests can be saved from entire extermination . . .
. . . it seems good policy to try and accomplish something that can be brought about. If we undertake to save too much territory as forest preserves we shall, I fear, fail entirely.[28]

Sargent was primarily concerned with areas where the forests were essential to the regulated flow of rivers.

As the forests affect the rivers, they should be made the subject of national investigation and preservation; but for no other consideration should the Government, either General or State, become a forester. Individuals can grow timber, and take care of it when grown, better than the Government, and the less Government mixes itself up with business of this nature, the better.[29]

Sargent's skepticism was well founded, for he knew that agricultural and certain business interests would oppose government possession of large land areas; at the same time he feared that government, with its complicated and not necessarily noble political considerations, could not effectively administer vast forested regions. Since he was only just then committing himself to an effort to save the Adirondack forests of New York State, he had yet to experience how entangled the question of government participation in forestry could become.

In the Census report, at any rate, he relied on evidence of the shrinking forest supply to make gloomy predictions. Although the *Report* awakened many people to a situation they had not considered seriously before, not everyone read

In the Nation's Forest

it uncritically. The most obvious flaw in the report was that only the timber trees with a diameter exceeding twelve inches had been counted. The factors of second growth and growth accumulation were neglected.[30] Thus the figures regarding forest depletion were perhaps more alarming than necessary. The critics—many of whom belonged to the lumber industry—seized upon this omission to discredit the *Report* as a valid authority, but to little effect, for the findings were sound in principle. Sargent had not stupidly ignored second growth or growth accumulations but had omitted them from his calculations because they were speculative items subject to variable conditions. If he had been allotted ten or twenty years to compile his findings, or if there had been previous reliable investigations, he would have been able to incorporate long-range considerations into the study. Because he did not, however, time proved some of his estimates to be exaggerated. It should also be observed that while he listed areas destroyed by fire on a state by state basis, he did not superimpose these figures on total forest acreage. Had he done so, the figures might have been less depressing. Later experts, using the *Report* as a reference, located mistakes or new information. Sargent himself found new species and distribution patterns which he had not recognized when he prepared the Census matereial. Botanists, inevitably, challenged some of the taxonomic decisions. Compared with the essential value of the *Report,* however, its errors and omissions were trivial. The message rang clear: if the forests of North America continued to diminish, if the public persisted with its casual plunder, the great wealth, with all its associated blessings, would be squandered within the foreseeable future. The statement was not original with the *Report,* but many of the supporting tables, maps, and data were. The conservationists found another foothold for their arguments.

News of Sargent's investigations spread quickly. Even before the *Report* was in print he had made a name for himself as an authority. He was occupied with Census work,

The Arboretum and Beyond

the Arboretum, and a wood collection for the American Museum when he accepted an offer to study the forests of the Northwest as an agent of the Northern Transcontinental Survey.

The Survey was the brainchild of Henry Villard, a railroad baron who, in 1881, masterminded the pooling of the resources of northwest railroad interests. Raphael Pumpelly, the geologist-explorer who became the Survey director, tells in his *Reminiscences* how Villard approached him, saying, "we are building a system of railroads through a vast region of which we know little. It is of vital importance to learn about its resources and their distribution to guide us in building feed lines. There should be made a survey with this idea in view."[31] The area in question covered more than 400,000 square miles, most of it unexplored wilderness. It was the country of Flathead and Blackfoot Indians, mostly confined to reservations, and some Crees from Canada.

Pumpelly, once a Professor of Mining Engineering at Harvard, was only too glad to take on the job since Villard's railroads were ready to finance the project generously (Pumpelly's salary for the first year was to be $10,000, exclusive of expenses) and give him a free hand in making the arrangements. In all, he recruited twenty-two experts, including Sargent, in various fields to participate in the Survey. Sargent, in turn, chose Brandegee—a second best to Cyrus Pringle, with whom he had recently quarreled—and H. C. Putnam, a Wisconsin lumberman and pine manufacturer, to aid in his part of the Survey. Andrew Robeson agreed to help.

Under Pumpelly's supervision, the Survey work began quickly. Many of the members did preliminary field work in 1882. Brandegee botanized on the east slope of the Cascade Mountains during the spring, and Putnam went to the Pacific coastal area. Pumpelly made reconnoitering trips, exploring the region that is now Glacier National Park.

Although he had been invited to join the Survey in 1881, Sargent cleared his desk of Census work before he went off

In the Nation's Forest

to the Northwest. At the end of June 1883, with the *Report* manuscript ready to go to Washington, Sargent was eager to head for the mountains. He wrote Engelmann,

I have to start for Montana. The party consists of Pumpelly, [W. M.] Canby [in charge of Economic Botany] and myself. The present plan is to push right through Missoula in Montana and there fit out a pack train and push northward through the Flat Head country to near the boundary and then westward through the mountains of northern Washington to the Cascades, cross the Cascades and come home by Portland and San Francisco. Whether we accomplish all this or not will depend on the condition of the roads, animals, etc.[32]

W. A. Stiles, later editor of Sargent's *Garden and Forest,* and Paul Dana, son of Charles Anderson Dana, editor of the New York *Sun,* went along as guests for the sake of the adventure which, according to Pumpelly's anecdotal account of the experience, presented itself in abundance.

Sargent enjoyed the strenuous work of the journey. Pumpelly met the party in Billings in early July, and together they crossed the Continental Divide, bearing northeast along Pumpelly's 1882 route before turning back toward the Cascade Mountains. The rugged terrain gave the men a hard time, especially during their first crossing of the Rockies. This was a two-week ordeal, which nearly ended before it began when six mules tumbled down an eight-hundred-foot incline into the Nyack Creek. Only one died, however, since the other five folded their legs under their bellies and landed on their packs. Later a horse lost his footing and fell fifteen hundred feet. Unfortunately, the horse was carrying Sargent's collections and all the guns. Despite the mishaps, which were taken in stride by the veteran explorers and their Indian guides, the party proceeded according to plan. The Rockies rewarded them with spectacular scenery; Sargent exclaimed that there was nothing grander in Switzerland.

The Arboretum and Beyond

The great glaciers, jagged peaks, the mountain lakes and gorges, the forests, were spellbinding.

"As we descended the Cutbank valley," Pumpelly recalled, "on the eastern side of the divide, we passed a succession of falls 1,500 to 2,000 feet high. At one point we watched, for half an hour, a great mountain goat standing immovable a thousand feet above us, his long, white hair seeming almost to touch the ground. He waited until our Indian, climbing all the time, had reached the vantage point—then with one long sprint he vanished." [33]

Scenery or no, Sargent found something to complain about when he returned to Boston in September. "The Botany," he informed Hooker, "was disappointing . . . the paucity of species in the northern Interior Region of the Continent is remarkable, although the country up to the summit of the 'Main Divide' is well watered and bears a very considerable forest composed, however, of very few arborescent species. Although several of the Coast trees reach these mts. following the high wet land along our boundary, I have indicated this in one of the Census maps." [34] Sargent's greatest pleasure in having made the journey derived from the knowledge that the route most likely had been traveled only once before by white men. And though he brought back few specimens for his herbarium, he returned with a concern for the rich Northwest forest areas and a new cause.

Sargent dashed off an article for the *Nation,* one of the respected periodicals of the day, in which he made the first proposal for what is now Glacier National Park. His language did justice to the beauties he had witnessed as he described how "[t]he explorers, standing upon the high peak which surmounts the pass, looked to the westward down the great gorge of the Flathead, breaking through the highest interior range; within this gorge Yosemites might be lost. At their feet were spread three mighty amphitheatres, swept clean of debris by recent glacial action; in any of these the population of an empire might find room to watch the manoeuvres of two contending armies." Using the scenery as bait, he lured his readers to the motive for his efforts:

In the Nation's Forest

95

We have dwelt upon the natural features of this region because here, if anywhere, there seems to be an entirely proper opportunity for the Government to establish a great forest preserve. In this region is situated the true dome of the continent, and here the forests are more important in their fluvial influences than in any other part of the country. They protect the snows which feed the three greatest streams of the continent—the Missouri, the Columbia, and the Saskatchewan. The constant flow of these rivers is dependent upon the preservation of these mountain forests . . . Such a reservation would contain perhaps some 8,000 square miles of mountain territory, absolutely unfit for agriculture or grazing, and only valuable as a reservoir of moisture.[35]

The park, with its sixty glaciers feeding 200 lakes, was ultimately established in 1910 and, indirectly at least, owes its existence to the explorations of the Northern Transcontinental Survey. On the other hand since the experts were unable to complete the work they had begun together, much of their effort was wasted.

In 1883 Villard's railroad pool broke up. Pumpelly was never quite sure what brought about the collapse. In part it was a general business depression and stock market decline that did not begin to reverse itself until autumn of 1884. In addition, there was a scandal involving a case of fraud running into millions of dollars; when he was exposed, the guilty party committed suicide. The Survey itself had caused dissent among the railroad backers, some of whom suspected it would not favor their acquisitive schemes. The establishment of national parks, for example, was not their idea of profit-making investment. Altogether, it seems that there were more problems than Villard could cope with successfully. The trust dissolved and so did the Survey. When Pumpelly tried to persuade a committee of railroad magnates that whatever results they had should be published, the chairman rebuffed him with a curt, "Mr. Pumpelly, when we want maps our engineers will make them, and when we

The Arboretum and Beyond

want coal we will send our men to look for it."[36] And that was that. Some of the work found its way into the geology section which Pumpelly prepared for the Census Office. The rest was never published. If nothing more, the country had learned of its great northwestern glacier clad mountains.

The scientists who participated in the Survey were disappointed when it was suspended, and Sargent was no exception. But, he rationalized, "From this time on, I suppose the Arboretum will keep me busy for several years, so I don't know that I entirely regret the giving up of the Transcontinental Survey."[37]

Despite his attitude of resignation Sargent had already promised to take on another forestry project. In November 1883, he wrote Hooker optimistically, "I am making a serious effort this winter to induce the State of New York to take possession of the whole Adirondack forest in order to preserve the flow of the Hudson River & Erie Canal ... I have really hopes of hurrying this about."[38] If he sincerely thought the Adirondack campaign would move quickly, it was because he had not yet been initiated into full-scale political warfare, or perhaps his confidence was a result of his victory with the Boston City Council. The trouble was that outside of Massachusetts, Sargent could not muster the same kind of support he stimulated on behalf of the Arboretum. When he became involved in the Adirondack dispute, he stepped into a political hornet's nest and had his first real taste of how politicians could handle conservation problems, a taste which left him frustrated and disgusted.

In dealing with the Adirondacks, the New York State legislature touched the hypersensitive concerns of the railroad and lumber industries. The Adirondacks had been in question for years. In 1872, the State legislature appointed a seven-man commission to inquire into the establishment of a New York State Forest Reserve. Among the commission members were Verplanck Colvin and Dr. Hough, Agent of the original U. S. Division of Forestry. The commission reported that the state owned only 40,000 acres in the Adi-

In the Nation's Forest

rondack region and, inasmuch as the holders of the remainder showed an inclination to merge properties to enhance their value in case the state bought them, the report recommended legislation forbidding further sale of state lands and their retention when forfeited for nonpayment of taxes.

This was the first of a succession of commissions which the legislators sent out to tramp over the wilderness of upper New York State. The politicians did what politicians often do when they want to avoid a controversial decision but also want to appease their critics: they resorted to fact-finding committees. And so it is no surprise that between 1873, when Hough's commission reported, and 1885, when Sargent's group turned in its findings, none of the interim commissioners produced any significant proposals.

Sargent was drawn into the investigations by Morris K. Jesup, President of the American Museum of Natural History in New York, for whom he was collecting wood specimens. Jesup, as President of the New York Chamber of Commerce, had been spearheading a public campaign advocating state ownership of the Adirondack area—cost notwithstanding—and had won the support of the Chamber in making recommendations to the state legislature. When they were not haggling over the problems of the wood collection for the museum, Jesup encouraged Sargent to lend his authoritative support to the effort to save the Adirondack forests from destruction. Naively believing he could succeed where others had failed, Sargent agreed to make his services available.

The forests of the Adirondack wilderness spread out over more than three and a half million acres of northern New York State. The principal argument in behalf of their protection was that they were essential to the Hudson-Mohawk river system, including the Erie Canal. The waterways, in turn, accounted for a good portion of the economic life of the region. Most people whose livelihood depended on the waterways had little notion that there was any relationship between the forests and the regular flow of the rivers. The

The Arboretum and Beyond

area, as Hough had observed in 1873, was mostly in the hands of private owners.[39] Some of them were farmers, who tried to squeeze returns from the hostile soil, some were land speculators, and some were business interests with large tracts. Among the last the most prominent were sawmill owners and railroad companies, who opposed any form of state control over the area. The other major property owner was the state, but its lands were so widely scattered in small holdings in remote areas that some had never been properly surveyed or marked. Since the lands were entirely unprotected, they were often denuded by timber thieves. Other regions, stripped of forest covering, had reverted to the state by their owners' failure to pay taxes. All commercial value having been exhausted, the owner, profit in pocket, willingly abandoned the land; or some hapless farmer gave up his battle with the soil.

In the two decades after the Civil War, the needs of industry and an industrial population created a growing demand for wood and wood products. Railroad owners who held franchises in the Adirondacks opened new lines with an eye on the profits from transporting lumber. The lumber business, which needed access to both source and market for its trade, was their friendly ally. By the time Hough's group made its survey, the increased activity had already taken its visible toll in denuded acres. As Sargent later clarified in his report, the problem was not that the lumbermen chopped down all the trees. In fact, he pointed out, "what they have cut down would hardly be missed from the forest."[40] The serious threat to the forests originated with the careless practices of loggers, who left branches and chips to dry out on the forest floor or debris around their logging camps, creating fire hazards. In dry weather, sparks flying from passing trains often started fires.

Even though the lumbermen could not see it that way, Hough had actually been sympathetic to their needs. Nearly all the experienced foresters, including Sargent, who had an interest in the Adirondacks, realized the importance of lumbering to the regional economy. But the evidence of

In the Nation's Forest

government activity and the rumor that some people favored a state preserve struck fear in the hearts of the lumbermen. They automatically assumed that the establishment of a state preserve would mean that they could not cut down a single tree. Even the more reasonable among them foresaw that any kind of state protection would impose costly alterations of lumbering practices that would result in a decrease in profits. Arguments for the long-term benefits of careful forest practices made no impression on them. The lumbermen and their allies went to war against the conservationists. They sent petitioners to the state capital in Albany who captured the ear of the legislature; the public campaign was carried out in the press.

Unfortunately, as sometimes happens when questions are debated in newspapers, the issues at stake were subject to distortion. The proconservation people painted the lumber and railway interests all black, and before long lumbermen might as well have been twirling waxed mustaches, and wearing top hats and black satin capes as they grasped their ill-gotten gains. The anticonservationists portrayed their detractors as scatter-brained theoreticians trying to put a false scare into the public. The "intellectual" man provided an easy target for public suspicion. The *Sun* of New York and the Albany *Evening Post* engaged in a sustained argument. The enlightened editors of the *Sun* took great pains to explain the beneficial influence of the Adirondack forests on the Hudson-Mohawk valley. The *Evening Post* countered, with questionable logic, that the forests robbed water from the rivers and that the state would actually be better off without trees. Trade journals, from Boston to Minneapolis took the position that the second growth in the forests was quite sufficient to replace what had been cut, but made no mention of what had burned down. On the side of conservation, the Boston *Herald* (Feb. 2, 1883) suggested that the Adirondack forests could best be saved by reducing the promise of profit in cutting them down. This, they proposed, could be achieved by removing the protective tariff on Canadian timber. Sargent

The Arboretum and Beyond

also favored this solution, but realized its political impracticality. Needless to say, that remedy found little sympathy among lumbermen.

In the face of the controversy, the legislature made a succession of fumbling gestures. Governor Grover Cleveland's Democratic administration, inaugurated in January 1883, maintained an invulnerable silence. Hough's old associate, Verplanck Colvin, was authorized to make new surveys and did such a slipshod job that he created a scandal. The *Sun* (February 9, 1883) attacked him: "he has wandered about the woods for a number of years without apparently any definite purpose in view, and has published, at the expense of the State, one or two volumes of reports of considerable size and profusely illustrated with curious and agreeable pictures. These reports have not, however, it appears, obtained the approval or consideration of those persons whose opinions on such subjects are valuable." Public opinion suddenly stirred in 1883, when word leaked out that the Adirondack Railroad Company was planning to extend its lines. The railroad held some 500,000 acres, purchased by its predecessors about twenty years before for five cents an acre; a substantial amount of territory was in immediate jeopardy. The same year the legislature voted to forbid the sale of Adirondack forest lands already in possession of the state, thus finally acting on the first recommendation of Hough's commission ten years earlier. But the legislators refused to commit themselves to any more than this token gesture. In 1884 they allotted $5,000 to the State Comptroller for another commission to report on a system of forestry for the Adirondacks. It was to this group that Sargent was appointed.

Jesup, whose sympathies and influence were well known in Albany, engineered Sargent's appointment, though his growing reputation would have been sufficient reference for the job. In any case, he accepted the position along with two lawyers and an interested businessman.[41] Sargent brought in Andrew Robeson to compile a map, which absorbed half the allotted funds, and Brandegee to help with

In the Nation's Forest

the field work. The Commission did precisely what it had been asked to do: it investigated. Not only did the men explore a good part of the region in question but they also inquired into "the relations which forests bear to the commercial and industrial interests of the State ... and heard and considered the views of a large number of persons interested, directly and indirectly, in forest property." [42] The Commissioners tried to be objective in their efforts to hear the arguments advanced by the lumbering interests.

Sargent and his colleagues compiled their information during the fall and winter of 1884, and the report was ready to submit by January 1885. It was a masterpiece of brevity. The general recommendations covered only thirty-one pages, and there were twenty-five additional pages of appendices. The document was calculated to catch the eyes of the lawmakers without putting them to sleep. The section devoted to existing forest conditions was obviously largely the work of Sargent, the only person with forestry experience on the Commission. He explained, in concise phrases, the values of the Adirondack forests and the hazards which endangered them, emphasizing the high frequency of fires and urging remedial practices. The balance of the report outlined a forest policy for the state and proposed three bills for the consideration of the legislature.

Recognizing the impasse in Albany, the Commissioners did not press for state ownership but concentrated on effective alternatives. Nevertheless they made their preference clear: "It must be conceded that if the people of this State are convinced that the preservation of the Adirondack forests is essential to their future prosperity, there is but one way by which they can be certain of accomplishing that end. Absolute control can be insured only by absolute purchase." [43] Before it could even consider outright ownership of the entire region, however, the state had to demonstrate its competence in the management of lands already owned. Since the responsibilities of forest administration demanded prolonged experience, the first of the proposed bills advised the establishment of a three-man, permanent,

The Arboretum and Beyond

unpaid forestry commission of an unpolitical nature. (The suggestion of a troika provoked the only disagreement among Sargent's committeemen. One of them, a lawyer, mistrusted plural executive offices.) The second bill provided for the rudiments of forest protection on private and state-owned properties, including fire prevention, and the authority for the Forest Commissioners to enforce these rules. The cutting of timber would be permitted, but good lumbering practices, such as the compulsory burning of debris, would be enforced for the safety of the forests. The third bill aimed to eliminate the waste which accrued on the abandoned lands which eventually returned to the state because of failure to pay taxes.

The proconservation press hailed the report and pleaded for positive action on the proposed legislation, but to no avail. By the end of April 1885, the newspapers were bemoaning the fact that the bills were doomed. Sargent, keeping in touch with developments in Albany, was depressed as he witnessed his recommendations fall behind an inferior compromise which, surprisingly enough, was the product of the original investigators who Sargent thought should have known better. He wrote Jesup that "[t]he Adirondack business is hopeless for the year; and it is better to have no bill than the one arranged by Hough, Colvin, Lansing and that crowd. The passage of any such bill will put off wise Adirondack legislation for years and destroy all our plans . . . The whole matter is simply disgusting from beginning to end." [44]

The strength of the recommended legislative package had been the terms for the appointment of the forest commission —whether singular or plural—in an unpaid, permanent capacity, thus guaranteeing the integrity of the office. The measure presented by Lansing was drafted with the aid of Hough, Colvin, and Bernhard Eduard Fernow, who later became Chief of the Forestry Division in Washington, and other authorities. Perhaps Hough and Fernow were simply trusting souls who did not share Sargent's suspicion of the political appointive process; and one can understand why

In the Nation's Forest

103

Fernow, as a professional forester with limited personal resources, would resent the idea of an unsalaried commissioner. At any rate, it was the Lansing bill that passed. The measure created a forest preserve out of the state-owned properties, and a five-man forest commission, with comforting salaries, to administer it. Furthermore, the bill did not set up strict controls on harmful lumbering practices. A few months after the bill was signed into law, Governor Hill, who had succeeded Cleveland in Albany, appointed three head commissioners. An irate citizen wrote anonymously to the New York *Evening Post* demanding that the Governor explain

> Why he appointed as a member of the Commission . . . a Democratic political worker for the northern part of the State, an acknowledged opponent of State forest preservation, the successful representative of the Albany lumber lobby organized to prevent any legislative act for the preservation of the Adirondack forests, a large manufacturer of Adirondack lumber, and a man immediately and constantly interested with his associates and friends in the purchase at tax sales of Adirondack forest lands.
>
> Why he selected as a second member of this Commission an active Republican politician of [New York] totally unfamiliar with the Adirondack question, and, moreover, disqualified for the position by previous public employment.[45]

The *Sun's* editorials were equally damning.[46] Sargent's disillusionment was complete, and the best he could say was "Thank Heavens I have done with the whole business."[47] He blamed himself for not having fought the Lansing bill harder, but it is doubtful that he could have prevented its passage. Despite his words, he did not "have done with the whole business"; for many years he continued to urge a decent program for the Adirondacks. It was a long time before he saw the fruits of his efforts, and in the meantime the forest lands continued to suffer abuse.

The Arboretum and Beyond

While Sargent's good work was being undone in Albany, he enjoyed more success in New York City. Almost simultaneously with the nefarious vote of the legislature, the Jesup Collection of North American Woods was unveiled for public display at the American Museum of Natural History. The spectators admiring the unique exhibition had little idea of the amount of work or the number of quarrels that had gone into its making, but they were happier for their innocence since the history of the Jesup Collection was unpleasant in many aspects.

The museum was a young institution, endowed in 1869 by a group of illustrious, wealthy New Yorkers, including J. Pierpont Morgan, Joseph H. Choate, and Morris K. Jesup. Its first collections were zoological, but by 1880 the museum directors agreed that it was high time to represent the other half of the natural sciences. Professor Albert S. Bickmore, founding spirit and by then Director of the Museum, had Harvard ties—he had once been a student of Agassiz's— and he turned to Gray for advice. During the summer of 1880, while Sargent was out west on the Census trip, Bickmore, in Boston for meetings of the American Association for the Advancement of Science, went to call on Gray. Gray referred him to Sargent, and Bickmore wrote immediately, hoping to catch the itinerant Census Agent in San Francisco. The letter made no definite proposals but indicated in a vague manner the desires of the museum to "begin a department of Economic Botany" with an emphasis on trees. Bickmore only went as far as to suggest "asking your advice, and when your government work is over that we might be allowed to employ your botanists, as Mr. Pringle, Mr. George Vasey and others to collect for us the specimens we desire."[48]

The man responsible for the whole idea was Jesup, one of the founders and a driving force behind the museum for over a quarter of a century. He was a self-made multimillionaire, who left a million dollars to the museum when he died in 1908. Like some of the other financial barons of the era, in a spirit of *noblesse oblige*, he gave a portion of

In the Nation's Forest

his energies and fortune to benefit the public. Jesup was not a scientist, but he was one of the most generous patrons of science of his day. Not satisfied with simple patronage, he involved himself in the administrative affairs of the museum and became its president in 1881, at a time when attendance was low and the trustees were discouraged. Jesup's prescription for the ailing museum was to take the natural sciences out of the classrooms and textbooks and fit them within a popular, eye-catching framework. When the time came to create an exhibition of Economic Botany, Jesup offered to pay the bills.

Two weeks after he got home from the West, Sargent took his wife on a week's trip to New York and Philadelphia. While in New York he called on Jesup to discuss Bickmore's proposal. The two men shared certain characteristics: they were both rich, hard-headed businessmen and enthusiastic, able administrators. This was the kind of dialogue Sargent enjoyed, for Jesup seemed a man with whom he could work and get things done. As he told Hooker, he felt that Jesup was "one of the very few rich Americans who wants to make the best use of his money & spend it for something better than nice houses or bad pictures."[49] The description is reminiscent of Gray's comment on Sargent.

Sargent agreed with Jesup that a portion of the work should be started while the Census investigation was still in progress, thus avoiding as much duplication of effort as possible. When he returned to Brookline from his conference with Jesup, he immediately put a rough outline of his plans down on paper, suggesting that the exhibition comprise all arborescent species growing naturally in the United States and exotic species of first-rate economic value, arranged scientifically along with their products and photographs of their natural habitat.[50] Within two days he had a reply from Jesup saying, "the programme you propose seems satisfactory and no doubt will meet my entire approval."[51] In view of the quick mutual agreement, Sargent could scarcely have imagined that this enterprise would cost him more petty aggravations and frustrations than any other work he would do. The formation of the collection dragged on for more than fifteen years and gave cause for major and minor quarrels not only with Jesup but involving Pringle as well. At the root of all the disagreements was the fact that Jesup, the man who provided the money, was not a scientist; Sargent, who was not paying the bills, was. The first item that Jesup requested after the draft proposal was an estimate of the cost. Sargent guessed the expenses would amount to something upwards of $10,000. This was more than Jesup had bargained for. He knew vaguely of Sargent's Census work and expected similar specimens for the museum. In a cool exchange of letters during the spring of 1881 Sargent defended his estimate and clarified his private views on the subject.

The collections in my department of the Census investigation have been made for the purpose of supplying material for certain series of mechanical experiments, undertaken with the view of determining the economic value of species, and not to furnish museum specimens, in any proper sense of the word.

... Your note conveys the impression that you think the expenses, entailed in the formation of your collection, excessive. While I regret this, and beg you to believe that all proper economy will be exercised by myself and by my agents in prosecuting the work, I must insist on the necessity of fully carrying out the scheme explained in my letter . . .

My time is so fully occupied that I do not feel justified in devoting any of it to your Museum unless in so doing I can be placed in a position to acquire new knowledge in the direction of my special studies, and to enrich by it a collection worthy of its almost National position, and of the importance of the subject itself.

It is not too late for us both to retire altogether from the undertaking, which unless carried out largely will add neither reputation to the Museum, nor credit to the parties most interested.[52]

In the Nation's Forest

The uncompromising Sargent left little room for argument. Jesup had only two choices. He replied quickly. "Do not for a moment consider that I have any intention or desire to cancel the arrangement between us," he said consolingly. "Your letter dispels all doubt in my mind. To have our museum contain that which cannot be found at any other will fully compensate for the cost."[53] With these words Jesup surrendered himself to Sargent's judgment and to the contribution of more than $100,000 for the perfection of the Jesup Collection.[54] He did not always defer to Sargent's point of view or part with his money with such docility. Nevertheless, it was Sargent's will that ultimately prevailed.

Sargent planned for the display to have whole tree trunks, around six feet tall, cut to show vertical, horizontal, and oblique sections, in both finished and natural states. The size and weight of such specimens made them far more costly to acquire, ship, and prepare for display than the small woodblock samples for the Census. Most of the actual collecting was done between 1881 and 1883. Jesup had been able to secure some railroad passes for the collectors from his friends. Cornelius Vanderbilt, for example, contributed the amount of fares on the New York Central & Hudson River line. (Vanderbilt expressed some irritation when he discovered that the amount exceeded $400 and that some of the fares had not been incurred on this line but on other Vanderbilt-owned lines.) Sargent's intimacy with railway magnates was also helpful.

By early 1881 the bulk of the exploratory and collecting work for the Census was finished, but many of the Census collectors were willing to gather specimens for the museum project also. Curtiss, Mohr, Letterman, and Pringle worked on both jobs. Curtiss was the first in the field for the museum, working the Florida Keys in February 1881. At the end of March, Sargent took a few weeks for a visit to discuss taxonomic puzzles with Engelmann in St. Louis; then he did some field work in Texas and Louisiana, "strictly on the five minutes plan,"[55] he wrote Engelmann, but most of the

The Arboretum and Beyond

Texas work belonged to Mohr. H. W. Ravenel sent specimens to New York from South Carolina. Sargent had to coerce Pringle to go out west, the latter showing some reluctance because he "seem[ed] greatly to fear Indians, [and] snakes,"[56] but by May he was in Arizona. The logs began coming into New York in the spring. Jesup watched their accumulation with sharp eyes and began worrying. On the first of September he figured that he had already spent $2,806.84 on the collection and had only fifty-three specimens in the building and a promise of sixty more on the way. At this rate, considering the additional cost of transforming the crude logs into display pieces, he would spend more than the original estimate. Moreover, as he told Bickmore, he was not happy with the "character of the collections,"[57] which did not seem to him adequate return for his expenditures. The logs he saw and the way they had been collected violated his idea of the functional.

One of the first questions that would present itself to the builder contemplating a wood's use would be the expense of getting these woods to the manufacturer, and it occurs to me that you are collecting woods from the most remote and inacessible parts where the cost of procuring it for manufacturing purposes will make its use prohibitory.[58]

This objection infuriated Sargent, and it was the substance of his quarrel with Jesup for years. The issue came up again and again. Sargent's refutation was always in the same vein.

In its scientific aspect a specimen of the smallest, rarest or most worthless tree is equally valuable with the most important . . . In scientific investigations it is impossible to foresee the practical results which, in the range of possibilities, are likely to follow in its investigations. A tree which you now look upon as worthless because it is rare and cannot be used as a source of lumber supply,

In the Nation's Forest

through its introduction into this collection may become of extreme value to the world as a subject for planting either in this country or some other . . . I hope you will not endeavor to separate *practical value* from scientific value in your mind when considering this collection. They cannot safely be separated.[59]

The argument between the two men was not personal at all; it rose from a conflict of ideas. Jesup wanted to popularize science and believed representative displays sufficient for the task as well as more attractive to crowds, which might easily tire of subtle differences. Knowing full well the public appeal of natural freaks, he longed to include deformed specimens, a suggestion which Sargent promptly vetoed. Sargent, as pragmatic as Jesup by nature, conceived a dual purpose for the exhibition, serving both science and the public. To perform either role properly, Sargent believed that the display must be complete in scope and thorough in detail.

The strained relations between Sargent and Jesup led to a bitter quarrel between Sargent and Pringle. For over a year all went well with Pringle in the field. In 1881, he was out west until November, working in difficult areas of Arizona, California, and Oregon. According to his agreement with Sargent he earned expenses plus two dollars per day paid by the museum, but since he did not think the salary sufficient he was allowed to take time out to collect additional sets of herbarium specimens which he might offer for sale later. When Jesup began to press Sargent, Sargent in turn hurried Pringle, and as a result Pringle was unable to do all the private collecting he had planned. Still, Sargent praised the specimens coming from Pringle, and the two men were on good terms.

Meanwhile Sargent accepted Pumpelly's bid to take part in the Northern Transcontinental Survey partly because it offered an opportunity to extend Pringle's field work. When Pringle was east in January 1882, he went to Sargent's Brookline office to discuss plans for the coming season.

The Arboretum and Beyond

They talked about the railroad survey and the work for Jesup. Considering what remained to be done, they concluded that Pringle could fulfill his museum obligations by the first of July. But Pringle declined the Survey job, saying that he preferred to spend the rest of the summer botanizing at his own pace in Arizona. His real motive for turning down the offer, as later disclosed to Jesup, was that Pringle resented what he referred to as Sargent's "imperiousness." [60] Pringle went back to California in mid-March. Sargent made no long trips during the spring, but worked in Brookline on the Census report, supervised the Jesup Collection and went over plans for the Arboretum since he had finally come to terms with the City's politicians. Jesup's impatience mounted. In April, Sargent estimated that 290 of the 406 prospective specimens for the exhibition were already in New York or on their way. Most of the outstanding balance was due from Pringle out west—50 specimens from California alone—and these should arrive during the summer. There were other details to consider, however. S. D. Dill, a nurseryman from Nova Scotia, had been retained on a full-time basis to prepare and care for the specimens. This was time-consuming work, proper cutting and polishing the surfaces, and he, too, proceeded too slowly to please Jesup. In some cases, by the time Dill got around to a specimen he found it in poor condition and asked for a replacement. Sargent, never happy with anything less than a perfect specimen, would agree, and Jesup would be distressed. Dill was also given the responsibility of building display cases. Furthermore, instead of the habit photographs he had originally mentioned, Sargent decided that drawings of flowers and fruit should accompany each wood piece, so he had Faxon make a couple of preliminary sketches to show Jesup what he had in mind. The substitution of drawings for photographs threatened to prolong the preliminary work even further.

In May, Jesup said he wanted to have the collection open to the public by October. Sargent, knowing it was impossible, tactfully reminded Jesup that "it would seem a mis-

In the Nation's Forest

taken policy to endanger their [the specimens'] beauty and usefulness for the sake of advancing by a few months the opening of the exhibit." [61]

Then, although Pringle made great progress during the spring, it became clear that both he and Sargent had underestimated the work. Even as he traveled, Pringle discovered new species to add to his list. He was so eager to complete his task that he abandoned his personal collecting almost entirely. To use his own histrionic phrases, "[f]rom dawn till dark through burning, dusty summer months I toiled in desperation." [62] This was not routine collecting but more strenuous work since he had to cut down whole trees and chop logs and arrange for their transportation. Jesup nagged Sargent, Sargent nagged Pringle, and Pringle's nerves began to fray. In September the issue finally came to a head. Pringle had shipped some specimens to New York at a cost of $800, and Jesup lost his temper when he saw the charges. Not only was Pringle slow about collecting, he complained to Sargent, but he was also unnecessarily extravagant when it came to making shipments. Naturally, Jesup left it up to Sargent to deal with Pringle. To Sargent the problem of money was nowhere near as trying as the pace at which Pringle worked. While it made very little difference to him personally how fast the collector sent specimens (he was not, after all, paying the bills) he wanted to soothe Jesup by holding out some assurance that the job would be completed quickly. In his exasperation, Sargent acted tactlessly and forced Pringle's hand.

Sargent's mistake was in not knowing his man. Throughout the summer, in spite of his displeasure with the situation, Pringle had registered only gentle objections to Sargent's commands and had tried to please. Sargent wrote Pringle at the end of September in San Francisco, where he was taking a short rest, and in a dictatorial tone ordered him out to the field again, this time to collect logs in Utah and Nevada. Pringle became angered on two counts. First of all, this was not part of the original bargain. He had thought he would finish up soon with California, Arizona,

The Arboretum and Beyond

112

and Oregon and was glad of it, for he did not like the work of chopping logs and he was tired of Sargent's attitude. But worse yet, in trying to intimidate him, Sargent hinted that he had neglected his museum work for the sake of private collecting. Pringle, furious, restrained himself from answering. Returning to seek some specimens in Tucson, he was greeted by a curt telegraph message from his chief: "I shall approve no more bills until I hear from you something definite and satisfactory." [63] Since Pringle had not yet been paid for September, this amounted to a whole month of accounts. In exasperation he sent his resignation by telegraph on October 26, left his specimens sitting in Tucson, and headed back to San Francisco.

Pringle's reaction took Sargent unawares, and he immediately tried to reverse the decision. Apologies were beneath his dignity, but he hastily approved the September accounts and tried to lure Pringle back with the argument that "[y]ou owe it to yourself to finish work." The effort failed. Pringle had had enough.[64]

News of the quarrel spread from coast to coast. Pringle rounded up support among the botanists in California, especially Parry and S. B. Parish. When he came east in November, he wrote Gray and Jesup to make sure they heard his side of the story. Parry, too, wrote Gray that "the entire blame rests on *Sargent* and that he has treated Pringle in a most disgraceful and shameful way without any cause." [65] Pringle told Gray that Sargent's treatment had been "outrageous" and, Pringle added, "I recollect saying . . . that I should endeavor to please Mr. S., but that he should never make me his hack. I expect him to be terribly angry and to give me a bad name." [66] As Pringle was a respected collector who took pains to defend his action, Sargent became *persona non grata* with some of his botanical colleagues for a time; indeed, his reputation never totally recovered from this incident.

Although Sargent's bullying treatment cannot be justified, it was caused in part by events of which Pringle could have no knowledge. Significantly, Sargent never made the excuse

In the Nation's Forest

that he was under pressure from Jesup, but it is likely that if Jesup had not been so impatient, the whole incident would never have occurred. Pringle was unaware of Jesup's behavior, or his evaluation of Sargent's action might not have been so merciless. Even so, at least one of Pringle's predictions proved to be dead wrong: Sargent never made any attempt to vilify him. When Jesup sent a copy of Pringle's self-defense, Sargent returned it with the comment,

> I fully realize Mr. Pringle's position, and, although disappointed in his want of manliness, do not, for a moment, doubt his entire honesty. He will, I am sure, feel differently towards me, as soon as he has time to cool down a little.
>
> I suppose, under the circumstances, you will pay his final account . . . I have no doubt he has earned the money.[67]

After all their difficulties, Sargent still regretted having lost Pringle's services. Brandegee was willing to take up where Pringle had left off, but to the very end Sargent still believed Pringle the best man for the job. By the end of the year, tempers subsided, but Sargent had earned a reputation for being hard on his collectors.

Considering the misunderstandings and conflicts of opinion, not to mention Sargent's multiple responsibilities to the Arboretum and the Census report, it is astonishing that the woods for the Jesup Collection arrived in New York as soon as they did. Early in 1883, Sargent directed the delivery of the specimens Pringle had abandoned in Tucson. Brandegee carried on in Arizona and California. Professor S. B. Buckley worked parts of Texas. Even the maligned Pringle sent down a few logs from Vermont in March. By midsummer, both Jesup and Sargent agreed that only some stragglers were missing, though this fact alone was not sufficient cause for rejoicing. Jesup bemoaned the numerous duplicates; Dill noted that the Arsenal building (on the

The Arboretum and Beyond

east side of Central Park at Sixty-fourth Street) used for storage of the logs was bulging on one side, having spread half an inch from the weight of the specimens. Furthermore, the collection was nowhere near ready to go on display since Dill had not prepared even a quarter of them. According to Jesup's schedule, the exhibition should have opened to the public almost a year earlier.

It was May 1885, before the public got its first sight of the Jesup Collection of North American Woods, and it was a triumphant day for Jesup. The *Sun* had nothing but praise for it:

> It is hardly possible to conceive that it can ever be surpassed in completeness or beauty of individual specimens. Engineers, architects, and mechanics will be equally benefited by a study of this collection, in which they will see for the first time valuable woods entirely unknown commercially, and learn the extent and variety of the forest resources of this country.[68]

So Sargent's stubbornness had paid off after all. Jesup was relieved because he thought, quite mistakenly, that his troubles were over. To begin with, the collection was still incomplete; among the missing specimens was the spectacular, therefore desirable, giant redwood. The accompanying illustrations of fruit, flowers, and foliage were nowhere near finished. They were being executed by Mary Sargent, for Faxon was busy with other things. Mrs. Sargent worked on the series of watercolors, at substantial cost to Jesup. The public was unanimous in its admiration of the pictures, and Sargent was justifiably proud of his wife's talent; but he wished Jesup had waited until everything was properly in place.

What really disturbed him, however, was that the wood collection shared the stage with a display of stuffed mammals. Although this fact did not seem to upset anyone else, Sargent objected that the arrangement interfered with the

In the Nation's Forest

continuity of the wood exhibition. After considering the problem for a while, he wrote Jesup: "nothing can be worse than the present mixture of mammals and woods," and prescribed a remedy in the form of a new structure to house the woods, herbarium, and a forestry library, coyly suggesting that it might be known as the "Jesup Building." And $15,000, Sargent figured generously, would cover everything but herbarium cases.[69] In view of the congestion throughout the museum, Sargent's idea was not entirely out of line. Museum officials had been pondering a new wing for the main building for some time. But neither Jesup nor the other directors were eager to make the botanical collection into the elaborate complex Sargent proposed. There were already murmurings among some of the endowers and scientists whose interests were strongly zoological that the wood collection was receiving more than its rightful share of attention and funds. The Board of Directors discarded the herbarium-library notion, but exhibition space was provided for the woods in a new wing added between 1890 and 1900.

Although the collection was on display, Sargent kept adding new species or replacing imperfect old ones and Mary Sargent continued to produce her water colors. The old Jesup-Sargent argument came up now and then, punctuating their relationship with disagreeable interludes. As late as 1894, Sargent gleefully reported to Jesup that he had found "several trees or varieties of trees not represented in your Collection and which we ought to procure as soon as possible."[70] Jesup must have groaned when he read the letter. All it meant to him was more bills and more space. He had just about recovered from the irritations of involved transactions over the giant sequoia *(Sequoiadendron)* specimen, but that, at least, had been worth the effort. He had it now, polished and ready to place in the collection. It was twenty feet in diameter and had come from a venerable tree some three hundred feet high. Jesup saw the picture of the fifty loggers who stood on the remaining trunk with plenty of room to spare.[71] Since Collis P. Huntington, a

The Arboretum and Beyond

California millionaire, made gifts of the redwood and *Sequoiadendron* logs, Jesup could scarcely complain about the time it took for them to arrive on the East Coast. Now, more than ten years after beginning the collection, Sargent wanted to send additional obscure specimens. Jesup was simply too weary to protest and told Sargent to secure the half dozen logs.

Finally, however, their tempers erupted in one of their periodic quarrels, and by far the most serious one, for it came near to ending their friendship entirely. In December 1894, Sargent was in New York and stopped in to check the progress of a set of new cases for the Collection, which was to be moved to its quarters in the new wing. To his horror he discovered that the cases were being built cylindrically, exactly as the old ones had been and contrary to his announced wishes. He stormed into Jesup's office and stormed out again, having made no progress. Still fuming when he got back to Brookline, he dispatched an apoplectic letter to his sponsor:

> If you remember, I felt this so strongly that I offered to pay myself for any additional cost that might be incurred in making the cases uniform according to my plan ... I am responsible for the scientific accuracy and arrangement of the Collection although I am deprived of authority in the matter ...
>
> A good deal of additional work in connection with the Collection has been laid for me but I confess I do not feel much like undertaking it if the results are to be as bad as you seem determined to make them; and I should feel like throwing up the whole matter and refusing to have anything more to do with the Museum were it not for the fact that my connection with this Collection is so well known among scientific people that I shall be made responsible for it whether I have anything to do with the arrangement or not. This, from my point of view, is the unfortunate thing in the whole matter and why I believe I have not been treated properly by you.[72]

In the Nation's Forest

Jesup sulked about the letter for a couple of weeks before he drafted a reply; he was not ready to yield an inch of ground this time.

> My feeling is that I do not merit the criticism . . . you do not invest with any significance the fact that my relations with the Museum partake of a dual character; i.e., as President and as the donor of a special collection . . . I ask you also to consider that while I confess my obligation to you for the knowledge, attention, and time you have expended . . . you are, I think, indebted to me for zealous co-operation in your plans, and the provision of the means without stint to make them successful. With the great success of the enterprise, your name has been and will always be associated.[73]

Once the words were down on paper, however, their author was fearful of Sargent's reaction, for he was still dependent on Sargent's advice in many matters. After showing his letter to members of his Executive Committee, he decided to send a gentler version to the effect that he had been hurt by Sargent's criticisms and declined to write at length for fear of creating further misunderstandings.[74] In place of a letter he sent Mr. Winsor, the Secretary of the Museum, to Boston to discuss matters personally with Sargent.

The Secretary seems to have had some success on his truce mission, for Sargent's subsequent correspondence was subdued if not submissive:

> For fifteen years I have given a great deal of thought, time and labor to this Collection. I am not sorry for it and I believe it is a useful thing, but I shall regret it sincerely if in doing what seemed to me right I have hurt your feelings or said or done anything to interfere with a friendship I greatly value. Rather than do this I should retire from all connection with the Museum. Your best plan I believe is to put the whole matter in my charge and

The Arboretum and Beyond

I will attend to the installment and the arrangement of the Collection with its additions, preparation of the labels, maps, water-colors, and everything connected with it and have it ready to open to the public next November . . . I could only do this, however, with the express understanding that no one was to interfere with me or my orders in any way.[75]

Jesup felt they had both cooled down enough to talk about their differences face to face in a sane fashion, a suggestion to which Sargent replied petulantly, "I shall be glad to go over again the matter of arranging the collection although I confess I do not feel like discussing this matter any further unless some entirely new views are to be brought forward." [76] By March 1895, Sargent reluctantly conceded on the question of the round cases, and his exchanges with Jesup were friendlier. But when in August Sargent realized that the display would not be reopening in November as ordered, he charged that "the whole collection [might have been] ready on the 1st of November if I had been allowed to have my way last winter." [77]

After the last argument, Sargent and Jesup never restored their friendship to its earlier footing although Sargent continued his work for some time. In 1899, Jesup belatedly laid down the law and said he would accept nothing but trees of obvious economic value as additions to the collection. Sargent, persisting in his all-or-nothing stance, shrugged the whole thing off, saying "[p]ersonally I shall be only too glad to be relieved of the bother of obtaining specimens needed to complete the collection," [78] and thereafter he sent no more.

There is a gentlemanly postscript to all this unpleasantness. Sargent had long desired a set of the woods for the museum at the Arboretum. Jesup not only agreed to donate the specimens (not exact duplicates but fewer, smaller, inferior pieces), but upon learning that Harvard could not finance their installation, gallantly offered to pay the $2,800 necessary for that purpose, asking in return only that the

In the Nation's Forest

exhibition space at Jamaica Plain be called the Jesup Room. Sargent expressed his gratitude in courtly phrases, and good form reasserted itself.

After Jesup died in 1908, there were few people on the museum administrative staff who took a real interest in the collection; the emphasis shifted more and more toward zoology, anthropology, and geology. Mrs. Sargent, however, continued to paint watercolors to complement the woods, carried on a long and bitter argument over payments for her efforts, and displayed considerable spunk and self-righteous artistic temperament in insisting on her rights. Her husband took offense at the omission of his name from a 1911 museum publication describing the collection, and protested:

> It was a matter of a good deal of surprise to me when I read that Mr. Jesup made this collection without any mention of my connection with it or that of Mrs. Sargent. Of course Mr. Jesup's only connection with the collection was paying for it. I worked twenty years on it entirely gratutiously [sic] and put in a good deal of thought and hard and disagreeable work in connection with it.[79]

Although the display won praise from the well-informed, it never had the popular appeal of the gems or mammals. Today nothing remains of it at the museum except a polished section of *Sequoiadendron gigantea* in the Warburg Memorial Hall; in the deep shadows of this room stand two bronze busts—one of Sargent and the other of his friend, the naturalist, John Muir. No one, apparently, knows what became of Mrs. Sargent's watercolors, but the woods were donated to the Oregon Museum of Science and Industry in Portland, where they lie in storage.

5

Changing of the Guard

February 13, 1883, Sargent to Engelmann: "For a man who in addition to being a chronic pessimist has a cold in the head you are certainly most good natured, and I go on bothering you, without feeling, I suppose, those pangs of conscience which it would be becoming to me under the circumstances to feel."[1]

February 22, 1883, Sargent to Engelmann: "You want more questions and I will try & arrange so that you will not be disappointed . . . Don't answer in your usual fashion & say 'don't bother about these things but do what I tell you.' . . . Had a long letter from Parry asking me to help him sell *something* of which he [has] 1000, but he failed to say what."[2]

June 7, 1883, Sargent to Engelmann: "Your letter was not necessary to remind me how very remiss I have been in not writing to you before. I am not at all happy at what you tell me about your bodily condition. Perhaps, however, here, as in other cases, you adopt pessimistic views, and that I shall hear of your 'climbing like a cat' this summer, the Swiss Alps . . . Won't you write me just when you expect to be in New York, and if possible I will run over and pass an hour or so with you."[3]

June 12, 1883, Engelmann to Sargent: " 'Pessimist' is a good word! I hope it may be the true word, the correct interpretation in this case. Meanwhile the 'catlike climbing' is an optimism, not likely to come to pass."[4]

October 3, 1883, Sargent to Hooker: "The Arboretum is getting on at last . . . Roads, belts, grades, etc. are making grand progress & I really begin to see daylight ahead. We have in the nurseries an immense stock of plants & certainly the largest number of living species ever collected together on this side of the ocean."[5]

November 11, 1883, Engelmann to Sargent: "I am thinking of your New York wood specimens. How would it do to split them through the center to more effectively season them—also to prevent cracking."[6]

November 25, 1883, Sargent to Engelmann: "Since you last came, I have been in New York to see how the woods are getting on. They look better since the fire has been started in the building; and, with the exception of two or three, from which the bark has nearly entirely fallen, I believe they can all be made decent enough. Of course the cracking is a great drawback, but I don't believe it can be entirely overcome in such large specimens."[7]

On the same day, November 25, 1883, Sargent sat at the desk in his improvised office at Holm Lea answering his mail, which included a long letter from Hooker on forestry problems. November 24 marked ten years since his official appointment as Director of the Arnold Arboretum, a coincidence which he probably failed to remark. November 26 would be his tenth wedding anniversary. He was father to five children, who were kept out of sight and earshot while he worked. They were like steps in a staircase, separated by approximately two years, beginning with Henrietta, age 9—Engelmann wistfully supposed he could no longer refer to her as a "little one"—on down through Bobo (Andrew Robeson), Mary, Charles, Jr., and Alice, the baby, who was not yet two. The senior Sargents, Ignatius and Henrietta, lived in separate quarters at Holm Lea, and Ignatius, almost eighty-four, was in poor health. Mary Sargent discreetly managed the small battalion of servants.

December 14, 1883, Sargent to Engelmann: "Weather

The Arboretum and Beyond

very warm & rain greatly needed. Water supply of Boston reduced to ten days. Bad but not as bad as Butler [Benjamin Franklin Butler, one-time Democrat, in 1884 presidential candidate of Anti-Monopoly and Greenback Parties] and the Bad Mayor Palmer [Albert Palmer, Mayor of Boston, 1883] whom we have also got rid of." [8]

December 23, 1883, Engelmann to Sargent: "Glad you got rid of that scamp, Butler—am ashamed of the Democrats for supporting such a selfish, unprincipled Demagogue . . ." [9]

In January 1884, Engelmann's health deteriorated, and in February he died; Sargent lost a favorite friend. Engelmann had been one of the few professional colleagues who had not been intimidated by Sargent's wealth and social standing. Gray, for all his academic status and familiarity with Boston's elite, was impressed by the Sargent affluence and caste, and knew very little of the man; perhaps he had no time for such musings. Engelmann, however, had teased, criticized, advised, helped, grumbled, and laughed. When he visited Holm Lea he took the formal routine as a matter of course and romped with the children in his friendly-bear manner. His last letter to Sargent, mailed the week before his death, must have been produced in great pain, for it was only two pages long and written at intervals over a ten-day period. He had not complained about his health, and only answered Sargent's queries on *Platanus.* [10]

"He was always cheerful, always interesting, and always zealous," Sargent said of him. "On slight acquaintance he appeared, perhaps, a little austere, but beneath this he was all good-natured jollity, and really one of the best companions I ever met." [11]

Sargent himself was a gentleman who, by attitude rather than appearance, impressed people as older than his forty-two years. He was large, handsome in the mode of his day, bewhiskered, inclined to overweight, shy, and formal. While gruffly affectionate with his children, he did not get down on his hands and knees and join their games. They called him "Professor" with profound respect and occasional

Changing of the Guard

terror. Both his manner and bearing were imperious, as Pringle said, but good breeding plus tongue-in-cheek wit gave him a quiet charm. Sargent seldom acted impulsively or willy-nilly. He tended to be silent at large social gatherings—which he loathed—unless, of course, approached on the subject of the Arboretum or trees; now and then he put in a word about the stock market or a wry remark about politics.

He had come a long way in the last ten years. From foreman on his father's estate he had become Director of the Arboretum and had secured the future of his institution. Without formal education in botany or horticulture, he was already regarded as an important authority on the trees of North America. Scientists in California and Europe knew his name. He owed much, he knew, to his father, to Hunnewell, to Gray, to Henry Sargent—who died in 1882—and to others who supported him morally and materially; but he owed as much, if not more, to his own willful determination.

He accumulated enemies. President Eliot disliked him because he had proved he could act effectively, independent of traditional University powers. Pringle, believing he had been humiliated, found sympathy among his botanical friends. Goodale, aware of Sargent's disdain, returned it in kind and kept a frigid distance. But these men still bore Sargent a grudging respect. Botany's pontiff, Gray, was startled by Sargent's achievements. Sargent was no rival for him, but the aging master feared for the solidarity of Harvard botany because he had an inkling that Sargent's Arboretum might eventually emerge as a competitor to its Cambridge godfather.

Sargent, absorbed in his work, created his own sphere of influence. Once he decided how something should be done, he did not deviate from this course, for he was not a flexible man. If necessary he paid bills himself or raised subscriptions among his rich friends; but he would not compromise or, should the situation arise, confess to mistakes.

Except for the incidental relief provided by his family

The Arboretum and Beyond

or business ventures, Sargent's world was his Arboretum, his trees. The metaphysical questions that puzzled Gray did not trouble him; politics and government aroused him only when they infringed upon his work or his financial stability; he made his friendships with people who shared his enthusiasms. He spent long hours, weekends, and sometimes holidays in his office, and weeks or months in the field; only reluctantly did he fulfill the social obligations of a Sargent. His birthright and wealth shielded him from the problems of Boston's growing slums. As he guarded his own privacy, so he did not meddle in others' affairs, either in a personal or public way, but held himself remote from the things around him. That the federal government since the Civil War had been characterized by weakness, bungling, and corruption only confirmed his opinion that government should mind its own business and leave private citizens to mind theirs.

Paradoxically, while Sargent was conservative in his politics, he was liberal-verging-on-radical on the subject of conservation. To protect the forests he welcomed the idea of government intrusion against the ravaging lumbermen, railroads, farmers, and fires. The dangers of destruction were real to him and the solution he sought was expedient, so he was not distressed by the contradictions in his political logic.

Sargent's aloof Boston soul found refuge in his study of trees. His pace was emphatic, marked by steady progress, and never mindful of any rhythm but his own. He never doubted his destination: how many times he wrote that the Arboretum was his life's work. Occasionally, some human incident would jolt him out of his work, only momentarily, and touch him deeply. The death of Engelmann moved him, as did the death of his father later in the same year.

In August 1884, following a long illness, Ignatius Sargent passed away. He was eighty-five, and his death had been expected by the family for several months; it was a sober occasion for his son, now entrusted with the estate and family fortune. The old man with his stern ways had encouraged

Changing of the Guard

and helped him from the start of his career. Father and son had not spent a great deal of time together, involved as each one was in his private interests, nor did they have a casual friendship, for both were guided by the strict forms of breeding into a relationship in which love was an unmentionable word. But the father's example had prevailed, and the son was the reflection of his image. At his father's grave, Sargent stood stoically, just as the old man would have liked; he displayed no more than tasteful concern and scarcely interrupted his work on the Adirondack report. In later years he remembered his father with warmth and affection.

Boston winters can be freezing cold, its springs no more than delayed, abrupt intervals between winter and the enervating humidity of a hot summer. If any one season can be called reliably pleasant, it is autumn, when colors run riot and the air is wonderfully clear. Sargent was at home in October 1887, when New England was at its best. As usual he found that the orderly life of his household had survived his absence as he revisited gardens, nurseries and herbaria in Europe. The Arboretum seemed in reasonably good shape; the roadways were still under construction, and Dawson was busy in the nurseries. Over in Cambridge, friends and colleagues welcomed Gray home from his six months in Europe, where he had done some work in herbaria and visited old acquaintances. Sargent had his research work for a silva of North American trees well enough in hand so he could promote his latest idea, a weekly magazine. He easily won the enthusiastic support of his friend Olmsted, and the two of them began mapping out details for the first issue.

Autumn conceded to winter, as it ordinarily does in Boston, around Thanksgiving. In the last week of November, Sargent learned that Gray was ill and probably dying. Like everyone else at Harvard, Sargent was stunned. Gray was old—seventy-seven—and, of course, he was mortal. But Asa Gray had seemed more than a man; he was an institu-

The Arboretum and Beyond

tion. Sargent was so sure of Gray's greatness that he began to make memorials to him before he died. It was Sargent who arranged for the bronze relief done by Augustus Saint-Gaudens. The sculpture rather amused Gray. But he was less pleased with Sargent's embarrassingly effusive article, written for the *Sun* on the occasion of his seventy-fifth birthday. Gray found the entire article, "about which nobody cared," full of mistakes.[12] For example, the notice credited him with an original paper which was merely a translation, and said he had been to Europe twice instead of four times. He was doubly irritated when Sargent had the tribute distributed in pamphlet form, mistakes intact. Sargent's concern for history—a concern which, unfortunately, he never applied to himself—led him to urge Gray to

> write out a brief account (with as many personal anecdotes of European naturalists as possible) of your three last European journeys. For you must remember that you have no botanical contemporaries (not a pleasant thought) to record all these things for you and that there is a long period of time, say from 1846 to 1865 or 1876 during which the going generation of botanists knows little about you except for your books. And then there are all your letters! I suppose it is hopeless to expect you to do anything toward putting them in order for publication, but could not Mrs. Gray do it under your directing eye? Many of them must relate to events which no one knows anything about but yourself; and a few short explanatory notes would greatly smooth the way for any future biographer you may have.[13]

As Sargent guessed, Gray spared no time for the sake of posterity, but after his death Mrs. Gray took on the task.

Although the thought of Gray's death had certainly crossed Sargent's mind, his illness, striking without forewarning, arrived as a bad surprise. A stroke which came in the last week of November left Gray speechless and helpless. Sargent made frequent trips to Cambridge to console Mrs. Gray

Changing of the Guard

and relieve her of practical matters which had been permitted to lapse. He relayed telegraph messages to Hooker and Thiselton-Dyer at Kew. They, too, were shocked, for not three months before they had seen Gray in relatively good health. Then, in mid-December, Sargent himself alarmed the Harvard community by coming down with a case of typhoid.[14] Fortunately the fever was not very serious, but it was frustrating for Sargent to be confined in bed, alternately shivering and sweating, as Gray's health declined. With his entire right side paralyzed, Gray lingered on until January 30, 1888, when he died quietly. Torrey, Brown, the elder de Candolle, and the senior Hooker were long dead; Bentham, Engelmann, Decaisne, and Darwin were gone; and now Gray. Joseph Hooker was old and in retirement, though prolific; Sereno Watson was also aging. Men of the nineteenth century who had made botany into a serious scientific discipline, who had, in a sense, made the study of plants a respectable profession, gave way to their students. In America, where the power of authority had been identified with a single man, an era came to its end.

It was no more than fitting that the first sentence of the first issue of Sargent's magazine, which came out under the title of *Garden and Forest*, mourned the death of Asa Gray. Sargent's elegy was a simple, touching praise of Gray's "wonderful intellect," [15] for this was certainly not the moment to mix criticism with reverence. Nearly six years later, however, Sargent dared to suggest that Gray had failed at an important point in his career:

> No man certainly ever worked harder or gave himself more cheerfully to labor. But, like other men of facile expression and great ambitions, he was too often led away from the main purpose of his life in efforts to excel in many directions. Perhaps Asa Gray lived too soon to have written an exhaustive *Flora of North America*, the work which occupied him at different times for fully half a century; but, looking at the two volumes of that half-finished book, we cannot but regret that other labors were allowed

The Arboretum and Beyond

to interfere with the completion of a work for which he was so specially fitted." [16]

Sargent's words flaunted his true colors: Sargent always got things done, as Gray had said; he never deferred to distractions; he always concluded what he began. That the *Flora* should be left unfinished disturbed Sargent because, in his orderly existence, everything begun must be completed. Privately, he confessed to Thiselton-Dyer, "Mrs. Gray does not like at all what I wrote in Garden and Forest about her husband and I did not suppose she would, but there is always such a temptation in this country for men to branch off into all sorts of things, leaving their work half finished, that the opportunity for a little sermon with Gray's Flora seemed too good a one to lose." [17] Thiselton-Dyer commiserated, "[I]t is lamentable that [Gray] never finished the Flora. He had capacity, opportunity, and a long life & he ought to have done it. God help American Botany now, with all you young sparks." [18]

For all their cordial friendship, for all the help that Gray had given, Sargent could never really understand his master's letting loose ends dangle; yet Gray's astonishing intellect awed him. As a personal gesture, he selected and republished two separate volumes of Gray's lesser writings, consisting largely of reviews, biographical sketches, and a few of the more important essays. It was a simple chore, requiring little of Sargent beyond making the selections and writing a short introduction. He set about it matter-of-factly, intending to make no fuss, and found, strangely enough, that he risked offending by his actions. Hooker, to whom Sargent wrote for advice on the contents, was helpful but visibly sensitive about Gray's reputation and anxious for posterity to treat his American colleague with kindness.[19] James Dwight Dana suggested that Gray's book notices with "criticisms which would offend should not be introduced." [20] Mrs. Gray stood guard over her husband's memory, jealously defending her privileged access to it. She ignored Sargent's work because she felt he trespassed on her territory, which was far

Changing of the Guard

from his intention. Sargent ceremoniously consulted her on his selections, but a coolness set in between the two. Mrs. Gray, meanwhile, handled the task of securing and editing her late husband's letters. It was a job that all his friends were eager to see accomplished, yet many of them found fault with her personal approach. Hooker vainly pleaded for Sargent to use his influence with her and have her put her money to better use, noting that he had "had much experience of this matter of attempts to force a dead author's claims to immortality on the public: most of which eventuate in The Widow paying the great part of the costs, & having to thrust volumes on the friends of the deceased."[21] Apparently questions of Gray's memory involved no outspoken disputes, but passed as a faintly disagreeable episode. Ultimately, Sargent's selections of the *Scientific Papers of Asa Gray,* published in 1889, were received thankfully despite a few typographical errors. The consensus among botanists was that much more of Gray's work could be reprinted usefully in similar volumes, but Sargent felt he had done his share and let matters rest there.

The semblance of unity among Harvard botanists which had prevailed out of respect for Gray during his last years vanished. Only the faithful Watson attended the Herbarium and continued its research. Goodale and Farlow were both caught up in their own special efforts; Goodale, particularly, ambitiously built his botanical museum. Sargent expressed the most concern for the deteriorating system despite the fact that he had been the first person to claim independence of Cambridge but, like the others, he was too busy with his own business to be of much assistance. When Sereno Watson died four years later, Sargent, who had come to know him better after Gray's death, lost another friend. "Watson's death will make a big gap in American botany," he wrote forlornly to Thiselton-Dyer. "He was an excellent man, industrious and of sound judgment, very silent and retiring, and entirely destitute of the American aggressiveness, but of late years I had grown to be very fond of him and shall miss him sadly. There is no one now to go on with the flora

The Arboretum and Beyond

and the possibility of our having a North American continental flora seems very remote, a not very creditable state of things for American botanists to contemplate."[22]

Sargent missed Gray a good deal. Gray had been in on the early discussion about *Garden and Forest*, brimming with inventive ideas. Because he had always been troubled by lack of funds, he had been unable to put out any regular publication from Harvard. Even without Gray's collaboration, however, *Garden and Forest* was a first-rate publication.

The magazine was not published officially by the Arboretum but operated as a private company with headquarters in the Tribune Building in New York; Sargent was not the editor but styled himself as the "conductor." As a major financial backer, along with Frederick L. Ames, Olmsted, and a few other friends, Sargent had complete control of the weekly. In effect, however, he exercised his authority only with respect to general policy and entrusted his editor, William Augustus Stiles, with the practical responsibilities. In forming policy, Sargent relied heavily on Olmsted, and the result of the collaboration was a format flexible enough to include many kinds of information. The single rigid standard seems to have been excellence: the paper was of high quality, the layout and typefaces tastefully chosen, the illustrations well reproduced, and the general level of writing remarkable. In short, it was well above the usual level of contemporary horticultural publications.

For ten years it was a quality publication. Stiles, who edited it almost until the end of its brief life, could not have been more happily selected. Bespectacled, bearded, thin, and timid in appearance, he was very versatile, delighting in subjects ranging from mathematics to football to music. His experience in journalism—he had been on the editorial staffs of the New York *Tribune* and the *Philadelphia Press* —and his educated interest in many facets of horticulture blended harmoniously in fulfilling the task at hand. The great wisdom in choosing Stiles was the priority given to his

Changing of the Guard

knowledge of journalism over his interest in horticulture or forestry. Too often horticultural magazines were run by horticulturists who had scant familiarity with the complexities of publishing. Stiles, on the other hand, could write, and he had good ideas and meticulous judgment. With Stiles in charge, and Olmsted and Sargent in the background, *Garden and Forest* was an immediate success; but it received praise instead of popularity. While the former was gratifying, the latter would have eased the financial crisis.[23]

In *Garden and Forest* plants were discussed in terms of taxonomy, morphology, geography, ecology, anatomy, history, agriculture, horticulture, economy, artistic value, and social and political contexts. Because its treatment was not strictly scientific, it was generally considered a horticultural magazine, but no aspect of plant life fell outside its range. Such a broad, and seemingly undisciplined, editorial policy could have resulted in a hodgepodge of unrelated information, but instead the magazine became an interpretation of the relationship between plant life and the several activities of man. Whether or not that elaborate intention was a conscious effort of the planners of *Garden and Forest* is mere speculation. More likely they thought of it as an attempt to increase the general knowledge of plants and to influence readers in specific matters. In its pages Sargent carried on his crusade for useful Adirondack legislation, Stiles denounced schemes which would spoil Olmsted's Central Park design, others pleaded for the salvation of California's statuesque trees. In issue after issue, articles on landscape design and aesthetic values instructed readers to discern between the tasteful and the grotesque.

Just how influential *Garden and Forest* actually was is a moot question. Generally it had a small circulation, but it did reach people who worked with plants—foresters, nurserymen, botanists, landscape designers, and others whose opinions were valued. In political matters, for example, it had no power on its own. But when quoted in a politician's speech or in the column of a popular newspaper, the words carried authority. The magazine did its small part to raise

The Arboretum and Beyond

the horticulturist from amateur to professional standing by exposing the wide extent of his activities and the science fundamental to his art. Gray's student, Liberty Hyde Bailey, would later go far to bring horticulture to maturity; meanwhile Sargent did his share in laying the groundwork.

On October 11, 1888, William Carruthers of the British Museum (Natural History) wrote to Sargent:

> We are all pleased very much with your journal, and I hope you may long live & maintain it at its present high level.
> We have had visits from three clear headed and cute American botanists—Dr. Britton, Profs. Trelease & Bailey. They meant work and did it in the Herbaria here.

These were kind words for *Garden and Forest,* which Sargent could not fail to appreciate. They are incidental to the casual remark about the trio of visiting Americans: Britton, Bailey, and Trelease. Those three were among the brightest of Thiselton-Dyer's "young sparks." With Gray gone, the new generation made itself heard. Nathaniel Lord Britton, whose self-confidence befitted his name, even in Gray's time had risen to challenge the accepted rules of nomenclature; he would be a force to contend with in the future. Bailey would do his monumental *Cyclopedia* and become the first bona fide Professor of Horticulture in the country. William Trelease fell heir to Engelmann's position in St. Louis and, on the advice of Gray, had been named Director of the new Missouri Botanical Garden. Other names, such as John Merle Coulter and Joseph Nelson Rose, were sounded frequently in American botanical circles.

Without Gray, however, there was no longer a focal point. Harvard, which for so long had been the center of American botany, began to see rivals in New York, Washington, and elsewhere. The new botanists competed and quarreled among themselves even though they collaborated. Within the plant sciences, fields of specialization became more

Changing of the Guard

refined. Sargent, single-mindedly studying trees, had no real competitors. Where woody plants were concerned, he was botanist, forester, and horticulturist all rolled into one. When he interfered in botanical controversies, it was always on the side of uniform order; he advised and editorialized on conservation problems, always on the side of strong protective measures. He contributed in quantity to *Garden and Forest* and worked steadily on his *Silva* which should not, God forbid, meet the same fate as Gray's *Flora*.

Arboretum problems still took precedence over everything. Sargent's persistent worry was that he did not have enough money to carry out all his projects. In the 1890's, he campaigned for funds and received them from H. H. Hunnewell, F. L. Ames, Jack Gardner, and Arthur Blake.[24] In an effort to raise $200,000 for "the completion, development and improvement" of the Arboretum, Sargent called for help; among the four men he got $62,000, with Hunnewell and Ames donating $30,000 and $25,000, respectively. It was another sample of Sargent's legendary ability to raise funds for the Arboretum. In fact, one of the few tales which have survived is that whenever he was in financial distress he gave a dinner party for his well-to-do, sympathetic friends. At a critical moment, the story goes, he arose to announce his own contribution to the cause and asked for reciprocal donations which, of course, he received. The story seems to contain some truth, for Sargent's donation in 1892 was $10,000 for books; he also turned over his collection of 5,000 books and 5,500 pamphlets to provide a nucleus for the library.[25]

Hunnewell earmarked his $30,000 to fulfill one of Sargent's dreams: a building to house the library, herbarium, and museum on the grounds of the Arboretum. The makeshift facilities at Holm Lea were both inconvenient and inadequate. Sargent's site for the new building was immediately off the principal entrance, which now joins the Arborway, to the Arboretum; he ignored suggestions to build near the Bussey complex, determined to have the Arboretum building independent in theory and practice. The architects

The Arboretum and Beyond

Horatio Hollis Hunnewell and Sargent at the opening of the first flower show staged in Horticultural Hall, Boston, June 1901

drew up plans immediately, no doubt strongly guided by Sargent's desires:

> ... a hundred feet long and thirty-nine feet wide and [consisting] of a high basement, two stories, and a high attic. The lower and principal story will be divided in the middle by an entrance-hall which will open on each side into a museum-room, and in the rear into a small work room in which is to be the stair shaft. The second floor will be divided into an herbarium-room, a library and

Changing of the Guard

four work rooms. By this plan the public can be admitted to the museum without interfering with the people working in the herbarium and library.[26]

Sargent insisted on numerous precautions to make the building "practically fire proof." He estimated that the new space would allow him to treble the number of herbarium specimens and put twenty thousand volumes into the library. For a man who usually thought a century ahead in making plans for the Arboretum, he was remarkably shortsighted about the building. He mistakenly stated that the space "ought to answer for a purely dendrological collection and I [w]on't attempt anything else either in the museum or herbarium." [27] Yet within less than fifteen years he needed a new wing.

A word about the design is in order. If Henry Hobson Richardson had lived a normal life span, it is very likely that he would have been the architect for the Administration Building of the Arnold Arboretum. As many articles in *Garden and Forest* testify, Sargent was a great admirer of his friend and neighbor's art, and as a director of the Boston & Albany Railroad had encouraged the selection of Richardson as an architect of railroad depots. Unfortunately, however, the building was planned by someone whose name has been lost, perhaps forever, in the great archives of Harvard University. Sargent apparently did not think it of sufficient significance to include in his reports. Assertively rectangular (though Richardsonian in some details) and quite what one would expect Sargent to order if given his own way, the building avoided the frilly patterns of the era. Sargent's architect solved his needs efficiently, simply, and undistinctively— functionally, we would say today. The construction work was quickly executed, and the staff was in new quarters by autumn 1892.

"Staff," by this time, was no longer just Faxon and Dawson. A lanky young man named John George Jack, who was only thirty-one, had been with the Arboretum for six years. A Canadian with no formal education beyond high school, his self-taught knowledge of plants earned Sargent's con-

The Arboretum and Beyond

fidence. He checked identifications of plantings on the grounds and provided the column of "Notes on the Arnold Arboretum," which appeared regularly in *Garden and Forest*. In 1891, Sargent recommended Jack's appointment as Lecturer in arboriculture. Jack's field classes at the Arboretum were geared for the interested amateur. The trial run in the spring of 1891 was an instant success, and the walks became an annual feature. Jack's friendly enthusiasm and familiarity with wildlife as well as plants made him a popular instructor. Somehow he had managed to overcome the handicap of red-green color blindness and was adept at identifying and selecting the plants he saw.

Jack's lectures added to the Arboretum's role as a public institution. Although classes were small, ranging between twenty-five and fifty, they effectively brought people into contact with the work being done by Harvard out in Jamaica Plain. Sargent could never have held a class himself; although he bore the title of "Arnold Professor of Arboriculture," he never taught a real class in his life. The rhetoric courses of undergraduate days had been futile, and nothing could prevail upon him to give speeches or lectures. He envied his silver-tongued colleagues. It must have been a family failing, for of his father Sargent wrote, "he used to say that he had never made but one public speech in his life and that it was in opposition to replacing the beautiful First Church in Brookline by a modern building. The congregation voted to pull down the old church." [28]

Technically, the Arboretum was twenty years old in 1892, when the building was completed and Jack gave his second round of field courses. Many of the young trees had had time to fill out and the roadways were near completion, though fresh gashes and grading still scarred the landscape. But Harvard's Arboretum was no longer a fledgling. It had a publication (indirectly), a research program, popular classes, and the capability of attracting large sums of money—a factor which scored high with the Harvard Corporation. The fifty-one-year-old Sargent might well have sat back, rested his gouty knees, and finished up his work on the *Silva*, but

Changing of the Guard

he found so little pleasure in the idea of relaxation and retirement that he never considered the prospect.

The following year, 1893, was a year of anticipation in the United States for reasons which had nothing to do with the Arnold Arboretum or with Charles Sargent except by remote associations. Communication media were primitive and techniques of public relations still in their embryonic stages, but people were agog over the Chicago World Columbian Exposition, the biggest fair in the United States since the Philadelphia Centennial Exposition of 1876. It was the 1893 "World's Fair." Olmsted and Sargent's nephew, Henry Sargent Codman, had accomplished something just short of a miracle by converting seemingly hopeless lakeshore wasteland into a smiling park. Codman, only twenty-nine years old, died suddenly after an operation for appendicitis in January 1893, before he could witness the full success of his efforts.

The most famous artists, architects, and sculptors of the era combined to proclaim an American renaissance and build a glittering white city frosted with plaster of Paris and decked with ornaments. The dreamlike quality was enhanced by the fact the elaborate complex had a functional life of about six months. Looking back from our vantage point, we call it tasteless and enjoy it only as we are inclined to take perverse pleasure in vulgar displays. But in 1893, hundreds of thousands of people gaped appreciatively at the gaudy revivals of classic forms. Sargent made the trip with his wife and his youthful landscape student, Beatrix Jones,* showing Miss Jones what should and should not be done. Given his admiration for bold, simple designs, he did not particularly care for The White City. However, he kept his opinions to himself out of loyalty to Olmsted and Codman.

* Beatrix Cadwalader Jones, later Mrs. Max Farrand, became a noted landscape architect. She redesigned the plantings at Dumbarton Oaks in the 1920's, was hired as a design consultant by the Arnold Arboretum on several occasions, and undertook many other important commissions.

The Arboretum and Beyond

Garden and Forest was kindly in its appraisal of the show, especially where the landscaping was concerned.

Nothing serves so well to demonstrate the place of horticulture in the opinion of the public in the 1890's as the generous provision of space for horticultural displays at the Chicago fair. There, alongside structures to house exhibitions of machinery, agriculture, works of art, mines, industrial products, and small international pavilions, a horticultural hall sprawled over 67,200 square feet, with an annex. There was nothing even remotely like it at the New York World's Fair of 1962–63 or Montreal's "Expo" in 1967. At Chicago, indoors and out, were special displays of azaleas, begonias, cacti, citrus plants, grapes, pecans, potatoes, and a wide variety of other edible and ornamental plants. Purists and professionals might—and did—criticize the doings at the Horticultural Hall, but the public obligingly admired them. *Garden and Forest*, politely offering several excuses to the horticultural committee, expressed editorial criticism of the offerings, both from the point of view of materials and their arrangement. "The broad landscape features of the Exposition are incomparably good," wrote a stern editor, "but such details as fell to the Bureau of Floriculture are often wrought in the stiff and conventional forms which, unfortunately, are still called landscape-gardening by a great body of our people." [29] At least the maligned forms were consonant with the architectural configurations. Bent on pleasing people rather than instructing them, the committees put on a show for enjoyment which serious-minded men like Sargent did not appreciate. Sargent's work was represented in another building: The American Museum of Natural History sent a duplicate set, comprising all 410 specimens, of the Jesup Wood Collection for inclusion in the New York State exhibit.

Chicago's extravaganza served as a reflection of popular American taste and, to a lesser extent, as an influence on it. Horticulture and forestry were of national significance, newsworthy subjects of economic importance. The Chi-

Changing of the Guard

cago fair gave exposure to the horticulturists and foresters as professional scientists. Americans were taking a genuine interest in horticulture, and this interest was no longer confined to the Northeast. With the closing of the frontier, intelligently planned, attractive planting—private and public—on a large scale made sense. The country was, necessarily, preoccupied with agriculture, yet, more than ever, the elegant garden was a symbol of prosperity and culture—and therefore a most desirable thing.

Early in November, as the chilling lake wind began its assault on Chicago's freshly deserted exhibition site, Francis Parkman died quietly in his home on the banks of Jamaica Pond in Boston. "Another of our big men has gone," Sargent told Thiselton-Dyer, "Parkman the historian who was our neighbor and one of our best friends. If you never read any of his books, I commend 'The Conspiracy of Pontiac' to you. It gives the best idea of the character of the country and the appearance of the forests before the white settlement that have ever been written." Although he won his fame as a historian, garden lovers knew Parkman as a grower of roses and a skillful propagator of lilies and poppies. Sargent had kept him supplied with new plants and called on him to trade horticultural confidences or talk about the West. Parkman, in exchange, had quickened Sargent's historical sensibilities, for Sargent thought him "far ahead of any [American historian] in method and literary skill." [30] They shared the pleasantest kind of neighborly friendship. When it ended with the historian's death, Sargent wrote feelingly to Mrs. Gray, "For his sake I am glad that Parkman has gone to rest, but it is impossible to find words to express our loss. He was more to me than all our other neighbors, and without him Brookline will never be the same. So many people are dead!" Sargent helped carry his friend's casket to its grave, but he refused to attend a Parkman post-morten appreciation, reflecting, "I have little liking for such functions which are chiefly useful in giving people a chance to talk about things they know least about." [31] Later he raised money for a memorial to mark the site of Parkman's home.

The Arboretum and Beyond

"So many people are dead!" Sargent's nephew Codman, the landscaper, had died the previous winter in Chicago. Parkman was dead, and so was Frederick Lothrop Ames, best known to horticulturists for his love of orchids but appreciated by Sargent as a powerful ally. Second only to Hunnewell in the magnitude of his financial support of the Arboretum, Ames was one of the original owners of *Garden and Forest* and a generous donor of funds. "Ames's death is a very serious blow to me," Sargent wrote Thiselton-Dyer. "He was in the Government of the College where I could always count on his intelligent support and assistance; and then he was one of the richest men in America to whom I could always go for financial assistance with confidence." Though not a sentimental commentary on Ames' death, it was an honest appraisal of his value to Sargent at a moment when the Professor was down in the dumps. "I wish you might come over here and talk over our Arboretum with me," he went on; "it gives me no end of trouble and anxiety. Not only do I have to raise the money for it, but pull wires with the University and the city authorities, build up the Herbarium and Library and establish precedents, as this is an entirely new undertaking. It is working out slowly and I hope in the right direction, but I shall hardly live to see it amount to anything more than a conception, all of which is rather discouraging and uphill work."[32]

Then, as if to compound his misery, Sargent came down with the flu at the end of the year and gloomily pronounced himself a "good deal of a wreck, mentally and physically."[33] The only benefit he derived from his three weeks in bed was that he had ample time to read and work up a strong dislike for Mrs. Gray's just published selection of her husband's letters. "I hope somebody will say that they do not add to the fame of the author," he remarked.[34] Perhaps he cheered up to read Thiselton-Dyer's quip that his wife, who was "pretty shrewd," was of the opinion that the book was mostly "piffle."[35]

So ended the year of the World Columbian Exposition, with Sargent weakened by his influenza, saddened by the deaths

Changing of the Guard

of Codman, Parkman, and Ames, worried about money, and unsure of his next move. He behaved testily, resigned himself to holiday festivities, and saw out the old year without regrets.

6

One Success and One Failure

Although Sargent may not have minded, the wood collection at the American Museum bore Jesup's name, and the Arnold Arboretum was the *Arnold* Arboretum, even though Arnold died before there was any arboretum at all. Such accidents play strange tricks. For example, while many Bostonians know about the Arnold Arboretum, only a few of them have any idea at all about Sargent. Botanists remember Sargent for two things: the taxonomic confusion he created in the genus *Crataegus* and his *Silva of North America,* usually called "Sargent's Silva." Often with pleasure, and occasionally with weariness and irritation, Sargent labored for nearly twenty years over those fourteen volumes.

Sargent's insistence on completing anything he started never prevented him from undertaking several projects simultaneously; if it had, he probably would have left nothing behind but the Arboretum. A silva was a logical sequel to the Census report. The Census included a great deal of information of practical value to foresters and others concerned with trees and forest products. While botanists were among the first to applaud the practical usefulness of the report, they were also aware that it could only perform a limited service for botany. Sargent was in no way blamed for this deficiency; everyone recognized that the contents of the report had been governed by the needs and restrictions of the Census Bureau. The botanical information was incomplete, and there were no plates to supplement the abbreviated descriptions. However, all the traveling, collecting, corresponding, compiling, and studying which Sargent had done on behalf of the Census prepared him to write a silva.

Sargent had dreamed about writing a silva ever since he began to study trees. His hopes materialized sooner than he expected, for during the spring of 1882, before he had even submitted his Census report to the Washington officials, Spencer Baird, Secretary of the Smithsonian Institution, approached him with an offer to sponsor a silva. Gray had been invited to prepare one back in 1848, and Isaac Sprague had drawn some color plates for it; twenty-two of them found their way back from the lithographer's, but Gray never published any text. When Sargent agreed to Baird's terms, the Smithsonian thought it had its man.

American botany needed an updated description of its trees. The standard references in the 1880's were F. André Michaux's *North American Sylva,* the last volume of which was published in 1819, and Thomas Nuttall's continuation of that investigation, published between 1842 and 1849. Although Nuttall's work was more recent, Sargent considered Michaux's superior.[1] Both works, remarkable when they appeared with their handsome colored illustrations, quickly became obsolete, largely by virtue of the amount of territory subsequently explored and opened up. Between 1845 and 1868, the United States acquired fourteen territories, all west of the Mississippi, and Texas entered the Union. Michaux had botanized only east of the Mississippi. Nuttall got all the way to the West Coast—up the Missouri into Oregon Territory, and in California as far south as San Diego, as well as part of the way up the Red River; he examined specimens sent to him from as far south as the Florida Keys. Impressive as this was, it still left great gaps in the United States of the 1880's and, consequently, in the knowledge of its trees. The only other significant generalized attempt in this direction was George Vasey's catalogue, with notes and brief descriptions of some species, sponsored

The Arboretum and Beyond

by the U.S. Department of Agriculture and published in 1876. Sargent's Census was more recent and thorough than that but still inadequate for botanists.

Sargent hired Faxon to do art work and take over the herbarium from John Robinson. Originally he thought that Faxon would prepare the illustrations for the Jesup Collection, but it was soon evident that this was more work than Faxon could cope with, so Mary Sargent took over the latter task. Meanwhile, Sargent discovered that the arrangement with the Smithsonian would not be satisfactory. ". . . [A]t the end of a few months," he explained, "it was found that at the rate the Smithsonian Institution was willing to pay for the work it would take at least seventy-five years to complete it." The Smithsonian lost its man, but Sargent stayed with the *Silva*. He made "another arrangement" for financing the project, thereby subtracting—if we accept his figures at face value—fifty-five years from the date of publication of the final volume.[2]

Faxon started drawing before Sargent began to write. Along with Arboretum problems, Sargent was burdened with the Census, the Jesup Collection, the Northern Transcontinental Survey, and the Adirondack report. All the time, of course, he had the *Silva* in the back of his mind. When Pumpelly asked him to join the Survey team, Sargent saw an expense-paid collecting trip in the Northwest from which the *Silva* could but benefit; each of the other undertakings contributed similarly to the project.

Still, North America was a vast area, and despite all his travels there were trees he knew only from books or herbarium specimens. "To be really understood," he explained in his preface to the first volume of the *Silva*, "they must be studied in the forest; and therefore, since the plan of writing this Silva was formed, I have examined the trees of America growing in their native homes from Canada to the banks of the Rio Grande and the mountains of Arizona, and from British Columbia to the islands of southern Florida. I have watched many of them in the gardens of this country and in those of Europe, and there are now hardly a dozen of the

One Success and One Failure

trees which . . . I have not seen in a living state."[3] The matter-of-factness with which he set out for the West Coast, Florida, Europe, or later, South America and Japan, was extraordinary in an age when the world seemed enormous to most people, and travel posed complicated problems. Botanists, necessarily, saw more of the world than most people. Hooker, who had been to the Antarctic and India, had a spirit of discovery and adventure beyond the floras. Sargent, by contrast, took a single-minded approach to his jaunts: he was bent on seeing trees and shrubs. One has the feeling that anything else he noticed was purely accidental. He traveled at that breakneck speed that Engelmann had once teased him about—the infamous "five minutes"—and this was his habit throughout his life.

In February 1885, he sent the Adirondack report to Albany; the Jesup Collection seemed more or less under control in the hands of Dill; and it would be several weeks before the warm weather thawed the grounds at the Arboretum adequately for new plantings. Rather than languish in Boston during another miserable winter, reading about the discouraging lack of progress in the New York State Legislature and working in the herbarium, he decided to take a trip to Florida. On second thought, he shifted his itinerary to the West Indies where, he suspected, botany had more to gain. In the company of Faxon, he sailed from New York in mid-February.

> We went from New York to St. Kitts, then to Antigua, passing a day at each in exploring the gardens & shores— then to Martinique where we had a couple of days. The first in the old & really wonderfully interesting & rich Botanic Garden [St. Pierre, which was destroyed during the eruption of Mt. Pelée in 1902]; and the second in the mountains where they are now establishing Cinchona plantations on a very considerable scale. St. Pierre is a charming old place, most picturesque, and the vegetation in the mountains, thanks to daily showers, seemed denser, if less mixed than that of Jamaica. From Martinique we

The Arboretum and Beyond

went to Barbados & then to Jamaica where [Sir Daniel] Morris gave me a hearty welcome & did everything he could for us. We were far too early, however, to find the trees we were in pursuit of in flower, & one must go to Jamaica in May or after the rains for good botany. The Garden there disappointed me. It is very pretty and admirably kept, but it is a garden almost entirely of exotics, while, of course, I wanted to see the West Indian plants. What a pity they can't establish somewhere in the W. Indies a collection of at least their trees! Even at St. Pierre the finest specimens were Old World or Brazilian species. At Jamaica such a collection is especially important because the original vegetation is fast being replaced by introduced plants... I went from Jamaica to New Orleans & passed a couple of weeks in Texas & Louisiana & then home to a terribly cold ... & disagreeable spring.[4]

So much for the West Indies! The weather was warm but the trees were not in flower and the botanic gardens had the wrong plants, so he accomplished less than he had hoped. What a maddening botanist-to-botanist letter it was, without a remark about the West Indians and their ways. One could believe that Sargent and Faxon had not seen another human being save Morris—also a botanist—during the entire trip. They had used every precious moment to absorb the novelties of the Caribbean flora.

During the spring and summer of 1885, Sargent was busy supervising the final plans for permanent planting at the Arboretum. But in September he went off again, this time to the mountains of North Carolina—via Newport, to watch the *Puritan* win the America Cup race, and New York, where he left his wife with some friends.[5] The fervor with which he collected and solicited specimens matched the diligence with which he plowed through the herbarium sheets when he was at home. There was the painstaking task of determining a specimen, a process demanding the scrutiny and evaluation of minute details, comparison with other speci-

One Success and One Failure

mens, and checking library references and cross references. When he lacked confidence in his decisions, he scrawled a hurried note to one of his many correspondents asking another opinion. The actual writing of the taxonomy and descriptions was usually easier than assembling all the necessary information, for even though he had the Census as a basis, it was not detailed enough for his silva. Besides, every year he learned new facts, reports of new species were published, geographic distribution lines had to be redrawn, and revisions made.

Faxon, who produced one plate, sometimes two, for every species which Sargent described, needed the head start he had. Sargent's time was so consumed with other matters that it was not really until the winter of 1885–86 that he was able to devote concentrated effort to the writing of the work. He came out of hibernation in April 1886 for another collecting trip, to Florida and the Keys, western Louisiana, and Alabama. Faxon went along, as did Sargent's brother-in-law (Henrietta's husband) James Codman, who, having no special interest in botany, enjoyed the warm weather and company. Sargent invited Gray, who declined, for he "did not care for that."[6] It was one of the rare occasions when Mary Sargent accompanied her husband on a collecting trip. The Secretary of the U.S. Light-House Board gave permission for the party to spend the month aboard the lighthouse tender *Laurel*, so the accommodations were not as primitive as those Sargent usually endured and were comfortable enough for his delicate wife. She had a chance to see, in their wild forms, some of the flowers she was drawing to illustrate the Jesup Collection; meanwhile, sketchbook in hand, she could enjoy the benign climate. Codman preserved the trip in photographs. In one, Sargent slouched in the tender parlor with his collecting gear, complete with floppy, broad-brimmed hat and sullen expression.

Sargent, satisfied that the time was profitably spent, irritated Jesup by announcing the arrival of more logs "to complete . . . your collection so far as that part of the country is concerned."[7] After spending the summer at home, with oc-

The Arboretum and Beyond

casional visits to Newport, Sargent went down to the mountains of southern North Carolina in September, made a return visit to the Florida Keys in November and December, trekked (again with Mrs. Sargent and Codman) to Texas and the forests of the Sierra Madre of northeastern Mexico in March and April 1887—he promised Jesup another half dozen specimens [8]—and then went back to the Keys for a third trip. [9] All the traveling made for a crowded schedule, especially at the pace Sargent marched through the forests. He was home for the late spring, however, supervising Arboretum plantings. Then, around the first of July, he sailed for Europe with his nephew, Henrietta and James' son, Henry Sargent Codman. [10]

Primarily, Sargent wanted to see various European gardens, nurseries, and arboreta. It was more than thirteen years since he had been in Europe, but this time he went as an authority instead of a neophyte. He no longer needed Gray's letters of introduction. Though his eye was no less critical, it was more experienced than before. Aside from visiting arboreta, he wanted to work in the herbarium at Kew to settle some doubtful points in his *Silva* research; he also planned to go to France to discuss arrangements for reproducing the *Silva* plates.

Young Codman, although only twenty-three years old, already exhibited promise as a landscape architect. After his graduation from the Massachusetts Institute of Technology in 1884, Codman had been taken on in Olmsted's office. A genial young man, he was a favorite of his uncle Charles, who liked the prospect of an interested, educated companion.

Arriving at London from Southampton, the two men established temporary headquarters at Brown's Hotel on Albemarle Street; from there they headed straight for Kew. Hooker, still active in research, had retired from administration in favor of his son-in-law, Thiselton-Dyer. With Thiselton-Dyer, Sargent enjoyed a camaraderie he had not known with Hooker; the two younger men were friends, as Gray and Hooker had been. Sargent indulgently compli-

One Success and One Failure

mented Kew, and proclaimed its arboretum particularly improved over his last view of it. The arboretum had been one of Hooker's pet projects, and Thiselton-Dyer was equally enthusiastic about it. Sargent inevitably compared it with the Arnold Arboretum, and Kew came off poorly by contrast; but he was diplomatic enough to make suggestions for improvements without alienating the Director's friendship.

The Asa Grays were also traveling in Europe at the time, and their paths crossed Sargent's in England; together, Gray and Sargent went to visit Lord Ducie at his baronial manor, Tortworth Court in the Vale of Gloucester, where they admired his horticultural displays. Sargent worked in herbaria, at Kew and at the British Museum, and shepherded Codman around to nurseries, gardens, and parks, with no dallying. Heaven only knows if Codman ever escaped in the evenings to sample London's higher or lower life. After some weeks in England, they crossed the English Channel to France. Edouard André, acting as Sargent's Paris intermediary, obligingly interrupted his vacation in Lacroix (Touraine) to meet him. André was to French landscape design what Olmsted was to American. He did Sargent a personal favor in arranging for the engraving and printing of the *Silva* illustrations in Paris, for Sargent would settle for nothing but the best. The text would be printed by the Riverside Press in Cambridge, a prestigious firm, but Sargent had little faith in American lithography. Also, the rendezvous gave Sargent an opportunity to present his nephew to André, a fruitful introduction for young Codman, who later returned to Paris as André's apprentice-pupil. Uncle and nephew proceeded through France, and on to Italy and Germany for brief tours, then back to England before returning home in early October in time for the New England fall color extravaganza.

When Volume I of Sargent's *Silva* appeared in 1891, it was dedicated to "Asa Gray, Friend and Master." Despite André's anxieties about plates, and Sargent's anxieties about everybody except Faxon, the book was out. It weighed

The Arboretum and Beyond

about eight pounds. Houghton, Mifflin & Company, the publishers, offered it at $25 a copy which, at the promised issue of twelve volumes,* meant the set would sell for $300, beyond the means of most individuals, but feasible for institutions. The reviewers were unanimous in their praise. Britton, who wrote up the *Silva* and *Garden and Forest*— he could have refused to do it if he had felt under pressure to be kind—spared no enthusiasm and predicted that "the result will rank with the works on science and art that are recognized the world over." He continued, "The book is sumptuously printed on heavy paper and cut with broad margins. The illustrations are superb, the descriptions are excellent, and the notes on geographical distribution, history and economic importance are of the highest interest and value." [11] What pleased Britton most was that Sargent chose the new American system of nomenclature over the conventional European system, which had been favored by Gray. The *Botanical Gazette,* while more subdued in its praise, welcomed the volume and acknowledged that "No one more competent could have been selected to undertake the work." [12] The English objected to Sargent's nomenclature, but this seems to have been the only point in contention. "Whether we regard it from the point of view of pure botany, gardening and woodcraft, or from the standpoint of art, typography and book production, it stands out in all respects as a most remarkable undertaking," purred the *Gardeners' Chronicle.* [13] John Muir, the naturalist and Sargent's close friend, was ecstatic over the *Silva.* In an article for the *Atlantic Monthly,* he was most enthusiastic: "Though accustomed to read the trees themselves, not written descriptions of them, I have read [the *Silva*] through twice, as if it were a novel, and wished it were longer." Muir offered the following description of Sargent at work:

While all his surroundings were drawing him toward a life of fine pleasure and the cultivation of the family

* The *Silva* actually ran to fourteen volumes.

One Success and One Failure

fortune, he chose to live laborious days in God's forests, studying, cultivating, the whole continent as his garden. Into this glorious field he set forth rejoicing, making ways everywhere, consuming obstacles, never counting the cost . . . His task seemed endless, but glowing enthusiasm carried him on. Flitting from side to side of the continent, he was now in Florida, now in Canada, California, Alaska; traveling thousands of miles every year, mostly by rail of course, but long distances by canoe or sailboat on the Florida coast, through swamps, along lagoons, and from one palmy island to another, jolting in wagons or on horseback over the plains and deserts and mountain chains of the West, now tracing the ways of early adventurers, to identify the trees they first described, now exploring untrodden wildernesses, like Charity enduring all things,—weather, hunger, squalor, hardships, the extent and variety of which only those who from time to time were his companions can begin to appreciate. While trees were waving and fluttering about him, telling their stories, all else was forgotten. Love made everything light.[14]

Muir's account of Sargent's emotional condition belies everything else we know of Sargent. There is more Muir than Sargent here!

Supplementary to the descriptive and systematic text, and the distribution and economic information, the *Silva* included historical notes and occasional tales of folklore. It was one of those instances in which the footnotes were as beguiling as the text. Jack added remarks on insects which attacked certain tree species, and Farlow commented on fungi. Sargent investigated the histories of the trees he described and the biographies of the people somehow connected with the trees. He delighted in offering morsels of curious information as though they were pieces of candy. Years later when he supplied the biographical notes for the Sargent genealogy, he wrote with the same kind of relish, revealing his enjoyment in relating quaint tales about his

The Arboretum and Beyond

family. The anecdotes of the *Silva*, and the genealogy, did not provide any continuous history; rather, they imparted a character and charm to the individual, whether an oak or a Sargent. Sargent appreciated the characteristic detail for itself, making little effort to place it in a wider context. Charm aside, however, the fullness of the information—he gave many more details than either Nuttall or Michaux— added immeasurably to his text. The *Silva* became, and remained, a standard classic.

After his work with the Census, the Transcontinental Survey, and the Adirondacks commission, Sargent had cause to be discouraged with the forestry program in the United States. He had diagnosed forest problems and suggested remedies; moreover, his work had been praised and cited by experts. It was, then, exasperating for him to sit back and watch year after year as the Washington politicians bickered on, allotting only token sums to the Division of Forestry. The most promising gesture to come out of Washington was the 1891 act to repeal the much-exploited timber culture laws. No doubt this was a good idea, for under the government's careless management, too many frauds had been committed in the name of the law. On the other hand, the honest settler was no longer provided with an incentive for planting forest groves. Another section of the 1891 law authorized the President to set aside by proclamation any portion of public lands as a forest reserve. President Harrison's first use of his power was to oblige conservation interests by declaring a 1,200-square-mile addition to Yellowstone Park, a concession which Congress had failed to make during eight successive sessions. Yet the 1891 bill was one of Congress's mixed blessings, for an accompanying amendment sanctioned timber-cutting on public domain lands subject only to regulations made by the Secretary of the Interior. It would take an iron-fisted Secretary to curb the waste likely to occur under this clause, and past performances offered little hope that cutting would be judiciously restrained.[15]

One Success and One Failure

Not all conservationists were as critical as Sargent of the 1891 legislation. While in solid accord on the necessity of government involvement to protect natural areas, they differed widely, and sometimes bitterly, on the nature and extent of that involvement. The crucial division within conservation ranks occurred between the faction that wanted the wilderness areas to remain untouched and viewed government as the defender of their virginity; and the faction that thought of the areas as natural resources to be used under government supervision. Further, subtler arguments arose in both camps: *how* government should protect; *how* to use the resources without waste. Sargent, though not opposed to use as a principle, did not trust the government's competence to control it, so until federal agencies could prove their proficiency in forest management, he sided with the aesthetic conservationists. Infighting among the reformers confused the public and compounded the difficulty of securing legislation, particularly on the federal level.

In 1893 a *Garden and Forest* editorial remarked that "[i]t can not be said that even the beginning of a rational forest policy is anywhere visible." [16] In the face of disappointments, the experts could do little more than pursue their efforts to inform the public and hope that an enlightened electorate would press for forest legislation. For a man like Sargent it was a frustrating spectacle. Mostly through the pages of *Garden and Forest,* he did his share in advocating measures to prevent waste and warned against its consequences. His words betrayed his despair with politicians, which lingered from the days of the Adirondacks debacle. "The Government," he wrote, "and not the people, are to blame for the present attitude of the country toward the nation's forests; and the whole theory under which the western lands have been managed is wrong and demoralizing." [17] As a recognized authority he had proposed what he considered to be logical and viable solutions to critical problems. The fact that, having solicited his views, politicians failed to act favorably upon them, or even to take the forest situation seriously, appeared to him as ludicrous and idiotic.

The Arboretum and Beyond

Sargent was too engrossed in his *Silva* and the Arboretum, and too vexed by the circumstances, to make forestry into a major crusade. Although he wrote an occasional editorial and kept abreast of developments throughout the nation, he was a rather passive agitator. Meanwhile, Bernhard Fernow, by 1886 chief of the Division of Forestry in Washington, applied the full force of his spirit and experience to the cause despite Congressional parsimony. One of Fernow's associates was Gifford Pinchot, a Yale graduate whom Fernow had directed to Europe to study forestry because the United States had so little to offer. By 1891 Pinchot returned and was already impressing his colleagues with his ability. Another associate was Henry Solon Graves, who had spent a year at Harvard, working part of the time under Sargent and Jack at the Arboretum. Fernow and Pinchot were among the most notable leaders of the forestry movement in the 1890's; they represented a new breed of professional foresters. Among them Sargent's words carried a good deal of weight. Sargent had no formal training in forestry, he did not deliver long papers on forestry methods, and he was conspicuously absent from forestry meetings, where his presence would have been desirable if only to add a little Harvard distinction to the group. But he was undeniably superior to everyone in his knowledge of American trees. The early volumes of the *Silva* proved that beyond a doubt.

Besides professional foresters and men like Sargent, whose scientific experience gave them authority, there were a few people who, from devotion to outdoor life and a passion for nature in its undisturbed state, became evangelists of conservation programs in general and of forestry legislation in particular. Among the naturalists, none was greater than John Muir. Of all the conservationists, his is the most familiar name today.

No two men with common interests could have been less similar in temperament than Sargent and Muir. The Scottish-born Muir was one of the last of the transcendentalists in the Thoreauvian sense. To the bewildered amusement of his scientific companions, Muir's enthusiasm for the sights,

One Success and One Failure

smells, and sounds of nature knew no restraint, whether he was captivated by a grand vista or a small flower. Gray, for one, admitted teasing him; but Muir, unabashed, took the chidings laughingly.[18] With his untrimmed beard flying above his wiry frame he roamed the forests, particularly in the West Coast mountain regions. Having explored the Yosemite Valley, he fought hard to have it set aside as a national park. His articles won popular support, and he did not shrink from confronting politicians. Although it was not entirely a one-man effort, Muir deserved most of the credit when, in 1890, Congress passed a bill embodying his proposals. With the same zeal he campaigned to protect California's sequoias and redwoods. In 1892 he organized the Sierra Club with like-minded people—some of whom had powerful connections—and within a few years the group mustered enough political strength to make a successful stand against a bill designed to redraw the boundaries of Yosemite Park. With Muir at its head, the Sierra Club became the chief spokesman for the aesthetic conservationists.

Muir achieved leadership in the conservation movement through indefatigable labor and his ability to communicate both his knowledge and his enthusiasm. People who refused to take his cause seriously wrote him off as a raving madman because his love of the wilderness knew no reasonable limits. For Muir, no superlative was too superlative to celebrate the wonders of nature. Face to face with some new pleasure in the mountains, he was known to break into a joyous jig.

So different were Muir and Sargent that it is hard to imagine their association progressing beyond a businesslike correspondence based on common objectives. Even by Boston standards, Sargent was a reserved character. Yet, somehow, Muir got through to him, and a strong sympathy bound the two from the beginning of their acquaintance. Perhaps Muir divined some mystery beneath Sargent's cool exterior; perhaps Sargent was fascinated by Muir's lack of inhibitions. On occasion, however, they did irritate one an-

The Arboretum and Beyond

other. Once on a hike through the Alleghenies, the two stood atop Grandfather Mountain to take in the view. Muir later recalled:

> I couldn't hold in, and began to jump about and sing and glory in it all. Then I happened to look around and catch sight of Sargent, standing there as cool as a rock, with a half-amused look on his face at me, but never saying a word.
> "Why don't you let yourself out at a sight like that?" I asked.
> "I don't wear my heart upon my sleeve," he retorted.
> "Who cares where you wear your little heart, mon?" I cried. "There you stand in the face of all Heaven come down to earth, like a critic of the universe, as if to say 'Come, Nature, bring on the best you have. I'm from Boston!'"[19]

Muir, apparently, could never quite understand what Sargent, or Boston as represented by him, was all about. Yet despite what appeared to him as spiritual shortcomings, Muir revered Sargent's knowledge of trees. He conceived of Sargent as an intellectual mastodon, exploring the forests with single-minded energy.[20]

Sargent and Muir had been vaguely acquainted through Engelmann for some time before Muir had occasion to call on Sargent at Holm Lea. By this time the naturalist was a well-known figure and accustomed to ceremonious receptions; the Sargent household still impressed him, but life at the estate was not as forbidding as surface appearances indicated. On his first visit in June 1893, he wrote his wife in California:

> We [Robert Underwood Johnson, editor of *Century Magazine*, and Muir] went to Professor Sargent's grand place, where we had a perfectly wonderful time for several days. This is the finest mansion and ground I ever saw. The house is about two hundred feet long with immense ve-

One Success and One Failure

157

randas trimmed with huge flowers and vines, standing in the midst of fifty acres of lawns, groves, wild woods of pine, hemlock, maple, beech, hickory, etc., and all kinds of underbrush and wild flowers and cultivated flowers— acres of rhododendrons twelve feet high in full bloom, and a pond covered with lilies, etc., all the ground waving, hill and dale, and clad in the full summer dress of the region, trimmed with exquisite taste.

The servants are in livery, and everything is fine about the house and in it, but Mr. and Mrs. Sargent are the most cordial and unaffected people imaginable, and in a few minutes I was at my ease and at home, sauntering where I liked, and making the house my own. Here we had grand dinners, formal and informal, and here I told my dog story, I don't know how often, and described glaciers and their works. Here, the last day, I dined with Dana, of the New York "Sun," and Styles [sic], of the "Forest and Stream," [sic] Parsons, the Superintendent of Central Park, and Matthews, Mayor of Boston. Yesterday the Mayor came with carriages and drove us through the public parks and the most interesting streets of Boston, and he and Mr. and Mrs. Sargent drove to the station and saw us off.[21]

There, at Holm Lea, the unlikely friendship was cemented. Muir, struck by the beauty of the place, wondered that the elaborateness of the household belied the simplicity of the man. By nature, Muir was the more talkative of the two, but there was ample time for a fair exchange. Muir did not have precisely the same ideas about forestry as Sargent. To the naturalist's mind, nature in its virgin state was quite perfect —"the face of all Heaven come down to earth." Sargent maintained no such romantic notions. In the tradition of Marsh he cleaved to his conviction that man, if properly instructed, could improve nature's random arrangements. Impressed by European examples, Marsh admitted that he considered artificial forests superior to spontaneous woodlands.[22] Sargent, doubting that any government agency

The Arboretum and Beyond

could carry out a massive program without bungling, resigned himself to fight for conservation. Despite their philosophical differences, Muir and Sargent shared immediate goals; they were both anxious to secure federal protection of the great forest areas.

With people like Muir generating public sympathy, men like Fernow and Pinchot discussing the more technical aspects of forest management, and publications such as *Garden and Forest* sowing seeds of alarm, Washington gradually became forest-conscious. With unjustified optimism, Sargent summoned Pinchot and two magazine publishers to a meeting in New York City in late 1894, and the group agreed to promote a bill in Congress to create a commission to investigate government timberlands. Congress showed no enthusiasm for the measure, but Wolcott Gibbs, head of the National Academy of Sciences and Sargent's personal friend in social and academic circles, salvaged the idea by suggesting a method for bypassing the legislature. On his advice, early in 1896, Fernow and Pinchot drafted a letter for the signature of Hoke Smith, Secretary of the Interior, requesting the National Academy, as scientific adviser to the government, to launch an investigation and submit a report outlining a "rational forest policy for the forest lands of the United States."[23] Although it took some smooth talking, Smith was coaxed into signing the letter and returning it to Gibbs. Gibbs selected Sargent as commission Chairman, partly because of his outstanding reputation and partly because he was removed from political maneuverings. Along with him, Gibbs appointed Brewer of Yale, director of the 1870 forest census; General Henry L. Abbot, formerly chief Engineer of the United States Army; Arnold Hague of the geological survey; and Alexander Agassiz of Harvard, naturalist and oceanographer. They were all members of the Academy. At Sargent's request, Pinchot, a non-Academy man, joined the group and subsequently acted as its secretary. During the spring session, Congress allotted $25,000 for expenses, and the commission prepared to go into action.

There is little doubt that either Sargent or Pinchot could

One Success and One Failure

have sat down and single-handedly written a report on the spot; Brewer probably could have done the same. Each was familiar with forest problems and current remedies. So little progress had been made in the preceding twenty years that Sargent could have used his Census report as the principal reference. Fernow himself thought the commission a waste of time and money and did not hesitate to say so.[24] His statements were mistaken for resentment at having been passed over in favor of Pinchot, but it was obvious to anyone who gave the matter a second thought that if there was to be a study group it should be as apolitical as possible. Sargent's choice of Pinchot seemed wise, for Fernow was perilously close to Washington pressures.

Sargent approached the task with mixed emotions. Unlike Fernow, he did not think the commission entirely futile despite his past experience with the Adirondacks. Meanwhile, he aired private misgivings to Thiselton-Dyer:

> I have got . . . another bad job on my hands . . . the task is exceedingly difficult and I am not at all sure that the problems can be solved. Not less than 20,000,000 acres of forest land have been withdrawn from entry and sale by the Government already and it is probable that this area will be largely augmented. Every one living anywheres near these forests is opposed to any scheme looking to their care or preservation, the distances are enormous and topography difficult and broken. On the whole I am afraid I have more on my hands than I can manage . . . I should be glad to decline this national business if I could properly do so, but there is no one else in the Academy with as much knowledge, perhaps, of the situation as I have, or whose special studies have been in this direction; and the least cheerful part of the whole business is that after we have slaved over the thing for years, perhaps, Congress will probably pay no attention to our recommendations. On the other hand, there has been in the last ten years a distinct gain in the country in the feeling that forest preservation is necessary and proper, and our re-

The Arboretum and Beyond

port, if it does nothing else, should give rise to a vast amount of discussion which ultimately may result in some good.[25]

To complicate matters, personal differences began to manifest themselves between Sargent and Pinchot. At first they disagreed over how to proceed. The eager Pinchot had managed to get a half-hour interview with President Cleveland, who professed sympathy for the Commission's cause. As Cleveland would leave the White House in March 1897, Pinchot felt the Commission should report by November and wanted to begin exploring immediately. Though equally eager, Sargent approached the problem with caution, planning to do some preliminary homework; Pinchot's upstart attitude nettled him a bit. Pinchot, chronically active, could not tolerate waiting for the full Commission to organize; he set out five or six weeks in advance of the others, at his own expense, taking his friend Henry Graves along as a companion.[26]

Sargent, Brewer, Hague, and General Abbot determined to take their westward journey in the summer. Gibbs, an ex-officio member of the committee, was too ill for rough traveling. Agassiz had no chance to visit the forests. By coincidence, Muir was east on business and in Cambridge in June to accept an honorary Master's degree from Harvard. Sargent invited him to return west as an unofficial member of the group, and they settled on a rendezvous in Chicago at the beginning of July.

Muir wrote his daughter, Wanda, from Hot Springs, South Dakota.

> I am now fairly on my way West again and a thousand miles nearer you than I was a few days ago. We got here this morning, after a long ride from Chicago. By *we* I mean Professors Sargent, Brewer, Hague, and General Abbott [*sic*]—all interesting wise men and grand company. It was dreadfully hot the day we left Chicago, but it rained before morning of the 4th, so that day was dust-

One Success and One Failure

less and cool, and the ride across Iowa was delightful. That State is very fertile and beautiful...

Nebraska is monotonously level like a green grassy sea—no hills or mountains in sight for hundreds of miles. Here, too, are cornfields without end and full of promise this year after three years of famine from drouth.

South Dakota, by the way we came, is dry and desert-like until you get into the Black Hills.[27]

He wrote again a few days later, from Custer:

My!! If you could come here when I call you how wonderful you would think this hollow in the rocky Black Hills. It is wonderful even to me after seeing so many wild mountains—curious rocks rising alone or in clusters, gray and jagged and rounded in the midst of a forest of pines and spruces and poplars and birches, with a little lake in the middle and a carpet of meadow gay with flowers. It is in the heart of the famous Black Hills where the Indians and Whites quarreled and fought so much...

We came here this forenoon from Hot Springs, fifty miles by rail and twelve by wagon...

We leave to-night for Edgemont. Here are some mica flakes and a bit of spiraea I picked in a walk with Professor Sargent.[28]

Pinchot joined the group shortly thereafter in Montana, and the whole party journeyed westward. Pinchot found further cause to disapprove of the Chairman: he neither fished nor hunted, and he did not have Pinchot's boy-scout temperament. "He tried to take thirty-six cans of condensed milk for [a side] trip, but was headed off... We used 6 or 7."[29] Sargent, naturally, collected specimens furiously all along the way, lugging his increasingly cumbersome possessions with him as the party sped from one place to the next. By the time he returned home near the end of October, he was elated by the success of the trip but was still skeptical about its consequences. He wrote Thiselton-Dyer:

The Arboretum and Beyond

This has been the longest, hardest and probably the most interesting and instructive journey I have made in western America . . . It has covered all the great forest regions from the northern Rocky Mountains along the northern boundary to the coast, and down through Washington, Oregon, California and Arizona to Colorado. I have had a good chance to review nearly all our conifers and have been able to extend the range of several of them, as this journey has taken me into parts of the country I have not seen before. The Commission will make, of course, a report on the condition of the national forests with various recommendations. Whether Congress pays any attention to this is an entirely different matter and I confess I do not feel very hopeful of future prospects in this direction.

Even though Sargent did not expect much from Congress in the way of forest legislation, he was pleased to suppose that the Republican presidential candidate, William McKinley, would defeat William Jennings Bryan, the "Cross of Gold" orator and Democratic proponent of free silver. "There is going to be a tremendous victory for sound money next month and the prospects for better times are certainly good," Sargent predicted confidently.[30] What the new administration might do in terms of a forest policy was still a moot question, but Sargent could sooner bet on a man with a sensible fiscal policy.

Shortly after returning from the West, Sargent sprained his ankle during a trip to New York. He had almost recovered from his misfortune when a fire destroyed a wing of his Holm Lea mansion on the day after Christmas. So it was the beginning of January before the Commission went into action—and then they moved quickly. According to Pinchot's suggestion, they decided to press their advantage with the lame-duck president. As Sargent had predicted, McKinley had been elected in November, but he would not be inaugurated until March. By the end of January 1897, the Commission produced a perfunctory report urging that

One Success and One Failure

President Cleveland proclaim, under the 1891 laws, thirteen new forest reservations totaling over 21 million acres— or more than double the area already set aside. The Commission made its report after consultations with the new Secretary of the Interior, David Francis, who proved sympathetic and endorsed the plan wholeheartedly. Sargent, on behalf of his unanimous commissioners, drafted the recommendations in a letter to Gibbs, who passed it on to Francis; Francis added his own letter of transmittal to President Cleveland, artfully concluding, "I respectfully suggest that the one hundred and sixty-fifth anniversary (February 22, 1897) of the birth of the Father of our Country could be no more appropriately commemorated than by the promulgation by yourself of proclamations establishing these grand forest reservations." [31]

Fernow, meanwhile, was appalled by what was happening. As he guessed, there was nothing particularly new in the Commission's propositions; furthermore, he worried that, should the President act upon the recommendations, Congress would raise such a fuss that not even the diluted bill for forest management and protection, currently under consideration, would be approved. A giant step forward in one direction might well mean two steps backward elsewhere. [32]

The ensuing uproar justified Fernow's fears. On Washington's birthday, precisely as Francis had advised, Cleveland proclaimed all thirteen forest reservations. It was, to say the least, a grandiose gesture and one best made by an exiting President with little left to fear from Congressional adversaries. According to Muir, this was Cleveland's last chance to redeem himself and the nation. [33] Cleveland either underestimated the potential strength of Congressional resistance or—more likely—having little to lose was willing to take a chance. By asking for so much, he hoped that at least half the reservations would pull through.

A representative from Wyoming accused the Commission of having conducted "by a sneaking still-hunt a so-called

The Arboretum and Beyond

investigation of the regions ... There is no hypothesis upon which they can explain their conduct except that they were endeavoring to exploit a theory and were afraid that the men who had practical knowledge would not take the same view as they did of the matter. So we of the West are to suffer as we have suffered before from the actions of men who sit in their studies and formulate pretty theories based on the action of European nations in densely populated regions." [34]

Twenty years later, Fernow offered a somewhat dramatized and prejudiced version of the subsequent events:

> The reservation policy had never been favored by the Western Representatives and Senators, who saw in it an impediment to settlement and development of the Western country, and now when without previous announcement or even competent investigation this large block of territory was suddenly withdrawn from entry or disposal, the storm broke loose.
>
> In a session of the Senate which lasted two days, including a Sunday, the proposition of impeaching the President and of annulling not only the reservations made by him but all of them was hotly discussed.
>
> It is difficult to say how exactly the disaster was averted; there were many conferences and influences brought to bear, but it is to the credit of the then Speaker of the House, Joseph Cannon, to have manfully assisted in preventing rash action. The Congress came to an end on March 4 without action, but also without having passed the appropriation bill for the government, so that it became necessary for the President to call immediately an extra session. [35]

Cleveland held his ground, but March 4 was his last day as President. At ten o'clock that morning, McKinley began his ritual approach to the inaugural platform. Congress, adjourned and called back into special session in the same morning, was in a state of bedlam, but there was just time

One Success and One Failure

enough to swear in the new congressmen. By midday, McKinley was President.[36]

Sargent did not delude himself about the fate of the forests. McKinley could not reasonably be expected to provoke the legislators' resentment at such an early stage in his term over the relatively minor issue of forest reserves when graver problems, including the likelihood of a war with Spain, already troubled him. Sargent guessed that the new President would try to rescind his predecessor's proclamation. Fearing the worst but unwilling to see his work swept aside without a fight, Sargent assembled his commissioners and succeeded in arranging a private interview with McKinley at the beginning of April. Sargent recalled that McKinley

> was alarmed by the protests of western politicians against the reservations and seemed inclined to revoke Mr. Cleveland's action. I went to see him alone at this time and had a private conversation with him. He told me he was going to break up the reservations and I had a very plain talk with him and explained to him that the President of the United States could not afford to put himself in the position of helping western timber thieves. We had a rather stormy interview.[37]

Since historians tend to portray McKinley as a genial, unsophisticated Ohioan with a long temper, Sargent's Boston arrogance must have been in evidence during this encounter. Apparently he argued effectively, for McKinley reconsidered his position and decided to let Cleveland's proclamation stand, though he refused to defend it. With half the nation clamoring for war, he had enough troubles without further antagonizing Congress. But Sargent, having gotten his inch could be satisfied with nothing less than a mile. He left the interview feeling the same kind of bitter disappointment he had known when the New York lawmakers had started tearing apart his proposed Adirondack

The Arboretum and Beyond

legislation. In his misery, he wrote to Thiselton-Dyer, "the outlook is not at all satisfactory and I feel anxious and discouraged about the results. Our final report, however, will be finished in a month and then this matter will be off my hands—a great relief." [38]

After the Sargent-McKinley meeting, the Commission's final report came as an anticlimax, but this, too, precipitated a nasty quarrel. General Abbot and Sargent wrote the report themselves, and all the Commissioners signed it without dissent. Like the Adirondack paper, it was direct and concise. The five appended bills proposed methods of forest management, protection, and administration by federal troops pending the establishment of a trained forest corps, as well as the creation of parks in the Mount Ranier and Grand Canyon regions. [39] By the time the Commission submitted the report through formal channels, it was the beginning of May and Sargent had abandoned hope for Cleveland's reservations; he no longer believed that any part of the recommendations would be enacted into law during the next few years. The necessity of admitting defeat was frustrating enough for Sargent, but when he discovered that Pinchot had double-crossed him, he was furious.

"The report was signed by all members of the Commission, including Pinchot," he remembered acidly. "A few days after he had signed it he was in Washington obtaining from the Secretary of the Interior permission to prepare what was described as a practical plan for the management of the forests on the national domain: in other words, he had gone back on the report he had signed a few days before." [40] Although Pinchot's biographer, M. Nelson McGeary, claims he only signed the report after suffering serious mental anguish, in Sargent's eyes he was no less than a traitor. [41] When Pinchot accepted a Department of the Interior appointment as a "special forest agent" shortly after, any doubts Sargent may have had regarding his motives vanished. His single consolation came in finding others who shared his opinion. Muir criticized Pinchot severely, [42] as did Abbot, who wrote:

One Success and One Failure

That Pinchot should think to grasp control of the forests is not surprising, for he is a man of limited capacity, but I did not think he would sign the report and then overturn it—and this he appears to have done ... It was a great misfortune that he was a member of the commission; but I do not wonder at your being mistaken in the man, for he has a good address and appears energetic and intelligent. —In fact he is the former; the trouble is in his head and, it would appear from recent developments, in the lack of appreciation of proprieties usual among gentlemen.[43]

Aside from considerations concerning the integrity of the report, Sargent, like Abbot, took offense at Pinchot's lack of good form. It was unthinkable that a non-Academy man who had been awarded the opportunity of participating in an Academy committee should turn around and insult its authority. While Pinchot's handling of the affair was inexcusably tactless—even a little stupid—the real issue dividing him and Sargent was the forest land itself. Pinchot's German training had made him an advocate of immediate forest *use* while Sargent fought for forest conservation until a responsible forest corps could be educated. The two wealthy aristocrats, equally stubborn and ambitious, also quarreled over employing federal troops as forest protectors; Pinchot disliked the proposal intensely. He downgraded Sargent as a mere forest botanist, while Sargent accused Pinchot of selling the forests down the river.

Sargent did not disguise his displeasure with the latest turn of events, and Pinchot quickly recognized his *gaffe*. He tried to make amends, and when Sargent refused his explanations, he finally gave up. There is little doubt that Pinchot was ambitious: otherwise he would never have risen as he did to the position of Governor of Pennsylvania. He took unilateral actions and allowed himself to be swayed by political considerations. Nevertheless, despite Sargent's prophecy, he masterminded many advances for American forestry, particularly in creating an operational Forest

The Arboretum and Beyond

Service, during his twelve-and-a-half-year tenure as chief of the Forestry Division, a post he gained after Fernow resigned to head a new school of forestry at Cornell University. (Ironically, Pinchot's job there ended when he was forced to resign for having taken a politically unpopular stand in favor of conserving certain mineral-rich lands.) Forestry could have gained more, faster, with Sargent and Pinchot as allies instead of enemies.

As far as Congress's action on the Commission's report was concerned, it was nearly as bad as Sargent feared. On June 4, the Sundry Civil Appropriations Bill suspended all but two of Cleveland's reservations for a minimum of nine months, and called for a new investigation of the areas—a humiliating blow to Sargent's prestige. The bill did grant authority to the Department of the Interior to administer national forest reserves but the measures fell far short of the Commission's recommendations. A *Garden and Forest* editorial, written by someone other than Sargent, articulated his views in milder words than he himself would have used.

It may as well be said that the character of the rules [for the governing of the forest reserves] published by the Secretary [of the Interior] is not a matter of serious practical moment. He has not the machinery nor the money to enforce them. Many of his predecessors have been earnest in their desire to check timber depredations on the public lands, to mitigate the dangers to the forest from fires, and to protect the mountain slopes from the pasturage of hoofed animals which destroy the forests wherever they tread. Like his predecessors, Mr. Bliss will be compelled to rely upon employees appointed for political reasons, and many of them in full sympathy with herders and speculators and prospectors and timber thieves who have had their way unchecked ever since they drifted into the west.[44]

Other men involved in forestry, however, and especially those who, like Fernow, had been entangled with the work-

One Success and One Failure

169

ings of government for a long time, were pleased with what little they had reaped from the bill. And to everyone's good fortune, McKinley ultimately proved to be an effective friend to forest management.

Sargent, who had begun his Commission work realistically, had let his hopes get the better of him and lead him into disenchantment. The episode with Pinchot gave him special cause for bitterness, and he had his bellyfull of politicians. After 1897, he ceased to take an active role in the national forestry movement. Instead, he devoted himself to the development of the Arboretum and the preparation of scientific publications, activities in which the rewards seemed commensurate with the expenditure of effort.

The Arboretum and Beyond

7

The Arboretum Grows Up

By 1900, the decentralization of botanical studies at Harvard which began near the end of Gray's lifetime was accomplished; Harvard botany could claim neither geographic nor academic unity. As B. L. Robinson observed, this segregation came "into being in no instance through previous plan or special design of the Governing Boards, but as the result of restricted gifts and legacies, or through the energy of the teaching staff backed by sympathetic support of interested patrons living mostly in Boston or its suburbs."[1] The early splintering which Gray had witnessed with sorrow in the 1880's was an established fact, and his successors were now firmly entrenched in their separate spheres of influence.

As Sargent predicted, Goodale's approach to the Botanic Garden in Cambridge differed radically—in Sargent's view, undesirably—from his own. Goodale, partly because he was not a taxonomist, showed little enthusiasm for the scientific arrangement which Sargent had worked so hard to perfect. The new director leaned toward displays with popular appeal; there was one bed to show plants which had been mentioned by Virgil, another for Shakespeare's plants, and enlarged greenhouses to shelter special displays of insectivorous species and other crowd-pleasing curiosities. Goodale also had to contend with that perpetual nightmare of all Harvard administrators, the Endowment Fund. Although

Sargent had done financial wonders for the Botanic Garden during his time there, he had by no means created enough of a fund to safeguard its future; furthermore, when he moved his domain to Jamaica Plain, he took most of his patrons with him, leaving Goodale in a budgetary vacuum. The new director chose to overhaul Sargent's system and seek his own sponsors. Goodale's real brainchild, however, was the Botanical Museum. The project, originating with Gray by way of inspiration from Kew in the 1850's, had never amounted to anything. Goodale, with his talent for public relations and his interest in popular education, convinced prospective donors of the need for, and value of, a building to house botanical displays, and by 1890 builders completed a new wing on the University Museum on Oxford Street in Cambridge, several blocks from the the Botanic Garden and Herbarium. In 1893, Goodale negotiated the purchase of the glass flower models, created by the Blaschka brothers, for which the Museum is famous. Goodale was a scientist, but he was also a forceful, ambitious man whose publications and lectures on plant physiology and appealing displays did much to popularize botany. He did not, however, go out of his way to assist the other botanical segments at Harvard. He took little interest in the Herbarium or the Arboretum and none in the Bussey Institution. His attitude conformed with the spirit of Harvard botany: competition, not cooperation, dominated.

The Gray Herbarium, as the library-herbarium-laboratory complex on Garden Street was called after Gray's demise, profited little from Goodale's imaginative management of the surrounding Garden; if anything, the Herbarium suffered the consequences of the misconception that it formed a single unit with the Garden. The money that Goodale's admiring public contributed in no way benefited the work performed by the taxonomists lodged in the building within the Garden. As a result of this situation and because of its administrators' ineptitude at raising funds, the Herbarium hovered on the brink of financial disaster for ten years after Gray's death. At the end of the fiscal

The Arboretum and Beyond

year 1898, the total income from endowment was $1,232.17, plus $1,806.31 from Gray's copyrights and $573.00 from sales of publications. There were no gifts for immediate use. The income amounted to only about half of the institution's minimum expenses. The Fisher Professorship passed from Gray to Goodale, stranding the Herbarium botanists in an ambiguous position. Mrs. Gray, who survived her husband, was wholly absorbed in the task of fixing a permanent niche for him in posterity and grew progressively fearful that the institution which had occupied him for half a lifetime was verging upon ignoble extinction. With Watson's death in 1892, the last of the old guard disappeared. By the mid-1890's the Botanical Museum and the Arboretum dwarfed the parent Herbarium in popular reputation and accumulation of funds, and Mrs. Gray began to feel desperate. Appealing to Sargent's loyalty and influence, she begged for his help but received only his restrained sympathy. "I am afraid that there is little I can do," he apologized, ". . . for I have more than I can manage to keep the Arboretum going."[2]

In 1897, however, acting upon Goodale's wishes, the University officials appointed a Visiting Committee solely responsible for the Herbarium, where in the past a single committee had served for the Garden, the Botanical Museum, *and* the Herbarium. The new arrangement, plus an anonymous offer of $20,000 in 1898 to establish an Asa Gray Professorship of Systematic Botany, injected new life and fresh money into the Herbarium. (Mrs. Gray ultimately proved to be the donor of the $20,000.) By 1899 more than $50,000 had been raised for the professorship and the regular endowment. B. L. Robinson, the first Asa Gray Professor, and his assistant, Merritt Fernald, thus provided with economic stimulus, plunged into the task of preparing a new edition of Gray's *Manual*. Robinson, an elegant, withdrawn, kindly gentleman, and Fernald, a small man with big ability and an ego to match it, represented the new generation of taxonomists. Sargent seldom found reason to consult either of them. Neither, for that matter,

The Arboretum Grows Up

did Goodale or Farlow. Lodged on the top floor of the Botanical Museum, he was engrossed in his study of the lower forms of vegetable life—personally donating an annual salary of $450 to pay for an assistant—his herbarium, his students, his endowment, and cared little for his botanical colleagues or the problems of their respective domains. Samuel Eliot Morison presents a harsh but accurate appraisal of Harvard botany at the turn of the century.

Unfortunately, no one of the three Harvardians [Goodale, Farlow, Sargent] could abide the other two. Each entrenched himself in his special herbarium, laboratory, or arboretum, and spent a disproportionate amount of time trying to bag all available students and funds; despite brilliant individual work in research (especially by Farlow in Cryptogamic Botany and by Sargent at the Arnold Arboretum, a department of the University that attained the very highest reputation), this jealousy prevented a well-rounded programme, and hampered Botany at Harvard for almost half a century. Closely allied to these botanical sub-divisions in subject-matter, and impartially detested by them all, was the Bussey Institution in Jamaica Plain.[3]

Only the courtly newcomer, Robinson, escaped the personal animosity of the others and quietly declined to participate in intramural rivalry even though the Herbarium felt the consequences of the hostile atmosphere.

As for the Bussey Institution, between 1880 and 1895, it was plagued by a shrinking income and forced to survive hand-to-mouth on rents collected from boarding horses and cattle, profits on vegetables sold for student consumption at Memorial Hall in Cambridge, small individual donations, and annual gifts from the Massachusetts Society for Promoting Agriculture. When, in June 1894, the Harvard Corporation, responding to Sargent's persistent demands for expansion room, transferred seventy-five acres of Bussey land (now called Peters' Hill) to the Arboretum, the Institu-

The Arboretum and Beyond

tion was deprived of $700 to $900 per year, a sum which it could scarcely afford to lose and which Dean Storer regretted bitterly.[4] Understaffed and poorly attended by students, the department received no sympathy from the Harvard botanists even though Goodale, Farlow, and Sargent had each been briefly associated with the Bussey staff. The Bussey Institution was orphaned among the Harvard divisions with botanical inclinations, and it was not until after 1908, when it was remodeled as a graduate school of applied biology, that it gradually began to play a significant role in the University.[5]

The tug-of-war, begun in earnest after Gray's death, grew if not inevitably perhaps naturally out of advances in botanical study and the resulting trend toward specialization. In that sense, developments in botany ran parallel with the changes which occurred within the University as a whole. Eliot's pioneering administration rescued Harvard education from its mid-century doldrums and drastically activated and streamlined it. The number of courses swelled while subject matter was refined. During the 1880's, for example, economics finally came into its own as a study, and the college listed ten courses in Political Economy in 1886–87 where ten years earlier there were only two tucked away under the heading of Philosophy. At the turn of the century the faculty included William James, Charles Eliot Norton, and George Santayana. No doubt rivalries existed in other departments, but they did not inflict the deep wounds that troubled botany, for each botanical competitor, because of its irregular and individual financial relationship with the University, was compelled to seek its own funds. Geographic divisions stood stolidly in the path of pooled resources. Robinson and Fernald, Sargent, and Farlow had separate herbaria; Goodale, the Bussey Institution, and the Gray Herbarium had separate laboratories; all had their own libraries. Unavoidably, this arrangement led to wasteful duplications of facilities and expenses; but since each man was absorbed in his specific study, no one tried to consolidate the materials. Yet, as Morison

The Arboretum Grows Up

noted, individuals in each institution made brilliant contributions to science under these trying circumstances, and it is doubtful if a cooperative effort would have improved their work. Surely, however, it would have simplified financial matters and relieved the administrators of the necessity of chasing separate endowment funds.

Goodale and Sargent fared best in this every-man-for-himself climate: the former on the strength of personal magnetism, public speaking ability, and an honest desire to popularize botany: the latter by virtue of his influential Boston connections and administrative excellence. Both men rewarded their sponsors with results: Goodale had his Garden, Museum, and glass flowers; Sargent, his Arboretum and *Silva*. To the eye of most potential donors, the work of the Herbarium botanists and the Bussey Institution agriculturists was inconspicuous and less attractive. Some people gave to more than one department at a time, but distributed their gifts unevenly. In 1901–02, for example, Sargent's old friend, Francis Skinner, donated $5,000 to the Arboretum and $20 to the Gray Herbarium while Francis Shaw gave $100 and $10, respectively.[6] People contributing to both places usually favored the Arboretum.

Relative success, however, brings small comfort to the fund-raiser if he falls short of his intentions. Sargent's ambitions for the Arboretum were grand, his appetite for endowment insatiable. He pleaded his cause effectively, and President Eliot made a special request for contributions in his 1899–1900 Report to the Board of Overseers.

> The City of Boston has finished the work of construction in the Arnold Arboretum which it began in the year 1883. The City has built three and a half miles of Telford and macadamized roadway, five and seven-tenths miles of gravel walks, solid stone walls on highway boundaries wherever such walls did not previously exist, seven entrances to the Arboretum with handsome iron gates, and has made all slopes or other changes of surface which the construction of the roads and walks made

necessary. It also bought, and turned over to the University for the use of the Arboretum, land to the value of $79,315.85. The total cost of the construction paid for by the City has been $371,768.82. Moreover, the City pays for maintaining the drives and walks, and for police protection: and this payment amounted in 1899–1900 to $8,500. The contribution of the City of Boston to this admirable collection of all the trees, shrubs and herbaceous plants which can be grown in the open air in the climate of Boston has, therefore, been large. [On page 245 of the same report, Sargent estimated the total expenditure at $661,084.67.] The University has contributed about 200 acres of land; but it is the scientific direction of the Arboretum by the University which has given to the collection its most characteristic value ... the collections are already a source of great pleasure to the public, and of valuable instruction for a few students; and every year adds to their completeness and beauty. The question remains, however, how the University is to be provided with the means of making the Arnold Arboretum an object lesson in all that relates to horticulture, arboriculture, and landscape gardening in New England. To accomplish that object a far larger endowment than any which the Arboretum now possesses will be necessary. It is obvious that, if adequate salaries were now paid to the Director and his assistants, the whole income of the endowment of the Arboretum would be exhausted by those payments alone. From the beginning the salary of the present Director has been little more than nominal. It is for the public to decide how an adequate establishment is to be maintained on these beautiful grounds where so excellent a beginning has already been made. The State, or the City of Boston, might do it; or it might be done by a great endowment provided by public spirited individuals.[7]

This hardly sounds like the same Eliot who resisted an alliance with the City in the 1870's. To some extent he had

The Arboretum Grows Up

been softened by the participation of his much-loved son in drafting final plans for the Arboretum. Young Charles Eliot was an apprentice landscape designer in Olmsted's office when the scheme was still on the drawing boards, and he labored many an hour over it, passing a good part of the spring of 1885 out in Jamaica Plain, supervising plantings and staking out beds in the shrub collection. Thereafter, until his premature death in the spinal meningitis epidemic of 1897, the younger Eliot's professional interests threw him into frequent, usually amiable, contact with Sargent.[8] President Eliot, however strongly sentimental he felt about his son, did not set University policy by his feelings. The Arboretum—its achievements, its reputation, its success in the face of his initial apprehensions and criticism—testified on its own behalf. In retrospect, Eliot appreciated the partnership with the City without which the Arboretum would have floundered and become a financial millstone.

The $188,400 which Eliot mentioned as having been received in gifts to the Arboretum since 1877 did not include Sargent's personal expenditures: his reduced salary; his trips abroad or collecting in various parts of the country; the purchase of books and periodicals to form a library; a portion of the financing of *Garden and Forest* which, while not an official organ of the Arboretum, spread its reputation; and who knows how many more outright or indirect payments of which there is no record. No one else at the Arboretum had access to the financial records, but there were occasions when funds were supposed to be so low that the staff suspected Sargent of paying wages out of his own pocket. During his lifetime, in one way or another, Sargent probably gave a quarter of a million dollars to the institution. At the time he donated his library, it contained many old and rare volumes.[9] The Director's largesse had facilitated the undertaking and completion of projects which under other circumstances would have been unthinkable. If conventional finances ran out, there was no need to abandon or suspend work in mid-stream. When *Garden and Forest* ceased publication after ten years of deficits, it was not for

The Arboretum and Beyond

lack of available funds but because the sponsors concluded that their money was going to waste. As Sargent bluntly told Thiselton-Dyer, "I have already sunk more money into the enterprise than I can afford and it doesn't seem worth while to go on with the certainty that it can never be made in our time a permanent institution." [10]

The fear that the same fate which befell *Garden and Forest* could one day undermine the Arboretum nagged at him. The agreement between the City and the University seemed to insure the permanency of the land as a park area, but in no way did the contract secure the scientific function of the institution. What, for example, would the Arboretum do after Sargent's death? His successor might not be adept at raising funds among the Boston patrons. At the turn of the century, Sargent yearned for the assurance that there was a million-dollar endowment guarding his life's work. The alternative which Eliot had mentioned so casually in his appeal, that is, that the State or City take complete control, was odious to Sargent, suggesting as it did the possibility that the Arboretum could be demoted to the level of a common park.

While Sargent found support for special projects either by soliciting subscriptions or delving into his own bank account, it was the day-to-day operational expenses that troubled him most, and here he budgeted small items scrupulously, like President Lyndon Johnson keeping the lights turned off at the White House. There was, in fact, no lighting of any sort in the Administration Building because the Director regarded electric lamps as extravagances, and candles or kerosene lanterns as fire hazards. On short winter days, no one could see to work after four o'clock. Yankee or not, the staff used supplies with Yankee thrift. The employee pay was very low. In 1896 and 1897, Jackson Dawson earned only $1,200 per year. In 1898 the highest paid outdoor laborer, Martin Daley, received $2.00 a day during a six-day week. Other laborers, their number fluctuating between five and twelve with the season, earned $1.50 or $1.75 a day. At the very bottom of the pay scale that year

The Arboretum Grows Up

was Alfred Rehder, treated as immigrant labor and assigned to menial tasks like weed-pulling despite his university studies and record of publications. At the end of each week he collected a grand total of six dollars, or a dollar a day,

Jackson Dawson, ca. 1900

for his efforts. Long years of service, at substandard wages, from the professional staff suggest Sargent's ability to quicken loyal sentiments. Dawson, Faxon, Jack, and later Rehder and William Judd lived out most of their lives working at the Arboretum with few complaints about salary, possibly taking some comfort in Sargent's ready acknowledgment that they were, indeed, underpaid. Ernest Wilson was the singular exception to the rule. His salary during the Arboretum expeditions to China came from subscriptions;

later he used his reputation to bargain for financial concessions. Conventional measures of economy to minimize operating expenses were not enough to keep the Arboretum budget out of the red. In 1899–1900, payments exceeded receipts by more than $8,000, and in 1900–01 by almost $5,000.[11] It cost approximately $15,000 for ordinary annual expenses, and the endowment did not yield even half that sum. To remedy the situation, in 1901–02, Sargent extracted $44,760 from sixty-three donors to amplify the permanent endowment. The gifts helped but in no way solved the problem of a sufficient, guaranteed annual income, and Sargent still had to solicit gifts for immediate use every year to pay his way.

A happier situation to ponder was Abby A. Bradley's gift of $20,000 in 1897 in memory of her father, William Lambert Bradley, an agriculture and tree enthusiast from Hingham, Massachusetts. Miss Bradley specified that the sum be applied to a specific project—not to the general endowment —which involved finding a task appropriate to the fund and agreeable to Miss Bradley. So it was that the Bradley Bibliography, the five volume *Guide to the Literature of the Woody Plants of the World Published before the Beginning of the Twentieth Century* was conceived and Rehder was rescued from the weed patch.

In March 1898, at the age of thirty-four, Rehder arrived in the United States with the dual purpose of making dendrological studies for Möller's *Deutsche Gärtenzeitung,* a German periodical, and of observing American fruit-growing and wine-making for the German government. To his immediate dismay and long-run good fortune, the mild-mannered German incurred the disbelief of suspicious Boston port authorities who insisted, finally, on checking his credentials with Sargent. Released by the Customs service, Rehder soon discovered that the money he made from writing magazine articles was not enough for even modest living by American standards. It was then that Sargent charitably invited him to weed the shrub collection to subsidize his

The Arboretum Grows Up

inadequate earnings. Rehder, unaggressive and embarrassed by a stutter, had more chance to prove he was a hard worker than a scholar, yet Sargent recognized his potential and after several months encouraged him to stay on with the tantalizing prospect of assembling the bibliography. Impressed by Sargent and the Arboretum, and uncertain of his career in Germany, Rehder accepted the proposal. He began working in the library, his quiet, kindly manner belying his capacity for producing enormous quantities of superior work. (His lifetime bibliography lists more than a thousand titles.) He was never too busy to answer a question, too preoccupied to look at another's work, or too impatient to do a thorough job. Sargent's luck was that, thanks to the Bradley Fund, he could manage to hire Rehder.[12]

By 1900 the Arnold Arboretum, for all its financial woes, was well on its way to being a traditional feature in the Boston landscape. Removed from Cambridge, the garden earned no place in Harvard folklore. A few students found their way over to Jamaica Plain to investigate the trees; some, no doubt, availed themselves of the serene pastoral environment in late springtime to indulge in romantic delights with agreeable young ladies—oblivious to the carefully labeled plantings. The only instruction offered on the premises as a regular class was Jack's peripatetic lectures each spring, and they had no bearing on the University curriculum. But Boston assimilated the Arboretum legend largely because its patrons played leading roles in Boston history. In 1935, Lucius Beebe, discussing sacred cows in his witty *Boston and the Boston Legend,* wrote: "Symphony in Boston is ritual, an integral and venerated part of the formal scheme of things as essential to the social well-being of Marlborough Street and Harvard Yard as the Arnold Arboretum or the lectures of the Lowell Institute." Beebe did not consider it necessary to identify the Arnold Arboretum for his non-Bostonian readers.[13]

The Arnold Arboretum was a place for families to stroll on a Sunday afternoon in May when the flowers were at

The Arboretum and Beyond

their best or in autumn when fruits and leaves turned dazzling colors; it was a place where the rich could drive in carriages, admiring the rolling landscape and awesome hemlocks. In the era of florid journalism, the Arboretum was even newsworthy, and many a long article on its beauties and research projects can be found on microfilm. Full-column feature stories, like the one bird-lover Emily Tolman wrote for the August 3, 1899, edition of the *Boston Evening Transcript,* provided restful interludes for the reader between stock prices or international crises.

Visitors to the Arnold Arboretum who never leave their carriage may miss many pleasures open to the pedestrian. Numerous enticing footpaths lead from the park roads into fragrant and flowery by-ways, where one meets only an occasional nature lover like himself or the robins and catbirds that hop fearlessly about his feet, or the gray squirrels that enjoy life amid the oaks and hickories. Many charming surprises await the pedestrian; but in all the Arboretum no walk is so wild and beautiful as that leading through the Bussey Hemlocks ... Take but a few steps from the carriage road near Hemlock Hill, pausing to drink of the cold spring that offers a refreshing draught to the passer-by, and you may find yourself in a primeval forest.

The arrangement of plants on the grounds had evolved into a compromise among Sargent's scheme for strict natural order according to Bentham and Hooker, Olmsted's aesthetic considerations, and ecological necessity. The existence of Hemlock Hill determined the location of the conifers. The angiosperms ostensibly began a pattern at the Jamaica Plain gate near the Administration Building with species of that primitive flowering beauty, *Magnolia,* and its close relative, *Liriodendron,* the Tulip Tree. Directly across the road, however, were the maples, which are considerably more sophisticated in their morphological development; so in terms of "natural" progression, the order

The Arboretum Grows Up

183

was immediately upset. The willows grew in a low, wet area which best suited their needs regardless of surrounding genera.

While Sargent sacrificed large-scale order in deference to competing interests and Olmsted's artistic wisdom, the trees were set out in groups according to genus and, where possible, by family. The pines, spruces, firs, and larches grew across Bussey Brook below the existing stand of hemlocks; the apples, cherries, and pears—all members of the family Rosaceae—bordered the Forest Hills entrance road; lilacs, forsythia, and *Chionanthus* of the Oleaceae decorated the banks of Bussey Hill road. The rhododendrons, many of which are temperamental and barely tolerant of New England climatic extremes, lived in a shady, sheltered location at the base of Hemlock Hill, while hardier azaleas were planted at strategic spots throughout the Arboretum. In effect the compromise design was a small loss for science and a great gain for beauty.

The shrub collection served as a repository for species which had no tree relatives. The shrubs grew in ten-foot-wide rows near the Forest Hills gate, and had they been placed end to end, the beds would have stretched out over a mile and a quarter. "The object of this special Shrub Collection," Sargent explained, "is to enable students, landscape-gardeners and nurserymen to compare readily the different shrubs which are available for planting in the Northern States; and to make the collection as valuable as possible for this purpose only well-known hardy shrubs are included in it. Less hardy and all imperfectly known shrubs will be found in more sheltered and less conspicuous positions." [14] On Peters' Hill, Sargent began his soon-to-be-infamous *Crataegus* plantation.

The Arboretum gave different pleasures to different people. For some it was merely a refuge from the commonplaces of the city. Amateur horticulturists came to learn about plants for the garden or simply because they loved plants. One person admired a solitary tree, another exulted in discovering distinctions between pines and spruces,

The Arboretum and Beyond

another watched wildlife, another appreciated vistas composed of subtle juxtapositions of textures, colors, and forms. A poet, perhaps, lavished upon himself Andrew Marvell's "green thought in a green shade." According to plan, the landscape concealed gentle visual surprises—a bend in the road turning into a distant view, a spectacular shrub planted in cunning harmony with its neighbors, a hushed grove of conifers—all thoughtfully calculated to look uncontrived.

Except for the few locations where existing stands remained as representatives of local woodland growth, Sargent determined the placement of each plant.[15] Jack, whose recollections of the early Arboretum years were candid, emphasized that "the Arboretum was a very personal thing to Professor Sargent, ... Since, in the early years he obtained the money for its construction and maintenance, he expended it as he thought best and without reference to any other authority. So, also, in the selection of plants and the planting of them he gave personal attention as no succeeding administrator is ever likely to do." Jack said he believed that Sargent had personal and economic reasons for ignoring the directive of the 1872 indenture to raise herbaceous as well as woody species. His Census investigations activated a preference for ligneous plants which were, in the long run, obligingly cheaper to maintain than herbs. That the Botanic Garden in Cambridge already had a good selection of herbaceous species made it easier for Sargent to disregard this facet of his obligation. Having made his decision early in his career, he never compromised by planting beds of herbaceous perennials, for aesthetic or any other purposes, and not even Wilson's Chinese lilies would find a home in the Arboretum. Before long the provision was forgotten by the few people who knew of its existence: they were satisfied that Sargent, though disobedient to the letter of the law, had done justice to its spirit.

One of the biggest attractions of the Arboretum was its horticultural novelties. They were never freak trees, for Sargent refused to have anything to do with malformed

The Arboretum Grows Up

specimens, but plants from distant gardens and forests that most people had never seen before. The introduction program started long before E. H. Wilson went to China: the Arboretum obtained *Acer rufinerve* from France in 1878; Bretschneider sent *Betula dahurica* from St. Petersburg in 1883; *Fraxinus anomala* came from the forests of Utah in 1874; Sargent introduced *Prunus maximowiczii* from Japan in 1892. By 1900, hundreds of trees and shrubs which before were unknown to American gardens grew on the rolling hills of Jamaica Plain for the pleasure and education of the general public. The world seemed so much larger then that a plant raised from seed collected halfway around the globe was still an object of considerable wonder. For a devoted horticulturist, regular visits to the Arboretum were *de rigueur* to keep up with the latest developments. Where patrons were involved Sargent often gave personal attention to their desires, favoring them with seeds or cuttings of rare plants, and paying calls to their gardens to give advice on planting and landscaping. (There was usually an observable ratio between the generosity of the patron and the amount of time which Sargent expended.) His frequent suggestions to eliminate dead, dying, or crowding trees sometimes struck his hosts as brutal; but having followed his instructions, they usually acknowledged his wisdom. A few people became quite dependent upon his opinions, like the elderly lady who was overheard to remark a few years ago, "Honestly, since Professor Sargent died I haven't the slightest idea how to plant my garden!"

For people professionally occupied with plants—botanists, landscape designers, park superintendents, nurserymen—the Arboretum had obvious advantages. A research scientist studying a particular group of plants could observe representative species from many parts of the world situated so close to each other as to invite comparisons; he could easily secure live material. Other professionals, most of whom were not trained in botany, drew two benefits from the Arboretum. First, the institution helped bridge the gap between

The Arboretum and Beyond

the practical plantsman and the research botanist. A nurseryman could, for example, ascertain the correct scientific name for a shrub without wading through difficult botanical jargon, see it living in the Arboretum collections, and offer it for sale on the market under the proper name instead of adding to taxonomic confusion by tacking on some misnomer. Secondly, the Arboretum was commercially useful. Sargent's favorite nurseries received seeds and cuttings of new plants from the Arboretum; those which did not get material at least picked up ideas about what might have market value. A landscape architect saw new plants and conceived new combinations to enrich his designs. The park superintendent could ask advice on street planting and learn how far apart to plant trees and which species would be most attractive and economical to maintain. Sargent had never carried out his plan for forest demonstration plots so foresters found less of immediate relevance to their profession among the living collections. But the possibility of studying the growth habits of a wide variety of trees, and Sargent's special familiarity with national forest conditions were aids to any forestry student. Following the instructions of the 1882 indenture to serve the public-at-large, the Arboretum staff spent nearly as much time identifying fragments of plants sent through the mail by home gardeners or amateur naturalists as they did answering professional questions.

The Administration Building, constructed in 1892, showed signs of overcrowding by the beginning of the new century. The museum and library occupied two large downstairs rooms. The Jesup Wood Collection duplicates, which arrived in 1902, dominated the former while Sargent avidly solicited literature to fill the latter. The herbarium and offices were upstairs. In this homely, functional building, Sargent passed most of his waking hours.

The Professor was a creature driven by habit and industry. When he was not abroad, on a collecting trip, or busy with some special mission, he adhered to routine just like his father, who had invariably occupied the same seat on the

The Arboretum Grows Up

same train between Boston and Brookline. Susan McKelvey, though she knew Sargent only in his old age, described the ritual as he had observed it for years:

> Professor Sargent's interpretation of a directorship may be described as "full time." He himself observed no Saturday half-holiday, indeed I am not sure that he was altogether convinced of its benefit to others. Sunday morning he considered the most satisfactory opportunity for work in his office, and it is my recollection that Christmas and national holidays fell into the same category. Daily he arrived early at the building, opened, read, and answered all the mail; once disposed of, incoming letters went into the waste-basket . . . He spent the remainder of the morning at work in the building or interviewing some of the many visitors. He was back soon after lunch and . . . went about the grounds; no ailing plant escaped his observant eye; each one was under surveillance. Unless weather made such outdoor work impossible, this routine was observed winter and summer, and few trips were taken to the environs of Boston or beyond which did not promise "results" as far as Arboretum interests were concerned.[16]

Mrs. McKelvey's remarks captured the essence of Sargent's behavior, but there were some fine distinctions which she overlooked. For example, Sargent did not discard *all* his incoming mail. There remain what appear to be complete sets of letters written by Hooker, George Engelmann, John Muir, Thiselton-Dyer, and a few others. In view of Sargent's respect for history, he appears to have made his selections with the thought that certain collections might be significant to some future chronicler. When he judged correspondents unworthy of historical consideration, their letters went into the basket unless they contained information to which he might refer at a later date. His own writing fell into the latter category. From the number and nature of the duplicates of his letters, he clearly had no system for keeping

The Arboretum and Beyond

copies. He did not keep any kind of diary. On the other hand, he liked to cut out newspaper items about the Arboretum and preserve them in scrapbooks.

Like others who knew the Arboretum in its first half-century or who investigated its history, Mrs. McKelvey drew the conclusion that "up to 1927 [the year of Sargent's death], the Arnold Arboretum was a 'one man' institution." The more one studies the evidence, the more wedded one becomes to this notion. Individual staff members made contributions to botany or horticulture and thereby to the reputation of the Arboretum, but it was Sargent who bound them together with his administrative and fund-raising abilities, with his example of relentless effort and stamina, and perhaps with his aloofness. He created a paternalistic regime, and his staff depended upon him with respectful adoration. Mrs. Rehder recalled her late husband as having worshipped the Director; Jack described Faxon's sentiments in terms of "extraordinarily faithful . . . unselfish cooperation"; [17] people who knew Wilson ascribed similar feelings to him.

In questions of administrative policy, Sargent neither solicited nor received advice from his staff. His operational dictatorship was balanced by the absolute trust in which he held his staff, his disinclination to meddle in their research projects, and his respect for the privacy of their personal lives. The accord between staff and Director was based on the principle of mutual respect and faith. The staff admired and trusted the Director's ability to govern and to insure their professional security—if not their prosperity—while he, in return, had confidence in their talent for turning out the kind of work that served the welfare of the Arboretum. Friendship did not enter into this feudal compact. Nowhere, not even in obituaries, does any staff member refer to Sargent as a friend, nor did he claim any of them in that relationship. The attitude was the only reasonable one in terms of the social forms of the day. The social chasm between Sargent and his staff was as obvious as it was wide. Rehder, Wilson, Jack, and the others were

The Arboretum Grows Up

unacceptable social partners for Sargents. Sargent might have overlooked the differences under other circumstances; he gladly entertained many kinds of people out of genuine friendship. But he had been weaned on the theory that business and friendship were incompatible, that social relations between an administrator and his staff could only undermine his authority. He remained remote, and the staff accepted his bearing without question or resentment. Indeed, they were somewhat awe-stricken by his grand manner, wealth, and authority, and they admired in him small signs of humanity which they would have ignored in a less prestigious person.

The Arboretum was a one-man institution, and Sargent was a one-institution man. He threw himself into whatever pertained to the Arboretum with such passionate intensity that he had little left in reserve for the other ingredients that combine to make a man's life. He treated his wife and children carelessly; social entertainments bored him; while he was careful with his money, he took his wealth for granted; he was indifferent to religion; he had no hobbies or recreations outside his work on the grounds at Holm Lea —which was really an extension of his profession—and riding horseback, which he did because he thought it was good for his health. He admired painting and architecture, attended an occasional sporting event, and expressed political opinions, but he did these things with detachment. The Arboretum, by contrast, commanded his total involvement; it was his single area of undistracted ambition.

In the outside world, he was an alien. That he knew and conversed with many of the great men of his day—Olmsted, J. P. Morgan, Eliot, Muir, his cousin John Singer Sargent, Wolcott Gibbs, Pinchot, H. H. Richardson, Francis Parkman —did nothing to cement his relations with life outside. He was happier with trees than with people; he "loved trees and shrubs and the beauty of fine plants as most men love children and grandchildren or as they love a fair lady . . . The hearts of people such as [this] came alive when they were in company with a tree of fine symmetry, their blood cours-

The Arboretum and Beyond

The Sargent family, ca. 1885; seated on the ground: Mary, Charles, Robeson; seated on the divan: Charles, Sr., Alice, Henrietta, Mrs. Sargent

The Arboretum Grows Up

ing in apparent harmoney with its sap; an example of the psychiatrist's term 'identification,' only that in the case of plant lovers their devotion was deep and profound and valid and tender and lifelong in its duration." [18] The psychological diagnosis may be a bit exaggerated, but the impression Sargent gave was clearly one of an obsessed man, respectably eccentric in his monomania. Visitors ignorant about the plants in the Arboretum irritated him in spite of himself whereas with better-informed people he relaxed and found a basis for dialogue. He neither loved nor despised his fellow man; the truth was that he gave humanity a small share of his thoughts. To a man comfortably stationed at the top of a social structure which he believed to be permanent, there was little to think about.

Once in a while the world distracted Sargent from his professional pursuits; something sent quivers through his idea of order and proper action. When President McKinley, whom he had backed on sound-money principles, reluctantly allowed himself to be talked into a war with Spain, Sargent's notions of intelligent politics were badly shaken as were those of several Boston citizens. The *Evening Transcript*, to which he always subscribed, denounced the war, and an impressive roster of leading citizens including ex-President Cleveland, Andrew Carnegie, and Samuel Gompers, joined to form the Anti-Imperialist League at Faneuil Hall in Boston on June 15, 1898. Sargent, long an opponent of big government, believed, as did many of the dissenters, that if the United States acquired an empire, Washington would assume wide powers to the detriment of the country as a whole.

Sargent's motives for opposing the war, then, were far from humanitarian. Nowhere did he reveal his sentiments so pointedly as in a letter to Thiselton-Dyer in February 1899, when American guns were silencing the Philippine nationalist insurrection led by Aguinaldo.

If I lived in England I should be a jingo. It is the business of England to civilize the world and boss the inferior

The Arboretum and Beyond

races. We are not equipped for that sort of work; we have still a great deal more territory than we need, more than we can look after or can occupy with our population; and the curse of universal suffrage is always with us—a perfect millstone round America's neck—a splendid thing in theory and for small communities where everybody is more or less educated and honest. It is a grievous failure, however, in our big cities, and it will prevent our ever having a public service which will enable us to compete with the rest of the world in the government of colonies. Americans are capable of doing a lot of good work; it is done, however, by corporations and individuals quite outside the government. There is no better proof of the correctness of this statement than the quality of the scientific work done by the Government as compared with that produced by the Universities. And what is true of science is true in every department of human effort here. Only the Navy and the lighthouses are really good in this country, and this is owing to the fact that they require so much technical knowledge that the politicians do not dare to monkey with them. I do not feel at all hopeful about the situation and I do not look forward with pleasure to those visits of the tax-gatherer which you think are so beneficial. We are going to have serious trouble sometime in this country. Lots of people are going to be killed and a lot of wealth wasted. If this results in the end in restricted suffrage the sacrifice won't be too great.[19]

Though he confessed to feeling "sorry for the miserable inhabitants of [the Philippines] if they are to experience the treatment our Indians have had at the hands of the politicians," [20] Sargent's real anxiety was unashamedly for the *modus vivendi* which had treated him so well.

The philosophical heritage to which Sargent was bound admired the self-made man. Earlier Sargents built the family fortune, leaving him free either to continue the mercantile tradition or to set out in another direction, and having

The Arboretum Grows Up

determined to do the latter, he enforced his decision with fierce intensity. He possessed neither the scientific imagination of a Gray nor the artistic intelligence of an Olmsted nor the administrative inspiration of an Eliot. Sargent's dogged pursuit of professional excellence was an affair of willful intellect, a powerful but graceless effort, however pleasing the results. Given this frame of mind, the tenuous connections between the Arboretum and the University and the other Harvard botanical units suited Sargent, allowing him full responsibility for the fate of his domain. Having submitted to his defeat over the arrangement with the City, Eliot sat back and gave Sargent a free hand, interceding only for funds on his behalf. Eliot's successor, Lowell, who ascended to the Harvard presidency in 1909, was too engrossed in the multiple problems of Cambridge and a massive building program to be very concerned with what went on in the Jamaica Plain tree garden, and so Sargent operated more or less independently until the end of his life.

As the new century began, Sargent approached his sixtieth birthday, his feverish anxiety for endowments rising with his age. The first phase of Arboretum development was completed, the plantings were assuming mature proportions, he had an agreeable staff, and his work on the *Silva* was nearing an end. What was he to do next? Sargent needed a program with public appeal to keep the cash flowing into his coffers, and the possibilities for plant hunting in eastern Asia fit snugly into this category. While Sargent's motives for organizing expeditions to the Orient were not entirely—or even primarily—mercenary, he was too shrewd to overlook their profitable by-products, and there was no reason why one plan should not accomplish several objectives.

The Arboretum and Beyond

Part Three. The Treasure Hunt

8

Journeys to the East

For centuries the Orient yielded its treasures to Europe and, eventually, via Europe to the New World. Spices, silks, fireworks, and other exotic objects lured adventurers and merchants. Marco Polo, the most celebrated of the China wanderers, brought back tales and tokens which filled his European contemporaries with wonder—or disbelief. Like any good explorer, he took notes on plants in the field and marketplace, reporting such extravagances as "certain pears of enormous size, weighing as much as ten pounds a piece and the pulp of which is white and fragrant like a confection"; [1] the botanist Emil Bretschneider, five centuries later, assured the world that the reference was to the Chinese quince, *Cydonia chinensis*. [2] After Marco Polo's journeys, westerners braved mortal dangers in quest of Oriental riches. And, after many others, Sargent determined to extract horticultural delicacies.

Before one can fairly discuss Sargent and the East, it is necessary to review Gray's work on Japan. Sargent himself summed up this aspect of Gray's research in his *Garden and Forest* obituary:

> In ["Remarks on the Botany of Japan," 1859, Gray] first pointed out the extraordinary similarity between the Floras of Eastern North America and Japan, and then explained the peculiar distribution of plants through the

northern hemisphere by tracing their direct descent through geological eras from ancestors which flourished in the arctic regions down to the latest tertiary period. This paper was Professor Gray's most remarkable and interesting contribution to science.[3]

It was remarkable less for its botanical observations than for its brave exposition of a theory of specific evolution in the manner of Darwin. This was the paper which signaled the approaching decline of Louis Agassiz. Gray based his speculations on the generic and specific affinity between the floras of eastern Asia and eastern North America, a resemblance made more striking because the floras of these regions had more in common with each other than did either with the western American flora. The phenomenon of identical or similar genera in the two areas had been remarked by Linnaeus in the thesis *Plantae Camschatcenses Rariores,* defended by Halenius in 1750,[4] and later by others; but before Gray tackled the problem, no one had produced a satisfactory scientific explanation of the peculiar distribution. Gray's paper, with its Darwinian overtones, exploded the conventional wisdom of Agassiz. To demonstrate the relationship between the two floras Gray could point to no less than forty genera which were to be found exclusively in eastern Asia and eastern North America.[5] As Sargent read them, Gray's observations suggested eastern Asia as the most logical and exciting source of horticultural novelties for New England.

Many other factors stimulated Sargent's curiosity about the east Asian flora. Asia was steeped in mystery. Despite the travels of Marco Polo and the subsequent establishment of overland trade routes to China, little was known about that country beyond its coastal or frontier areas before the latter part of the nineteenth century. Europe had been getting small quantities of Oriental plant material for some time. Linnaeus listed several species from the Far East based on collections which came into his hands from various sources, often in a roundabout way.[6] In the mid-1500's,

The Treasure Hunt

Portugal at the height of its glory as a naval power, dominated Oriental trade. Jesuit missionaries wrote of the botanical wealth of Asia; some, like George Joseph Kamel, collected plants which Linnaeus inspected. The Dutch, established in Java in the late sixteenth century, occupied Taiwan in the seventeenth century for thirty-eight years before Chinese pirates threw them out; they failed to get a foothold on the mainland. The British, committed to their empire-building program, were familiar if not always welcome visitors in east Asia during the late eighteenth and early nineteenth centuries. British horticulturists, with mercenary intentions, encouraged by the financial success of *Chrysanthemum* varieties and other florist flowers, showed some enterprise in getting ornamental and economic plants back to England. They had vague notions of what might be found from the dried specimens and occasional plants or seeds that trickled into England from amateur botanists and plant hunters. When the Horticultural Society of London commissioned Robert Fortune to bring back plants from China, its specific instructions, viewed in the light of later explorations, indicated only a superficial knowledge of the flora of that land.[7] Between 1843 and 1862, Fortune made three journeys to China and a fourth to Japan; the second and third voyages were financed by the East India Company with tea seeds as the prime objective. Fortune braved parts of inland China as well as the coastal areas and made a dent in east Asian plant wealth. Some of his discoveries came to America via Europe.

As far as Americans were concerned, however, there was little botanical activity in the Orient until Commodore Perry reached Japan in 1853. Charles Wright, who followed in Perry's wake, made herbarium collections for Gray but took no pains to select ornamental species. Dr. George Hall, originally from Bristol, Rhode Island, and a one-time physician, sent the first significant shipment of live ornamental plants from Japan to Boston in 1861, entrusting historian Francis Parkman with the honor of propagating them in his garden, where Sargent most likely saw them. When

Journeys to the East

Hall returned to America in 1862, he left Asian plant materials with Parsons Nursery in Flushing, Long Island.[8] His were the first meaningful horticultural introductions directly from Asia. Sargent's first direct transaction with eastern Asia was in 1876, when William S. Clark, who had left the presidency of Amherst College to establish an agricultural college at Sapporo, Japan, sent a small collection of native seeds—including the tree lilac and *Cercidiphyllum japonicum*—to the Arboretum.

Russian explorers, the best among them being Carl Maximowicz and Grigori Nicolaevich Potanin, collected mostly in Northern China, often in parties morally and financially subsidized by the Czar, who had ill-disguised territorial designs; the Russians, while increasing botanical knowledge, achieved little in the way of introductions of horticultural species. Later in the 1800's, after Gray's paper on Japan had been published, two French missionaries, Père Jean Pierre Armand David and Père Jean Marie Delavay, made extensive collections in China; but like the Russians, their horticultural discoveries were incidental to botany. Père David, however, found the delicate dove tree which bears his name, *Davidia involucrata*.

That the riches of the Orient were still largely untapped is not surprising considering the political climate of nineteenth-century Asia. Perry and the United States helped make Japan, which had been hostile to foreigners since the early seventeenth century, accessible. China was another matter. Britain, by virtue of supreme naval power, was the front-runner in China trade. Its only connection with the mainland, however, was via Canton where British "Red Hairs" were confined to a trading area and denied entry to the city proper. In 1840, provoked by the flourishing opium trade carried on by English merchants, the Chinese launched a small-scale war over the issue. British seamanship prevailed, and Britain walked away from the treaty table in 1842 with four new treaty ports and the island of Hong Kong. New wedges were driven into China's wall. Britain, France, Russia, the United States, Germany, and Japan, estab-

The Treasure Hunt

lished "spheres of influence" through separate treaties with the Chinese authorities and perched along the coastal perimeter like fleas on the back of a great dog. Like fleas, the intruders ate no meat but sucked blood and caused excessive irritation; like a dog, China was powerless to eject them but resorted to continuous diplomatic—and occasional military—harassment. The Chinese and their Manchu rulers had little liking for, or understanding of, the western intruders whom they considered inscrutable barbarians. The barbarians returned the sentiments, but there was profit for both sides in trade.

Travel inland at any distance from a foreign treaty area was always a risky business for westerners. Sprawling over a vast area and lacking effective central government, China was still essentially a feudal country, divided by tribes and dialects as well as geographic barriers. It had the chronic troubles of feudalism: war lords; ancient, complicated rivalries; little communication between one community, or one location, and another; and a usually well-founded suspicion of outsiders, especially non-Chinese. It was a credit to Fortune that he survived his inland journeys; he claimed to have done this sometimes by masquerading as a Chinese from a distant province, although some people doubt that he could have passed for a Chinaman.[9] The missionaries had their bad moments, for the Chinese appreciation of Christianity was a fickle affair. As late as 1905, Tibetan monks tortured and shot Père Soulié, a plant-collecting missionary. All in all, China did not endear itself to foreign explorers, and it was the man of luck, pluck, and purpose who succeeded as a collector. Given the hazards, it is surprising that so much, rather than so little, botanizing was accomplished by Europeans.

Sargent had often expressed his desire to plant in the Arboretum every tree capable of withstanding the New England climate. European plants or propagating materials were relatively easy to acquire by exchange or purchase, as were the plants of western North America. There was, however, no way for Sargent to get plants directly from eastern

Journeys to the East

Asia. At the moment, his chief source was Dr. Bretschneider at St. Petersburg, whose special interest was in collecting seeds of trees and shrubs in the mountain regions near Peking. He distributed his seeds generously, and their progeny proved more successful at the Arnold Arboretum than in any other location except the Jardin des Plantes in Paris.[10] Other species came to Boston via Kew or Paris. As far as Sargent was concerned, the omens were auspicious: Gray's paper presented a theoretical foundation, Bretschneider's seeds prospered, and Japan was friendly to westerners. Knowing no one more suitable for the job than himself, Sargent determined to make his own investigation of Oriental forests. He had neither the time nor the physical strength to spare for the perilous exploration of China's wilderness. Tiny, westernized Japan, however, promised horticultural treasures and was an area he could cope with in a reasonably short trip. Clearing his way for absence, he spent the winter and spring of 1892 working on the *Silva* and seeing to Arboretum business while giving what little help he could over in Cambridge, for Watson died in March. It was, then, the end of July before Sargent began his voyage to Japan. Sargent could have sent a collector rather than go himself, but he preferred to make his own judgments. Moreover, he was restless. Boston chroniclers cheerfully repeat anecdotes about Bostonians who never passed a night in another city, or of those who suffered in doing so. Sargent was quite the opposite. He became depressed and irritable if he stayed at home too long and began yearning for a change of scenery. Naturally, as a botanist he was filled with curiosity about specimens in other parts of the United States and in other countries, but other botanists managed to travel less. He seemed to thrive on his intervals in the field, relishing the strenuous pace and physical activity as much as the trees. Above all, he wanted to see his beloved trees and shrubs in their native habitats.

Sargent invariably took company· on his long journeys, preferably someone who shared his enthusiasms. Invited for the Japan excursion was Philip Codman who, like his older

The Treasure Hunt

brother Henry, learned the profession of landscape design in Olmsted's office. Uncle and nephew left Boston at the end of July, heading out to Vancouver via the Canadian Pacific Railroad. They sailed for Yokohama on August 7.

The American traveler landing for the first time in Yokohama is surprised at the abundance of arborescent Lauraceae, which here, with evergreen Oaks and Celtis australis, make the principal features of the woods which cover the coast-bluffs and surround the temples.[11]

Sargent restricted his explorations to Japan's two principal islands, Hokkaido, which was then called Ezo or Yezo, and Nippon, which was known alternately as Hondo or Honshiu. The two islands fall roughly between the thirtieth and forty-fifth parallels, corresponding to the area from northern Florida to central Maine in the eastern United States. Sargent, concerned with northern climates, spent a good portion of his time in Hokkaido or, when in Nippon, usually stayed north of Tokyo. Arriving at the end of August —not the best time to see flowers but a fine opportunity to collect fruits—Sargent and Codman went straight from Yokohama to Tokyo. He scanned gardens and nurseries, and then set out northwards in the direction of Nikko, searching, among other things, for a seed-bearing tree of the brightly colored maple, *Acer nikoense*. The effort yielded no immediate rewards, but he saw plantings of stately *Cryptomeria japonica* and learned the charming legend of the poor man who could only offer seedling trees to decorate the tomb of the founder of the Tokugawa dynasty and whose gift grew to be the noblest of all.[12]

Traveling by rail between major destinations, and taking time out in the field along the way, Sargent and his nephew reached Hokkaido by mid-September. It was this region that most closely approximated the New England climate. There and in northernmost Nippon they spent nearly a month combing forests, gardens, and nurseries. Sargent went first to Sapporo, where he hoped to meet Professor Kingo Miyabe,

Journeys to the East

an accomplished botanist at the college there. Miyabe, unfortunately, lay ill and received his American visitors apologetically. He was, however, able to provide them with a knowledgeable guide named Tokubuchi who proved helpful.[13] As for Miyabe, he eventually regained his health and became an invaluable source of seeds for the Arboretum.

It was, apparently, in Sapporo that Sargent met James Herbert Veitch, an English horticulturist, who joined him for a couple of weeks. The city itself, according to Veitch, had little to offer outside the college since it was relatively new; but the flora was astonishingly varied. Sargent could count forty-six kinds of trees on a single hillside; it was a collector's paradise. Still with the assistance of Tokubuchi, they explored other parts of the island and then crossed back to Nippon during the first week of October. Veitch related their adventures there:

> Beyond the village of Awomori, the northernmost port of Nihon [Nippon], lies a tall blunt mountain, Mount Hakkoda, the summit of which is capped with *Abies Mariesii*, and naturally strong was the desire of Professor Sargent ... and myself to see this little-known conifer in its native surroundings. Mount Hakkoda is but six thousand feet in elevation but owing to its lying at some distance, to the path approaching it traversing more than one considerable rising, the ascent and descent occupied altogether three to four days ... Splendid isolated specimens of forest trees it was frequently our good fortune to meet with ... Within a few hundred feet of the top of the mountain we came to a collection of low straw huts in which we passed two nights. They were too low to stand in, and as they were without window and chimney, we were only too glad to remain at full length to avoid the fumes of the smoke of the large fire rendered necessary by the intense cold. Immediately above these huts lies the forest of *Abies Mariesii*, a most handsome and striking Fir. The forest occupies but a limited area; it

The Treasure Hunt

is by no means thick, nor are any of the trees of great size. In winter the snow must lay there several feet deep. At the base of the trees is an almost impervious mass of tough thick Bamboo, to get through which, even in the wood-cutters track, was often no light task. Off the track there is no other course than to cut one's way with a hatchet.[14]

Sargent made light of the rigors of the climb, but in contrast with his companion, was disappointed by the *Abies,* which he later wrote off as a "handsome but in no wise striking or remarkable tree, which in all probability will flourish in severe climates."[15] He was more excited by finding fruits of *Magnolia salicifolia* on the lower reaches of the mountain because he had never seen its flower nor, so far as he knew, had any other botanist. He saw Japanese Azaleas in several locations and thought they did not surpass in beauty their American cousins from the Alleghenies. But he returned to Boston with seeds of the Kaempfer Azalea (*Rhododendron obtusa* var. *Kaempferi*) from high elevations as far north as he could find it growing in hopes they would prosper in New England.

Veitch parted with Sargent and headed back to Sapporo with Tokubuchi, but not before volunteering to collect for Sargent in central China. Ostensibly in training to manage the Veitch nurseries in England, he was impulsive and preferred travel adventures to the sedentary work at home; nothing pleased him more than a legitimate excuse to explore the exotic Chinese interior. Sargent, who liked Veitch, fell in with Veitch's plans and agreed to make arrangements for an expedition. Meanwhile, he and Codman began their trip back to Tokyo. Passing again through Nikko, they succeeded this time in gathering half a bushel of seeds from the elusive *Acer nikoense* despite some competition from a stiff wind which threatened to scatter their harvest. They left Japan early in November, having spent no more than ten weeks there, sailing for home from Yokohama. Sargent's

Journeys to the East

luggage included seeds of about two hundred species and varieties of plants and 1225 sets of herbarium specimens.[16]

Sargent's published account of his trip, accompanied by drawings which Faxon made from herbarium specimens, appeared first in *Garden and Forest;* the series was later printed as a single, elegant volume, *Forest Flora of Japan.* It was in no sense an enumeration or systematic description of Japan's forest trees. Instead, Sargent collected his observations and wrote them up informally, emphasizing the relationships between the Japanese and eastern American floras as Gray had done before him. Family by family he progressed through the Japanese forests, now and then telling a pertinent legend or commenting on Japanese forest practices. The narrative was charming but self-effacing. There were no personal adventures to assist his biographers, and one reads along suspecting that he failed to see anything beyond the trees, though he finally cast a few reflections on the new Japan, with its economic and social ailments arising from what he called "the hasty and often ill-considered introduction of European methods." [17]

One of the first things Sargent did upon his return was to follow up his conversations with Veitch about China. He wrote a letter outlining a proposal to Harry Veitch, the young man's uncle and sponsor, the proprietor of the Royal Exotic Nursery, at the time one of England's finest. The elder Veitch replied in avuncular tones that his wandering nephew ought to stay home for a while and experience the more practical, if less romantic, aspects of running a nursery. Though Chinese plants might prove commercially valuable, they must await another collector at another time. Despite further proddings from the eager nephew—who had obviously expected his uncle's reaction but still hoped to gain approval through Sargent's good offices—Sargent judged the situation to be a family affair and decided not to interfere. Having no offhand knowledge of anyone else qualified to undertake such a mission, he temporarily pushed the idea to the back of his mind, and perhaps would have abandoned

The Treasure Hunt

it entirely had he not received some letters from Augustine Henry, an Irish doctor in the Imperial Chinese Customs Service.

Henry, like many of the other early collectors of Chinese plants, was neither trained in botany nor interested in horticulture; he developed into a collector to defend himself against the tedium of his Chinese existence.[18] Henry confessed sadly to a friend,

> Life here is very monotonous. I am sorry to say there is not even a tiger . . . I have got various armaments, but I am a wretched shot, which is curious, as I play tennis very well and have not a crooked eye, and my hands are steady, but perhaps I am a "butter fingers" . . . Though we are bereft of ladies' society—I lately exported the two missionary ladies that were here homewards and now we have none—we get on pretty well. The country is charming but I cannot get much away. I am now studying botany a little.[19]

In the last half of the nineteenth century, the Chinese grudgingly allowed westerners access to the interior. During his first stay in China, nearly eight years, Henry was based in I-ch'ang * on the Yangtze River, a thousand miles from the sea in the province of Hupeh. His duties as a doctor for the Customs Service—a curious arrangement originating in the 1850's by which foreigners collected customs duties from western traders for the Chinese government—required his presence in the city. Since he was not free to wander off on long adventures, he made only two extensive botanical expeditions in the region.

A few miles upriver from I-ch'ang, the Yangtze tributaries had carved miles of gorges, and along the cliffs and ledges grew a bewildering abundance of plants, many of which

---

* Modern Chinese place names have been taken from the 1968 official standard list of mainland China names prepared by the Geographic Names Division of the Army Map Service. Wilson's and Rock's names are used throughout the text; modern equivalents appear in brackets.

Journeys to the East

were spectacularly beautiful. Fortunately, the British Foreign Office encouraged plant collecting, and Customs officials were supposed to investigate the flora in their respective areas for what they could discover about Chinese drugs and vegetable products, so Henry's initial collections were strictly in the line of duty. His own curiosity, however, soon exceeded the little that was asked of him as a botanist, and on week ends when Henry was not occupied in I-ch'ang, he went off to the gorges. After carefully gathering specimens, he returned home to press, dry, and label them. Eventually he taught some Chinese natives to help him.[20] Henry sent his collections to Kew, where the botanical staff received them with enthusiasm. Thiselton-Dyer urged him to continue his work and supplied him with botanical advice.

The Gray Herbarium purchased a duplicate set of specimens collected by Henry from Kew, and Sargent may have seen them, but Henry apparently knew nothing of Sargent until Mrs. Hugh Law, an Irish friend of his, suggested that Sargent might use some articles on China in *Garden and Forest*.[21] By the time Henry wrote Sargent it was 1894, and the Customs Service had shifted him to their station in Takow, Taiwan. Sargent not only welcomed material for the magazine, but was especially eager to purchase a set of the Hupeh specimens, and anything Henry could send from Taiwan, for the Arboretum.

Meanwhile, Henry's collections made an impression on English horticulturists, notably the Veitch firm. Despite one somewhat disappointing experience with sending a man to China, Harry Veitch thought there still might be valuable horticultural species in the Chinese wilds. When the Veitches hired Charles Maries to go to the Far East in 1877, they feared that Fortune and the others had already exhausted the Chinese field. Maries actually reached the I-ch'ang gorges but retreated hastily after natives stole his luggage, and he reported nothing spectacular from the vicinity. Henry's specimens now indicated otherwise. Moreover, the Veitches had long coveted seeds of *Davidia involucrata*, the Dove Tree (of which Henry sent a herbarium specimen);

The Treasure Hunt

if it proved hardy in England, it would justify the expense of sending a man after it. The Veitches selected Ernest Henry Wilson to be their plant hunter.

Except for Sargent, no one was more important in the early development of the Arnold Arboretum than Wilson.[22] Ernest Henry Wilson was born in Chipping Campden, Gloucestershire, in February 1876, the eldest son of Henry and Annie Wilson. He began life in modest circumstances. Upon completion of his secondary schooling he entered training in the nurseries of the Messrs. Hewitt in Birmingham where he began as a "nursery-lad." The nursery business was a thriving one, and nursery work was a respectable and potentially profitable trade for a man of Wilson's station; if one enjoyed plants and outdoor life, as Wilson apparently did, it promised a secure and pleasing future.

By virtue of his excellent performance at Hewitts', Wilson gained a position as a gardener at the Birmingham Botanical Gardens in 1892. Simple gardening, however, did not satisfy his ambitions; his sights were fixed higher. With a full load of work in the gardens, he used his spare time to study botany at the Birmingham Technical School and succeeded so well in the subject that he won the Queen's prize in a competitive examination sponsored by the Board of Education. By 1897 he was employed as a gardener at Kew and attended botany lessons in addition to his horticultural duties, performing both tasks admirably. Having decided he preferred botany to horticulture and, determined to become a teacher, he enrolled at the Royal College of Science at South Kensington. He had scarcely begun his studies, however, when the Veitch firm, acting on a recommendation from Thiselton-Dyer via George Nicholson, Curator of the Gardens at Kew and Wilson's superior, proposed that he journey to China for them. Wilson accepted the proposal at a salary of £100 plus expenses for the first year.

Expeditions were an old story to the Veitches, and they had no intention of sending Wilson out green into the field. First they put him through six months of training in their Coombe

Journeys to the East

Wood nurseries and directed him to study Henry's specimens in the Kew herbarium. Their young trainee worked hard for them, seizing any information about China and its vegetation. In April 1899, Wilson sailed for China on Cunard's *S.S. Pavonia* via Boston.

He had only five days in Boston and spent most of his time with Sargent at the Arboretum and at Holm Lea, where he was supposed to learn what he could about packing and shipping seeds for long trips from the Orient.[23] Since Henry's latest letters were prodding Sargent to set up some kind of expedition in western China, Sargent quizzed Wilson thoroughly on his plans and privately formed a high opinion of the Englishman who knew his botany and did not let the sense of adventure go to his head. Wilson, in turn, was much impressed by the Arboretum and its director, and profited from discussion with Sargent and Jackson Dawson.

The second leg of Wilson's journey was a train ride from Boston to San Francisco, a cross-continental ordeal of plains, mountains, and deserts. Wilson spent the dark hours buried in literature on the Chinese and their customs, trying to form a mental image of China. By daylight he gazed from his Pullman window and listened half-credulously to a brakeman's lurid tales of the exploits of Frank and Jesse James. After spending a few days in San Francisco, he set sail for Hong Kong; he arrived there the first week in June.

Then, as now, Hong Kong was a British outpost, thriving port, and a gold mine of gossip about the mainland. In his short stay on the island, Wilson heard first- and second-hand accounts of China's troubled political temper. Mostly in reaction to the humiliating Sino-Japanese War of 1894–95, a Chinese secret organization, the "Society of Righteously Harmonious Fists," nicknamed the Boxers by the English-speaking residents, was carrying out a semi-private reform movement, the prime objective of which was to drive out the foreigners, particularly the missionaries, who were the traditional scapegoats of Chinese politics. The government,

The Treasure Hunt

while not participating openly in the movement, showed its sympathy by abstaining from any interference with it. The Boxer movement had originated in Shantung, where the Germans claimed a sphere of influence and aggravated the inhabitants; Boxers murdered two German missionaries and terrorized the other non-Chinese. The agitation spread like brush fire to other provinces. It seemed an inauspicious time to wander about the interior, especially as Wilson planned to travel, for he might easily be mistaken for a missionary. Yet most people, including Henry, who was now stationed at Szemao [Fu-hsing-chen] in Yunnan—Taiwan had been in the hands of the Japanese since the war—did not think there would be any trouble in that province.

Boxers or no Boxers, Wilson had no patience to sit around in Hong Kong for long, especially since there was an epidemic of plague on the island. According to his instructions, he had to get to Henry. After making local inquiries as to the safest route for his journey, he proceeded by boat to Haiphong, that well-known port in what is now North Vietnam but was then the French protectorate of Indo-China. Inasmuch as the Hong Kong natives were in quarantine, he had to make the journey without benefit of an escort. From Haiphong he headed for Hanoi. So Frenchified was the city that Wilson, who spoke no French, not to mention Chinese, had trouble disembarking from his river boat. At his hotel, finally, he found an English-speaking Frenchman who helped him out of his linguistic difficulties.

Szemao was accessible only in a roundabout way, and Wilson had to go via Mengtsze [Meng-tzu]. Up the aptly named Red River he journeyed to Laokai, an outpost on the Indo-Chinese side of the Yunnan border. En route he heard that Chinese had attacked foreign residents and burned the Customs House and the French Consulate in Mengtsze. In view of the Boxer scare, most westerners, even on an official level, automatically attributed the hostilities to political motivations. A few, like Henry, though he kept a revolver nearby, thought there would be no more trouble;

Journeys to the East

but Henry's optimism was no help to Wilson in Laokai. French officials warned him to wait for an all clear because four travelers had been murdered in the mountains during the raid. Had Wilson been one week earlier he might well have met a similar end. As it was, however, he checked into the newest hotel in town where, to his relief, he could converse with the French proprietor's English wife.

As Henry suspected all along, the Boxers had played no part in the Mengtsze incident. The villains were a gang of outlaws who had fled to the hills, eluding the Chinese authorities for weeks; meanwhile Mengtsze was quiet. Wilson might have made the trip in safety, but failing to receive clearance from the French, he waited in Laokai, frustrated and baffled by the delay. The town was unbearably hot, the rainy season was in full swing, tropical fever ran rampant, and every day the French buried at least one of their soldiers. During his eight weeks in Laokai, he tried to busy himself with the vegetation, but it was jungle and of no practical interest to him; otherwise, he was harassed with problems. The French authorities suspected him of being a spy, an English captain in disguise. (The Dreyfus scandal was international news again and the French military establishment was very sensitive at the time.) Perhaps it was hard to believe that Wilson was a plant collector, but the situation added mental strain to his physical discomforts.

While the French discouraged him from making the Mengtsze journey, it became clear they had no intentions of preventing him. In mid-July he learned that the road was considered safe and decided to try it if he could locate an English-speaking guide. Again language deficiencies interfered with his plans, and neither the French nor the natives cooperated. He was nearly ready to abandon the whole expedition when a man he described as "a Chinese of very unprepossessing appearance who smoked opium freely and had been discharged from the Telegraph service for incompetency" materialized as his deliverer bearing the following note:

The Treasure Hunt

My Dear Sir,

Before I have wish to do a interpreter with you, because I am very sick cannot to going, at now I have a friend he have learned him English for two years at Hongkong, if you wish to get a interpreter he can do.

Your small servant,
LIMAY [24]

Wilson had no idea who Limay was, but he hired his friend, for he could, indeed, manage some English.

Wilson assembled his belongings and, with his interpreter, he arrived in Mengtsze on September 1, just in time to admire a gruesome display of the heads of the freshly apprehended outlaws. With the help of the American Commissioner, Mr. W. F. Spinney of Salem, Massachusetts, he organized a caravan of fifteen or more mules and drivers and agreed to transport stores for the Customs officials at Szemao. "I left on the morning of September 8th," Wilson recalled, "and, being unable to speak any Chinese, traveled very much as a parcel and enjoyed the trip." [25] He decided quickly that the "easiest way to climb . . . a mountain is to hang on to the mule's tail, and let him drag you up." The trip took seventeen days; Wilson had been nearly four months in coming from Hong Kong.

Szemao, he judged on first sight, as "the most God-forsaken place imaginable," [26] and he marveled that Henry could abide the life there in the company of only five other Europeans.

He failed to take into account that Henry, through his long years in China, had learned to cope with, if not to relish, his isolation. Not only did Henry botanize, but he mastered a local dialect (Lolo) and made friends among the Chinese, studied tribal customs, and came to sympathize with Chinese problems. Perhaps this existence was sometimes wearing, but it was tolerable. Wilson had not been in China long enough yet to understand such an attitude, and his early experiences had been thoroughly unpleasant. However, a

Journeys to the East

time would come when he, too, would learn to know China. For now he only wanted to hear about the Hupeh plants, and Henry was delighted to oblige him.

Henry anticipated Wilson's arrival for months. He spread his meticulous notes before his guest and added other information from memory. As Wilson's English sponsors foretold, Henry's advice was to work in the general area of I-ch'ang. The climate there closely approximated that of England, and the flora was rich in ornamental species. Henry also provided a crucial bit of intelligence: the location of a single *Davidia* from which he made a collection in May 1888.

Wilson could have spent more time with Henry profitably, but Henry was unexpectedly summoned to Mengtsze to relieve Commissioner Spinney, so Wilson traveled with him, and they completed their dialogue in Mengtsze. At parting, each was greatly impressed with the other. Henry, like Sargent, predicted Wilson's success in China, for despite his ignorance of the language he behaved well with the natives. He suggested that Sargent find this kind of person to lead an expedition because there was much to be accomplished in China.[27] Wilson, meanwhile, made an uneventful return to Hong Kong for the Christmas holidays, passed the time agreeably with an old friend from Kew, dispatched his first collections to Veitch, and replenished his supplies for the next stage of his trip, which took him from the island via Shanghai, up the Yangtze, to I-ch'ang.

Since I-ch'ang was to be home base for the next two years, Wilson organized himself there. He purchased supplies and outfitted himself for the wilderness. On the advice of Europeans, he bought a sedan chair, less to ease his travels than to impress the Chinese, who considered it as a sign of prestige. Later on, the chair turned out to be very useful for avoiding wet feet. Following Henry's example, Wilson hired natives to help him collect, and began his field work by making short trips to the gorges upriver from I-ch'ang with the dual purpose of getting to know the flora and of training his men. He bought a Chinese boat which could double as

The Treasure Hunt

shelter and transportation. By the middle of April 1900, the party was ready to strike out. Their objective, to obtain specimens of *Davidia*.

Wilson carried a half sheet of notebook paper on which Henry had drawn an area about the size of New York State; somewhere near the border between Hupeh and Szechwan, Henry had marked his *Davidia* tree. The paper looked like a proverbial pirate map for buried treasure. Wilson relates the tale of the *Davidia* quest in his *Aristocrats of the Garden* (pp. 275–294), and it is sufficient to say that the journey was adventurous. The party went through villages where anti-Christians and Christians had been at each other's throats, priests had been attacked—in one case murdered—and the superficial tranquility of the inhabitants belied their fuming rivalries. In such situations a less tactful man might have met a quick and undignified end, but Wilson kept his head and pushed on toward *Davidia*. After ten days the party reached its destination, a village called Ma-huang-pao, where Henry had once stayed. The people remembered Henry and *Davidia*, and a man proudly led Wilson to the tree, or at least to the spot where the tree had once grown, for tree there was no more—just a stump. The tree had been cut the year before to provide beams and posts for a new house. Wilson could not sleep that night.

The downcast group went back to I-ch'ang, where Wilson made other plans for seeking *Davidia* the following season a thousand miles to the west, where Père David had originally discovered it in 1869. In the meantime he would collect all he could in Western Hupeh and erase his first failure from his mind. Then, on May 19, he was collecting southwest of I-ch'ang when he stumbled on a fifty-foot *Davidia* in full bloom. The spectacle, far more beautiful than he had imagined, nearly took his breath away. "The flowers," he wrote, "and their attendant bracts are pendulous on fairly long stalks, and when stirred by the slightest breeze they resemble huge butterflies or small doves hovering amongst the trees." [28] To the end of his life Wilson thought it the most beautiful of north temperate zone trees. In November he

Journeys to the East

succeeded in gathering large quantities of seed. In north-western Hupeh the following year, he found more than a hundred *Davidia,* but he could secure only a very few seeds from them.

Having achieved his main objective, Wilson relaxed and continued his general collecting. Since, as Henry forecast, he found the flora there so rich in species of horticultural value, he usually stayed close to his base at I-ch'ang, a bustling commercial city in which there were plenty of Europeans should he feel the need for Occidental companionship. From May to mid-September 1900, threats of Boxer hostilities made him uneasy. All the Protestant missionaries evacuated their posts, and officials warned Wilson that he must stay at his own risk, for no one could guarantee his safety.[29] Fortunately, he avoided any serious incidents.

In the low altitudes in the vicinity of I-ch'ang proper, the climate was too warm to serve Wilson's purposes.[30] But at higher elevations upstream, cool temperate vegetation lined the limestone cliffs in the gorges. Even after he had visited more remote parts of China, Wilson believed that northwestern Hupeh was the hardest going. Few people inhabited the Yangtze mountains; those who did lived nearly exclusively on potatoes and suffered from goiter. Though the Chinese were more often friendly than not, it was diffi-cult to find accommodations for the entire collecting party. While the craggy cliffs supported a wild flora, the arable land was less generous in its yield, and crops grew poorly so the food supply was low. Roads were practically non-existent, and where there were roads they were very poor. Navigating the gorges by boat was one danger; crossing them by fragile bridges was another. Yet there were no serious casualties during the first expedition. After each long tour in the field Wilson and his men would return to I-ch'ang to sort and mail specimens and seeds, fill out field notes, replenish their supplies, and refresh their spirits for their next engagement with nature.

In early 1902, by the time he was ready to return to Eng-land, Wilson had amassed herbarium specimens of nearly

The Treasure Hunt

2,600 kinds of plants, and hundreds of species of seeds and bulbs for the Veitch nurseries. His work had been confined to a relatively small geographic area, hardly farther than Henry's roamings, but the vegetation was so varied that he had not needed to make long trips. He left China via Shanghai and arrived in England in April.

Nearly the first thing he did was to hurry out to the Coombe Wood nurseries to inspect his *Davidia* seedlings. There was not a single plant in sight; the seeds had arrived a year before him, been treated and sown, and not one of them had germinated. The nurserymen watched and waited nervously for *Davidia* to show signs of life, but the seeds took their own time as though refusing to submit to human impatience. Then, in May, thousands of young plants suddenly poked through the ground. Wilson had his reward, and the Veitch firm heaved a corporate sigh of relief.* Moreover, Wilson had introduced several other ornamental plants which would be popular in English gardens for years to come, such as *Magnolia delavayi, Rhododendron discolor, Malus theifera, Abies fargesii,* and two species of maple. In short, he had handsomely justified expenses.[31]

When he had left England three years before, scarcely anyone knew the name of Ernest Henry Wilson. By the time he returned, he had acquired a small fame. *Gardeners' Chronicle* had printed articles on his travels and collections. Botanists and horticulturists eagerly sought him out, and Wilson, while reluctant to elaborate on his adventures was proud of his achievements and flattered by the attention.

In June he married Ellen Ganderton of Edgebaston, Warwickshire. Mrs. Wilson, a small, quiet girl, thereupon embarked upon a lifelong mission to domesticate her exploring husband, a task at which she never entirely succeeded though she tried her best to provide comfortable

---

* Plant propagators have since learned that they cannot just put *Davidia* seeds into the ground and expect them to sprout like radishes. They require a warm period followed by cold treatment, which can be accomplished in greenhouses before outdoor planting. Under artificial conditions, *Davidia* seeds can be germinated in six months or so.

Journeys to the East

surroundings at home to contrast with the Chinese wilds. She suffered feelings of neglect and envy; she grew jealous of his long absences in China or other parts of the world; and she was never reconciled to living in the United States. She was not well liked, in general, by Wilson's colleagues who resented her attempts to interfere with his travels. If this judgment sounds harsh, it may be balanced by the fact that Wilson always referred to her in his letters with admiration and affection, and perhaps the marriage furnished them both with greater happiness than was apparent on the surface.

It is not surprising that Ellen Wilson wanted to keep her husband at home. They had been married for less than a year when Harry Veitch shipped him off for a second time. Wilson had demonstrated that earlier collectors had only scratched the surface of China's plant wealth. The first set of introductions had already generated interest in England, and the Veitches reasoned that a second trip would be a sound commercial investment. This time they ordered Wilson to bring back the Yellow Poppywort, *Meconopsis integrifolia,* a pretty plant which English horticulturists had heard of and wanted for their gardens. Though little was known about it, rumors of its beauty aroused excitement among garden lovers. In January 1903, Wilson waved goodbye to his bride of seven months and headed for the land of the Yellow Poppywort.

Wilson left for Shanghai in January 1903 and arrived on March 22. He was not at all apprehensive, as he had been during his first weeks in China in 1899; in fact, he derived a special satisfaction from his familiarity with the city and the routine of dealing with the Chinese. His ultimate destination, however, was not familiar territory. From Shanghai he traveled as before, north to Nanking and westward on the Yangtze to I-ch'ang. Having paid his respects to old acquaintances there and reengaged about half a dozen of his collectors, he continued westward and left Hupeh province behind, journeying far into Szechwan. At Sui, [Sui-hsien] where the Min and Yangtze rivers converge,

The Treasure Hunt

he turned north on the Min, and finally, in June, he arrived at his base in Kia-ting [Lo-shan] at the junction of the Min and Tung rivers, about fifty miles northwest of the Yangtze. The journey of nearly 1,500 miles into the heart of China was comparatively easy going, for Wilson traveled the busy waterways, which were less dangerous than the Chinese roads. The trip was not without adventure, however, as the river was not always friendly above I-ch'ang. The boat and Wilson survived, but one of the crew drowned and several men were injured in falls. They were fortunate in shooting rapids which claimed other boats and lives before and behind them. Wilson took blood and gore in stride, accustomed as he had become to Oriental attitudes, and observed somewhat coolly, "life is cheap in this part of the world." [32]

Kia-ting, while not as large as I-ch'ang, was an important commercial town and communications center situated on one of the main roads to Tibet. From there Wilson and his caravan traveled long distances along good routes and thus were able to cover more ground than they had in Hupeh. Wilson worked the field primarily in two directions from Kia-ting. The first was due west through mountainous country along the Tung river to Tatsien-lu [K'ang-ting]. Here he collected at high altitudes, often above the tree line where he found mostly herbs, which interested him less than ligneous plants, though he liked the lilies. His second main route was north-northwest from Kia-ting to Sung-p'an, a distance of nearly three hundred miles.

Though intent on finding *Meconopsis integrifolia*, Wilson began with a methodical exploration of the flora closer to home base. One of his first trips was a six-day journey to the massive, flat-topped, sacred mountain called Wa shan, eighty miles from Kia-ting. The country was rough. At Wa shan, weather consisted of an almost constant thick, penetrating mist; the cliffs were so steep in spots that once Wilson nearly lost his footing and was indebted to an alert coolie for saving his life; his pet dog had to be blindfolded when carried up the ladders needed to scale the top. In four days, Wilson collected specimens of 220 different

Journeys to the East

species. The most exciting of these were Rhododendrons, of which he gathered 16 species and which bloomed in glory at the upper reaches of the mountain, clinging to crags and cliffs, "in thousands and hundreds of thousands." [33]

On Wa shan, Wilson found a yellow *Meconopsis chelidoniifolia*, but not the species he hunted. For that he ventured to Tatsien-lu, almost to the Tibetan border, the center of trade between China and Tibet. High above sea level at 8,400 feet, surrounded by treeless mountain peaks, the town seemed attractive from a distance, but Wilson discovered on closer inspection that it was "a meanly built and filthy city." Though situated officially in China, the population was predominantly Tibetan. Today Tibet remains one of the few regions of the world that still seems remote and mysterious to westerners; then it was virtually unknown save by a handful of adventurers. Many men who had been known to cross the border into Tibet had never been heard from again. Tatsien-lu, however, was reasonably safe and easy to reach.

Wilson, while charged with collecting plants, had taken careful notes on the people and their customs throughout all his Chinese journeys, and close to Tibet he became fascinated by the Tibetan culture that had seeped across the frontier. In his visits to Tatsien-lu he made a number of friends, including the chief official known locally as the king. He learned about the lamaseries but conceived no sympathy for the mysticism of Lamaism. He was also much interested in the frequency of polyandry among the Tibetans, a practice which he viewed with the clinical eye and furrowed brow of a monogamous, Christian, British male. Wilson sensed himself as a participant in a great adventure, visiting places where few, if any, westerners had gone before. He recorded his impressions, often in an appealing, subjective fashion. One is thankful, finally, that it was Wilson and not Sargent who explored China, because it is unlikely that Sargent would have written about anything but the flora.

The Treasure Hunt

Near Tatsien-lu, Wilson found *Meconopsis integrifolia* and so crossed off the main item on his list. The area was good for collecting, and during his second expedition he returned to the Tibetan outpost three times, using a different route each time. On one occasion early in 1904, he and his party, investigating higher altitudes, crossed the high passes; bitter winter weather still prevailed, and the bearers suffered frostbite and snow blindness.

Wilson's problems did not begin and end in the field. On his first journey, Boxer agitation had nearly terminated his efforts; on his second, famine threatened to be his downfall. Food was scarce in Szechwan in 1904, so labor was hard to get and harder to keep. Worst of all was the difficulty of feeding a group of fifteen or twenty men for several days in the wilderness, wondering whether the next village would have enough food to sell and sufficient shelter. He learned he could not expect much from Chinese inns except the barest protection against the elements; he often had to put up with stinking, windowless huts, crawling with vermin of remarkable variety. But after a good day's collecting over rough terrain, he could sleep almost anywhere if the bugs did not bite too often. Plant collecting in China offered the kind of life an ordinary man would flee. Wilson was not being stoic; despite his repeated complaints about roads and accommodations, he liked it. Sooner or later he could understand how Henry had endured the wretchedness of Szemao.

Wilson made two trips to Sung-p'an, the most distant town in northwest Szechwan. The second, more arduous journey, took 52 days. In August 1904, he quit Kia-ting by the great north road leading into the fertile Ch'eng-tu Plain, and began a gradual ascent. "Having cleared the low country," he wrote home, "I got amongst some magnificent mountain ranges covered with a luxuriant flora, and in places well forested. The sides of these mountains are so steep that a flying-machine would be necessary to properly explore them. Species of *Meconopsis* occurred in plenty, and when collecting the seed we had to tramp about in snow nearly a foot deep."[34] Here, with the Yellow Poppywort, were *Mecon-*

opsis punicea, a scarlet species, *M. racemosa,* a prickly, blue-flowered form, and *M. henrici,* a violet-blue-flowered species. During this trip Wilson discovered a new species of *Incarvillea,* one of the few cold-hardy members of the African violet family.

In Sung-p'an, which was even closer to the Tibetan border than Tatsien-lu, Wilson found himself among the Sifan tribes, a people of Tibetan origin, who behaved in a friendly, gentle manner. The climate was delightful, the hunting good, the people and plants interesting. Wilson preferred Sung-p'an to any other town in western China.

Each time he struck out from Kia-ting, Wilson experienced an adventure within an adventure, so the story of his expedition reveals itself—as perhaps is fitting—like a series of Chinese boxes. He led his men across unmapped lands, where it was said no foreigner had been before, to the ancient kingdom of Pa in eastern Szechwan. He climbed one of the five holiest mountains in China, O-mei shan, which he could see from Kia-ting. Like Wa shan, its flora was rich in species, and it contained outstanding forests of *Abies delavayi,* a silver fir. Here, too, he collected Rhododendrons.

Early in 1905 Wilson was ready to go home, having abundantly fulfilled the demands of his employers. He had shipped back around two thousand numbers of seeds and plants and five thousand numbers of herbarium specimens, many of which eventually proved to be new species. Horticulturally his mission succeeded, though *Meconopsis* never received quite the acclaim accorded *Davidia* because it was only marginally hardy in Britain and seldom survived in the United States. By March, Wilson reached England and settled down, after a vacation, to working over his collections. The Veitch firm, satisfied with the Chinese harvest for the time being, had no plans for his future so, in January 1906, Wilson accepted an appointment as a botanical assistant at the Imperial Institute in London, where he worked on Hong Kong collections. He did not know whether, or when, he would see China again.

The Treasure Hunt

9

E. H. Wilson: Our Man in I-ch'ang

While Wilson searched China, Sargent was back at the Arboretum trying to find his own collector for a Chinese expedition. His visit to Japan, the short-lived hope that young Veitch might undertake the work, the letters from Henry, and the passing visit from Wilson whetted his appetite for Oriental plants. Though he received seeds and plant material through Bretschneider and the nursery firm of Regel and Kesselring in St. Petersburg, and from the Veitches, the quantities were limited. What really fascinated Sargent were Henry's specimens from the I-ch'ang gorges. An expedition of this type would involve expenses considerably beyond the capabilities of the ordinary Arboretum budget, but Sargent did not worry, for the time being, about the financial aspects; first of all he needed something—or, rather, someone—to finance.

For all his eagerness, he was not foolhardy. After all, one could not hire just any botanist or gardener for such an important and dangerous mission. The man ought to have a solid background in both botany and horticulture. Sargent would have preferred a man familiar with China and Chinese, but Henry reassured him that one could get along without knowing the language. Wilson proved that point, for he never bothered to learn the tongue and surrendered himself to the mercy of interpreters. Since Bretschneider had had experience in China and knew a good deal about

E. H. Wilson

223

collectors, Sargent asked his advice. Bretschneider had little in the way of practical suggestions and referred Sargent back to the Horticultural Society of London, which had sponsored Fortune almost sixty years before, a referral which, though well meant, was neither helpful nor original. Unquestionably, Henry would be the best person for the job, and Sargent tried every way he could think of to entice him to lead an expedition, offering to match his pay as a Customs official during the special leave he would have to take for field work. Even Henry thought the proposal extravagant. For a while it looked as though he might accept the job on more modest terms, but he finally begged off. He felt too weary, he said, to do vigorous work. His fatigue was less physical than psychological; he admitted that he had grown sick and tired of China and was looking for a way to shorten his days there.[1] He promised to give assistance to anyone Sargent might send, and in the meantime he provided information about expenses and procedures for an expedition.

Sargent made a short trip to Europe early in 1900 and talked over his hopes with Thiselton-Dyer, but the Boxer uprisings temporarily discouraged him from making a serious effort at recruiting an English collector. Although Wilson fared well enough at I-ch'ang, there was no telling how dangerous the disturbances might become. Sargent kept an eye on the headlines and feared the worst. Until the political climate improved and he could get hold of precisely the right man for the job, he had enough to do. Since his work with the National Academy's commission on forests in 1896, he had had no outside obligations and could concentrate on the Arboretum and his own research. Moreover, after 1897, when the combined forces of Stiles' death and depressing financial records brought *Garden and Forest* to an end, he disposed of another burden. He approached sixty without showing any signs of slackening his pace to accommodate his age. He worked hard to finish off the *Silva,* which had run to fourteen volumes, and he completed the chore in 1903. Before the manuscript was

The Treasure Hunt

out of his hands, he made plans to publish an abbreviated version of it in manual form. He traveled frequently on short excursions and occasionally on longer ones. In the fall of 1897, he joined Canby and Muir for a trip to the Canadian Rockies and Alaska, rejoining them a year later for the fruiting season in the Alleghenies. Sixty or not, in 1900, he was still going strong, in defiance of gout, over-weight, and an official life expectancy of 46.3 years.

In his sixty-first year, nearing the end of two decades of work on the *Silva*, he felt strangely melancholy and restless, and started thinking of making a long journey, perhaps to see a bit of China himself. There were so many trees to see! He laid out a trip around the world. Then he wrote Muir in California and talked about the great Siberian wilderness, a scene which the naturalist found irresistible. Sargent also tried to lure his English friend H. J. Elwes to join him, but Elwes was preoccupied with other projects and declined the invitation. (In the long run, Sargent was probably happier without Elwes, whom he once described as "a gentleman [who] has already been pretty much all over the world. The only trouble is that he talks too much and too loudly and positively, and so much that he has gone around the world without really seeing anything.")[2] The third member of the party would be Sargent's eldest son, Andrew Robeson.

Robeson had graduated from Harvard, Class of 1900, at the age of twenty-four. He matured into a likeable, easy-going fellow for, while he resembled his father and grand-father Sargent in appearance, having the same large-framed, heavy body and handsome face, his personality was relaxed and extroverted. With his well-bred manner and his good-humored attitudes, he made a perfect foil and companion for his father, whose interests in horticulture he shared. Much to Sargent's delight, after Harvard, Robe-son decided to make landscape architecture his career and entered into a business association with his brother-in-law, Guy Lowell. It is quite possible that Sargent hoped his son would succeed him as Director of the Arnold Arboretum

E. H. Wilson

because, to some extent, he groomed him for the role. If the Hookers could have their dynasty at Kew, why not the Sargents at Jamaica Plain?

The 1903 trip around the world was part of Robeson's education. Muir came east, and the three travelers set sail for England on May 29. Sargent had his usual calls to pay: Thiselton-Dyer at Kew; Hooker, still very much alive and spry though not feeling very well at the time; Maxwell Masters at the *Gardeners' Chronicle;* Elwes, just beginning his collaboration with Henry, who was home from China at last, on *The Trees of Great Britain and Ireland*, Britain's answer to Sargent's *Silva;* Harry Veitch for news of Wilson and a look at the Chinese material; the gardens and parks he wanted to show Muir and Robeson. All obligations and visits were quickly accomplished, and they were off to the continent taking a winding route through Europe to reach St. Petersburg.

In Europe they visited more parks, gardens, and art galleries. Painting was one of the few things which could distract Sargent from his trees and shrubs. Robeson evidently amused himself well, but Muir was unhappy with the program. For a man who liked wide open spaces in the unkempt wilderness, who shouted the glory of God from mountain tops, Europe's manicured gardens seemed unnatural and confining; museums inspired him even less. But he bore his irritation jokingly, looking forward hopefully to the Siberian forests.

The travelers went to St. Petersburg via Berlin. St. Petersburg, when it was the capital of czarist Russia, an elegant, gallicized, romantic city—if one could overlook its feudal miseries—was a delightful place to be in August. From there they proceeded to Moscow and south to the Crimea. "The most superb thing in nature that Russia had to offer," exclaimed Robeson, "was the voluptuous floral display of Mt. Kasbek, a spur of the Caucasus range, where 10,000 ft. above sea level the luxurious profusion of wild flowers was astounding." That sight was more to Muir's liking. The collecting was good, and Sargent gathered specimens

The Treasure Hunt

furiously. From Tiflis through the Dariel Pass they headed back to Moscow to board their train for Siberia. Robeson recalled:

> We entered Siberia by way of the Chita branch of the railway and spent 28 nights upon the train, during 10 of which we did not remove our clothing, owing to the miserable sleeping car accommodations.
>
> In Russia every traveller takes his bed clothing with him, and through ignorance of this custom we found ourselves in a sorry plight. Often where bedding could not be hired we were compelled to drive the streets all night.
>
> I was impressed with the vast forests and broad steppes of Siberia, and as we sped over the Amor R.R. [eastern branch of the Trans-Siberian R.R.] . . . the original one of the country, we passed many trains filled with Russian convicts. They were crowded into small box cars, lighted with tiny barred and grated windows.
>
> At Harbin, in Manchuria, we found the Russian government was secretly mobilizing her troops, and everybody professed belief in the permanent occupancy of that country by the czar's minions. Harbin is a new town and tenanted by soldiers and Russian officials exclusively.
>
> . . .
>
> We expected to return to Harbin, where the Eastern China R.R. commences, but while en route thither a bridge went down with 40 passengers and we were compelled to retrace our steps.[3]

Nearly a month on a train, particularly in Siberia, would be enough to sour the most hardened travelers. There was little chance to collect except close to the railroad tracks. And poor Muir was cooped up on board when he longed to leap into the forests and exchange some fresh air for the odious stale fumes of Russian tobacco. Yet Sargent seemed satisfied enough, profiting from his limited view of the

E. H. Wilson

Siberian forests. Robeson amused himself with nonbotanical observations: "The better class of Russian women are the handsomest in the world, but the military officers do not present so fine an appearance as do those of the German and Austrian armies." From Siberia and Manchuria, the trio finally reached Peiping and investigated the neighborhood.

They crossed the Yellow Sea to Korea—and new and exciting flora, little explored—Japan, and then back to Shanghai. Muir, exhausted by the pace and aware that his objectives did not often coincide with Sargent's, decided to strike out for himself and parted company with the others, without hard feelings. The Sargents traveled south by boat, putting in at various Chinese ports, all the way down to Singapore and Java, "huge hothouses or conservatories of nature, so profligate is their floral display," exclaimed Robeson, savoring his metaphors but less interested, in a practical way, in the flora there than in Korea. However, the botanic gardens at Singapore enchanted the elder Sargent. This was one of Kew's branch operations under the direction of Henry Nicholson Ridley, and the lush vegetation was beautifully and usefully arranged.[4]

Completing their circle of the globe, the wandering Sargents returned to the United States across the Pacific to San Francisco and did the last cross-country lap by train. Sargent, pleased by the trip, said it had been his best yet.[5] They had done it all in about six months and had collected quantities of herbarium material.

Useful though it might have been, the voyage did nothing to solve Sargent's China problem. He had only been around the edges of the country. Nowhere had he found anyone sutiable for exploring the inland regions. Meanwhile his enthusiasm for Chinese plants had waxed rather then waned. Returning to work on his *Manual of Trees* he hoped for an opportunity to get them.

Sargent's eagerness infected Jack, who decided to make a trip to the Orient on his own in 1905. The question arises as to why Sargent did not raise funds to pay for the trip and

The Treasure Hunt

have Jack do his collecting, but whatever the reason, Jack financed himself. He did not penetrate the dangerous interior of the Chinese mainland but concentrated on the northern coastal towns, where he looked for outstanding cultivated species. He spent the greater part of his time in Japan and Korea, the latter more or less virgin territory from the collector's point of view. Because of the Russo-Japanese War, however, he could not travel freely in Korea. After nearly a year in the Far East, he returned with specimens of 650 kinds of seeds and seedlings of both wild and cultivated plants, including some which had never been grown in the United States. While this was a satisfactory record, it did not prove to be remarkable and disappointed Sargent who, despite his better judgment, had secret hopes for spectacular introductions.

By the time Jack came back, Sargent, having completed the first part of his *Manual,* was out of the country again, this time on a six-month jaunt with Robeson in western South America with the overt objective of scrutinizing the Chilean flora and the ulterior motive of establishing diplomatic relations with Latin American botanical institutions. He scheduled the trip in winter in order to catch summer south of the equator. Sargent was too old for any rugged overland travel, so they crossed Panama and sailed down the west coast of the continent, stopping to collect at Guayaquil, around Lima, en route to Santiago, where they arrived in December of 1905. Sargent did some botanizing in central Chile and thoroughly enjoyed the benevolent climate though he looks particularly grumpy in a snapshot taken by an amateur photographer in Santiago. The route home was complicated: first, the Straits of Magellan to Buenos Aires, then England, and back to the Arboretum by mid-April 1906. If the itinerary appeared somewhat impractical, Sargent had a perfectly practical reason for making it: he had made up his mind to snare Wilson.

Wilson had recently accepted a position as botanical assistant at the Imperial Institute in London, and because it was a government appointment, he considered it a situa-

E. H. Wilson

tion which he could not treat casually. To all appearances, he was a man prepared to settle down to botanical research and retire forever from the field. Sargent, in his usual rush, had budgeted little time in England. He made his approach in an abrupt, matter-of-fact manner after discussing his ideas with a few of his English friends who were acquainted with Wilson. With a minimum of fanfare, he asked Wilson to make an expedition for the Arboretum similar to the two he had made for the Veitch firm, offering a somewhat higher salary. By Sargent's reasoning, Wilson should leave England in November to arrive in Boston by December and be in China for the beginning of the 1907 flowering season.

Sargent's proposal caught Wilson off guard, for he had not even properly settled into his work at the Imperial Institute. The idea of going back to China tempted him, and had he been a free agent he would have accepted without hesitation. But he had to think of his professional security and his wife's advanced state of pregnancy. While he did not flatly refuse Sargent's proposal, he would not commit himself either way. Sargent, accustomed to getting what he wanted, left England optimistically feeling that Wilson would eventually concede.

Wilson was in no hurry to make up his mind. A daughter, Muriel Primrose (after *Primula wilsoni*, a violet primrose which bloomed the day of her birth), was born at the end of May. Her arrival, the protests of his wife, and his own practical concerns induced him to turn down Sargent. The latter, having been confident of a positive answer, was much annoyed and did not bother to conceal his feelings. "I do not at all approve of your idea of not going to China," he began his reply. He indicated that he could consider increasing his salary offer and that he would try to find a position in America for Wilson after he had completed his expedition; perhaps a place would be open on the Arboretum staff. Except for what he said about payment, however, he could not make any firm promises.[6] The tone of his letter put Wilson on the defensive. He quickly set forth his excuses:

The Treasure Hunt

It is not altogether to be expected that you & I can look on this Chinese business from exactly the same standpoint. There are many difficulties in the way, difficulties which are well-nigh insuperable, but which you cannot be expected to appreciate in the way I do. Putting sentiment aside, I have to throw up a Government appointment which if at present modest has possibilities. Secondly, I have to leave behind my wife & child & these have to be provided for. Thirdly, there is the possibility of the pitcher going once too often to the well. There are other things of might which have to be considered & the possibilities of obtaining suitable employment on my return do not appear to me to be brighter in the future than in the past.[7]

The obstacles as he stated them were reasonable enough to justify an abrupt refusal, but Wilson's words were not those of a man about to turn his back on an offer. Sargent, sensing hope, applied to his English friends for aid. He asked Henry, George Nicholson—who had been Wilson's supervisor at Kew—and Ellen Willmott, a beautiful lady, avid gardener, and admirer of Wilson's introductions, to use what influence they could to convince Wilson to make the expedition. Willingly they all tried, and they all arrived at the same conclusion: Wilson would go if he got more money. Miss Willmott suggested that the only other drawback might be Mrs. Wilson, who had impressed her as a stubborn, small-minded woman obstructing the career of her gifted husband.[8] Wilson himself finally indicated that a larger salary—say $13,000 for a two year period—would make it possible for him to go.

Sargent, dependent on private subscriptions to finance the exploration, checked with his sponsors and was gratified to find them willing to put up the extra funds. Within a few days, he informed Wilson that he would not only meet his financial demands but would also make every possible effort to provide him with a permanent position on the Arboretum staff following his return from China.[9] The

E. H. Wilson

effect of Sargent's revised offer was magical. His wife's objections notwithstanding, Wilson responded warmly:

> So you have captured me after all! Twelve months ago I would not have believed it possible for anyone to have persuaded me into revisiting China on any terms. Since it has come to pass be it said that there is no person or Institution I would rather serve than yourself & Arnold Arboretum—Kew alone excepted.[10]

Sargent, triumphant, believed Wilson's price worth paying if he did as well as before. In the weeks before Wilson left England for the United States, the two men exchanged letters and worked out plans for the expedition. Sargent reported victory to his backers and collected their checks. The list of sponsors, Sargent's acquaintances from Boston, sounded like a page from the Social Register. There was a Weld, two Hunnewells, three Thayers, a Sears, two Ames's, each contributing a minimum of one thousand dollars.[11] Miss Willmott subscribed £200. Provided the trip went well, Sargent would favor the donors with horticultural treats from China but, in essence, the contributions were personal gestures to Sargent for the benefit of the Arboretum.

Wilson arrived in Boston shortly before Christmas 1906 and spent only a few weeks there before his departure for the West Coast. One of Sargent's best traits as an administrator was that if he trusted a man's judgment, he allowed that man to use it. In Wilson's case, it would have been folly to do anything else. The two men agreed that Wilson would work in the general area of his first expedition, the I-ch'ang gorges, but Sargent encouraged him to cover new fields at his discretion, thus allowing him considerable freedom. He was supposed to concentrate on woody plants, with an emphasis on conifers, but not to the exclusion of herbaceous species. His assignment also included gathering orchids for Oakes Ames, ferns for Hermann Christ of Basle, Switzerland, and lily bulbs for the Farquhar nurseries in Boston, and for Miss Willmott.[12]

The Treasure Hunt

Armed with Sargent's loosely worded instructions and letters of credit, Wilson left Boston for the Orient, suffering a nerve-wracking but harmless train wreck in Omaha and a soporific ocean voyage via Honolulu and Yokohama to Shanghai, stopping only for a quick glimpse of Japan. According to plan, in Shanghai he met Frank Meyer, a Dutchman who collected for the U. S. Department of Agriculture under the supervision of David Fairchild. Sargent knew Meyer's work and had criticized it severely because Meyer did not make herbarium specimens of the plants from which he gathered seeds. Nevertheless, Sargent and Fairchild had worked out a bargain by which Meyer would explore the Wu t'ai mountains under Sargent's direction and thus liberate Wilson for wider fields, where he would watch for economic plants for the Department of Agriculture. Wilson's first impressions of Meyer were mixed, mostly negative. Meyer was hard-working and enthusiastic, but he had "no sense of humour," a quality that Wilson evidently considered useful in dealing with the Chinese. Moreover Wilson worried that "he has very little sympathy for the yellow race, & ignores their manners & customs . . . [but] whilst he glories in roughing it & in the superiority of the white race, I fancy he will modify his views & methods somewhat after a time. I seriously hope so for when he comes to reside amongst the Chinese he will find that his present methods are not calculated to get the best from his men." [13] As tactfully as possible, Wilson tried to bring Meyer down from his high horse. They discussed the Wu t'ai project at length, and Wilson left Meyer a set of instructions for collecting, emphasizing the importance of herbarium specimens, field notes, and photographs. After making a few necessary arrangements with the banks and shipping authorities in Shanghai, Wilson began the familiar journey up the Yangtze to I-ch'ang, where he arrived during the last week in February.

Wilson handled preliminary routine tasks, immediately purchased a boat and fitted it out to approximate, as far as possible, the comforts of home. Word of his arrival had

E. H. Wilson

preceded him, and several of the men who had worked for him before offered their services again because they knew he paid good wages by Chinese standards and treated them well. So many men volunteered that Wilson had to turn some of them away. This evidence of their high regard flattered him, however, for Europeans were seldom popular with the local inhabitants. "So you see, Professor," he reported to Sargent, "that so far so good is the order of the day." The only difficulty he encountered was a currency exchange crisis which would increase the cost of the expedition.[14]

Sargent, fortunately, was unperturbed by additional expenses. On the other side of the globe, he traveled vicariously, studying the literature about Chinese plants and dispatching encouraging letters to Wilson. He kept in touch with Harry Veitch and planned a trip to England for early summer to take another look at Wilson's earlier introductions. As news of Wilson's first discoveries trickled into his office, Sargent rejoiced.

As he had done in the past, Wilson made his first excursion, a short one in the I-ch'ang gorge region, testing his equipment and men, and renewing his familiarity with the flora. In May he made his first long trip, northwest to Hing shan [Hsing-shan], along the watershed between the Yangtze and Han rivers; he followed the Szechwan border, crossed Shensi province back to Ch'u-shan in Hupeh, and returned by a slightly different route to I-ch'ang. The party made the nearly 500 miles in about forty days, over exceedingly rough territory.

> This region is a perfect *terra incognita*. It has never been surveyed, & the maps are all wrong. Save Henry & myself (& we only traversed a fragment of the whole) no foreigner has ever set foot there. And really there is little reason why they should for a more poverty-stricken area would be difficult to imagine . . . For days together we saw no living soul from noon till night & we had to arrange our stages from house to house . . . With fine

The Treasure Hunt

weather, a good flora, & wonderful scenery it would be odd if one did not enjoy the trip rough & fatiguing though it was. The same I fear cannot be said of our men, & I shall long remember the delight with which they received the order to turn their faces Ichang-wards. Poor beggars! they had a rough time living on maize which they had to pay famine prices for.[15]

Wilson was satisfied with the trip except that there had been a late and unfavorable flowering season in the area. Even so he found over 500 species in flower and collected 3,500 specimens.

Meyer, meanwhile, was not faring so well. He had traveled to Wu t'ai as directed. He informed Wilson petulantly, "I can say, with a small alteration, like Caesar did I came, I saw, I know. And—my knowledge is painful. The Wu t'ai shan n.l. is an utterly barren region!"[16] If nothing more, he had spared Wilson the pain of finding that out for himself, but that was no consolation to Meyer, who now wished he had been sent to western China, where he might prove himself as a collector. The Department of Agriculture was pleased enough with the economic plants Meyer sent back during the expedition, but he failed to find much in the way of ornamentals on Wu t'ai shan or anywhere else, and Sargent criticized him accordingly. Wilson expressed little surprise at Meyer's mediocre results, complaining, "He wants to be all over the country at one & the same moment. This is fatal to results."[17]

Wilson's second long trip was farther but faster than the first: down the Yangtze valley to the Lu shan—mountains in western Szechwan—almost as far west as Tatsien-lu. This was the region where Père David had collected, and it was rich in ligneous species including the Chinese Katsura tree, *Cercidiphyllum japonicum* var. *sinense;* a new species of Styrax, *Styrax wilsonii;* and *Lonicera nitida.* Wilson and his party accomplished the entire trip in three weeks, two of which they spent traveling, and the third in intensive

E. H. Wilson

collecting. And so, for the rest of the summer, all went well. Sargent, returning from England, where he had admired Wilson's plants, received only good news and forwarded Wilson's letters to *Gardeners' Chronicle* for publication because, as he explained to Wilson, "every one in England, and indeed in the whole horticultural world, is now deeply interested in your Chinese explorations." [18]

In September, Wilson came down with what he called "a malignant form of malaria" which forced him to remain in bed for twenty-two days.[19] The malaria left him weak long after he was out of bed. His work suffered, for he fell ill during the fruiting season when he should have been out collecting seeds. By November he felt stronger and was able to pick up many fruits in the gorges; he had plenty of winter work in I-ch'ang what with packing his shipments and preparing specimens. But the lost time upset him. "With so much to do," he wrote, "& so much more I should like to do, I often wish I could multiply myself into several presences." [20] Sargent magnanimously dismissed the delay as a case of "very hard luck." [21]

To make up for lost time, Wilson wanted to start off as early as possible in the spring of 1908. But to his dismay he ran into obstacles right away; the Chinese authorities had just put a limitation on the number of cartridges which a foreigner could import, restricting them to five hundred. Wilson did not want to undertake long spells in the wilderness without sufficient security and, with the assistance of the American Consul General at Hankow, he received permission to acquire the ammunition he required. Next he discovered cracks in the bottom of his boat, which had to be repaired before he left. Finally, it was early March instead of mid-February when he started up the Yangtze for Kia-ting, which he planned to use as a base for the next several months. At the end of April, he led his men up the Min River valley to the city of Kuan [Kuan-hsien], and southwest by land to Tatsien-lu, a trip of twenty-five days in rugged country, often at altitudes above 10,000 feet at near-freezing temperatures.

The Treasure Hunt

For days the road led through virgin forests with magnificent Conifers & Birch, with Larch over-topping all. Here & there we had to hew a path-way for ourselves, & how we managed to wade certain wild mt. torrents in safety will remain a mystery for I am unable to explain. One night we slept out in the forest under an impoverished shelter of spruce boughs. However, in spite of obstacles we got there & secured a good haul of material.[22]

Between Kuan and Tatsien-lu they passed through the semi-autonomous feudal districts of Woki, Wassu [Wa-ssu ch'ien] and Mupin [Pao-hsing] near the Tibetan border; the tribal folk regarded them curiously but left them to pass in peace. Perhaps because of the lingering effects of malaria, Wilson felt strained during the trek and suffered from neuralgia. By the time he returned to Kia-ting, he had a nasty summer cold. A short rest, however, sufficed to restore his energy. He may have been amused to read Sargent's dour account of Meyer's arrival in the United States and the end of the Wu t'ai episode:

Meyer has arrived in San Francisco where he was interviewed by the reporters and where quite a long story of his hardships, etc., was published . . . To show how badly he grasped the situation I will tell you that among the conifers from Wu t'ai, of which he sent herbarium specimens gathered in the winter with some grafts but no seeds, were certainly three new species of Picea, perhaps four, a new Larix, and a very remarkable Pine which may be the same as the one cultivated near Pekin, and these were in addition to two or three new species of conifers which had previously been collected on this mountain. The field, you see, was a very rich one, although he thought it not worth his attention. Unfortunately every one of the grafts he has sent us failed, so the results from that mountain are nothing.[23]

E. H. Wilson

At the end of his letter, Sargent mentioned he was sailing for England in August to consult with Veitch about getting up another Chinese expedition.

"Leaving the city of Kia-ting on the 4th of September 1908, we followed the main road to Yachou Fu and stayed for the night at Kia Kiang, a small city." So begins Wilson's account of his next adventure, one which took him to Wa-wu shan—the third mountain of the triangle, Wa shan and O-mei shan being the others—and across the Laolin, or wilderness. Wa-wu shan was not an easily attained objective. The party made camp near the base in an old wooden temple. "A priest and one attendant were in charge; the rooms, though dingy and damp, were alive with fleas . . . I had my bed arranged in a large hall where three huge images of Buddha looked down benignly upon me." [24] He had to grope his way up treacherous pathways to the summit, mostly in heavy rains, only to find the flora disappointing. He did, however, note about ten species of *Rhododendron*. The Laolin was the interior part of the triangle formed by the three sacred mountains. It is likely that no white man crossed this savage country from north to south before Wilson. The region was only sparsely populated and the weather miserable. Because of a heavy mist that obscured his vision, Wilson saw no more of the flora than what chanced to grow in his footsteps. It was, all considered, a wretched experience, but an accomplishment as a novelty.

For the remainder of the autumn, Wilson and his men busily collected seeds. The conifers which he had been instructed to gather with special attention fruited poorly that year, but otherwise the harvest was good. Chinese politics provided him with diversions of another sort. In Kia-ting in late November, he heard the latest bulletins:

The startling news reached here the other day of the sudden demise of the Emperor [Kuang-hsü] & Empress Dowager [Tz'u-hsi], how or by what means we here do not know though all sorts of ugly rumors abound. [Palace

The Treasure Hunt

secrets were well guarded, and the true story of their deaths was never revealed. Historians tend to agree that the Empress Dowager died a natural death, but some think she engineered the end of the Emperor before she breathed her last breath.] Strict mourning has been proclaimed throughout the length & breadth of the land & is being rigourously enforced. Shaving the head for the next forty days is forbidden; blue buttons are to be worn on all hats . . .

The late Empress Dowager can scarcely be called a good woman or a noble character from any standpoint of civilized culture or morality, but has ruled with a strong & unimpulsive will. Her death means that certain all-powerful ministers & Viceroys will control the destinies of China for some years to come. Jealousies carefully hidden whilst the late Empress ruled will now hark out & it is hard to prophesy what may happen. Secret societies of an anti-dynastic nature abound everywhere & in certain parts are very strong. Now is their opportunity.

No one could say what might happen next. Wilson's guesses did not stray far from the truth, in a general way. He was frankly relieved to be leaving China, for he wrote, "I think China will be a very good country to be out of until the new Emperor is firmly established on the throne. I am very glad the death of the Empress-Dowager did not take place earlier in the history of our expedition." [25] He spent three more months in China, making the river journey from Kiating back to I-ch'ang, sorting and packing material for mailing, and then proceeded on down the Yangtze to Shanghai. He sailed in April 1909 to rejoin his wife and daughter in England.

Except for the want of conifer seeds, Sargent felt that Wilson's accomplishments more than justified expenses; in fact, they exceeded his expectations. In numerical terms alone, the results were impressive: 2,262 packages of

E. H. Wilson

seeds, 1,473 kinds of living plants and cuttings, 30,000 herbarium specimens of around 2,500 species, and 720 photographic plates.[26] Furthermore, Wilson's introductions generally proved to be of first-rate horticultural quality. Jackson Dawson worked hard, and the Arnold Arboretum madly grew little Chinese plants.

There was something characteristic about Sargent's attitude toward his various enterprises, whether he did them himself or ordered someone else to execute them: he was thorough, sometimes headstrong and, once he determined the course of his project, oblivious to external influences. One suspects after reading the correspondence that Wilson's lengthy discussion of Chinese political intrigue contained a veiled hint that this was not a propitious moment to dispatch a new expedition. Any American newspaper would have supplied Sargent with the sequence of events as accurately as one could know them, but Wilson's on-the-spot, experienced advice was to let China rest for a while. Yet Sargent, having made his bed, was determined that someone should lie in it.

During the summer of 1908, Sargent went to England to discuss with Harry Veitch the prospects for a new expedition. His idea was that the Veitch firm and the Arboretum could raise subscriptions to co-sponsor a collector in the northern Chinese provinces. Veitch quickly fell in with the plan, and because England seemed a better source of collectors than the United States, Sargent left it to him to find a man. Ideally they hoped to secure the services of George Forrest, a Scotsman who had already made a superlative collection of Yunnan plants for some patrons of the Royal Botanic Garden at Edinburgh. Either out of loyalty to Sir Isaac Bayley Balfour, the Regius Keeper of Edinburgh, or because he preferred Yunnan to the northern reaches, Forrest turned down the offer, making several excuses—mainly that he knew nothing of the northern dialect. That he knew any Chinese at all put him far ahead of Wilson. Sargent blithely asserted that "if he knows one dialect he will soon be able to pick up another," and suggested proposing a higher salary, but Forrest could not be bought.[27]

The refusal irritated Sargent. As an alternative he nominated William Purdom, a young man who had worked at Veitch's Coombe Wood nursery and was now on the horticultural staff at Kew; Sargent had once offered him a position at the Arboretum. Veitch had a talk with Purdom, who was flabbergasted at the idea that he travel to China. Apparently a cautious man, he took nearly a month to reach a decision which, after all, might be crucial in his life. Early in January he decided in favor of China and prepared to leave England by the end of the month.

Purdom received a high-speed version of the pre-China indoctrination program Wilson had once endured. Henry came down to London from Cambridge for a week; while he did not know the country Purdom was supposed to explore, he had good first-hand experience with China and could make educated guesses as to what Purdom should watch for. Purdom studied Wilson's specimens at Kew and looked over the Chinese plants at Coombe Wood. He stuffed his head with as much information as he could absorb in three weeks and sailed for Boston at the beginning of February. Sargent and Dawson primed him for a few days at the Arboretum and packed him off with a set of instructions to board the *Empress of Japan* which would take him to Shanghai. Sargent thought highly of him, and he appeared fit for the job. Once in China, Purdom made contact with Wilson, who was en route to England—suffering unexpected pangs of regret about leaving China—and they spent a week together, the veteran giving the novice what hints he could.

Inasmuch as the general area of his first year's collecting would be in the northeastern provinces, Purdom used Peiping as a base. The Chinese still observed a state of official bereavement for their departed rulers, and Peiping, especially, was in tumult over preparations for the funeral. Purdom, therefore, was the victim of numerous delays and did not get out in the field before early May. His first journey

E. H. Wilson

was northeast to Jehol [Ch'eng te] and up into the Wei-ch'ang mountain district near the Mongolian border. He fared well enough with collecting, but he was in physical misery, sporting two huge boils on his neck and cursing the water supply for his affliction; belatedly he boiled every drop he drank. Fortunately the abscesses did not amount to anything serious, and Purdom kept up his work. In September, according to orders, he went to Wu t'ai shan. No doubt he knew of Meyer's experience there and had no desire to repeat his predecessor's mistake. Yet contrary to Sargent's contention that Wu t'ai shan was a rich collecting ground, Purdom discovered Meyer's comments on the flora to be true; except in the immediate vicinity of the temples there was scarcely a blade of grass on the whole mountain. Purdom tried to break the bad news to Sargent gently, softening the blow by reporting lovely virgin forests in the neighboring mountains.

In 1910, Purdom collected mostly in Shensi province, and, in 1911, he was in the farthest northwest province of Kansu near the Tibetan border. The high altitudes in Kansu enchanted him. "The Italian proverb says, 'See Naples and die,' he wrote, "but a traveller arriving at this spot wishes not to die but to live there forever." [28] During the three years he spent in China for this expedition, Purdom labored hard and earnestly to fill the demands coming from Sargent and Veitch, but in the end he disappointed them. Several circumstances operated against him to contribute to his difficulties. China was in political shambles and openly hostile to Europeans. Once Purdom nearly lost his life in an attack by brigands; fortunately, he only lost part of his collections and two horses. With all the confusion, some of the packages which he mailed from remote places went astray. The areas he worked were not as rich in novelties as Wilson's territories to the south. In Kansu, for example, he collected several species which duplicated Wilson's finds in Szechwan; in this instance, he hoped the northern forms would prove hardier. Purdom hated carrying cum-

The Treasure Hunt

bersome photographic gear around; like Wilson he had brought the old-fashioned glass plate camera and wished, as an afterthought, that he had a camera with film because, less skillful than Wilson, he kept breaking plates. One problem, viewed from Sargent's and Veitch's end of the operation, was that Purdom's shipments of seeds and living material often arrived in a useless condition because he waited too long to send them or packed them carelessly. Political unrest might excuse some delays but could not account for all the failures. At the outset of his expedition, Purdom had not been sufficiently impressed with the fact that only half the work of the collector of ornamental plants was done in the field; the other half was the not-so-glamorous, tiresome task of pressing and drying specimens, packing living material, making lists, and sending seeds. Wilson too had his failures; thirty-two cases of lily bulbs which he sent to Farquhar in Boston perished, and nothing could be salvaged from the rot. Wilson's failures, however, were exceptions; Purdom's were common during his first eighteen months in China. Repeated urgings from Sargent to improve the quality of his herbarium specimens, to take more care in shipping live material, and to dispatch seeds as quickly as possible got results, and later shipments excelled the early ones.

Neither Veitch nor Sargent could refrain from comparing Purdom to Wilson, and since Wilson happened to be one of the best collectors of his time—and among the best for all time—Purdom was doomed by the contrast. His outstanding accomplishment was his discovery of the wild Moutan Peony, never before collected in the field by a westerner. When he left China in the spring of 1912, his sponsors felt that he had fairly earned his pay but that the expedition as a whole was very disappointing because so few new species had been introduced. Veitch, whose interests were necessarily commercial, complained more vigorously than Sargent. Purdom himself was none too pleased, pleading that the northern flora was too similar

E. H. Wilson

to Wilson's. Sargent, who could afford to take his disappointment more graciously than Veitch, was nevertheless unwilling to accept Purdom's excuse at face value:

> Of course Purdom has not been successful. It was unfortunate that he came into direct comparison with Wilson who is evidently a much more competent collector, and of course Wilson was in a country richer in species. I do not think, however, that it is fair to say that the flora of Purdom's region was similar to that of Wilson's collecting ground.[29]

Sargent's doubts were reasonable and probably based on Bretschneider's listing of the collections made by the Russian explorer, Potanin, from Shensi and Kansu in the 1880's and 1890's, including many species which Wilson never saw.[30] But it was too late to argue the case with Purdom and of little value to indulge in sad speculations of what might have been. Sargent preferred to take pleasure in the Moutan Peony and to write off the Purdom expedition as otherwise unremarkable.[31]

During the three years that Purdom explored northern China, Wilson made his fourth expedition in Hupeh and Szechwan. The trip culminated in disaster for him, perhaps bearing out his old superstition that the pitcher would go to the well once too often. Wilson had left China and returned to England in May 1909. Sargent suggested that after a vacation period and a few months in his native country, Wilson should come to the Arboretum to work over his herbarium. The Director could not, however, make any long-range commitments. "When this work on the herbarium is done," he wrote, "possibly some arrangement for other work connected with the Arboretum can be found, or perhaps you will care to undertake another journey." [32] In truth, it was easier for Sargent to raise subscriptions and keep Wilson in the field than it was for him to juggle the Arboretum budget

The Treasure Hunt

to provide a permanent salary for him. For the fourth expedition Sargent got almost half the funds from British investors —including money raised by Balfour at the Edinburgh gardens—in return for a share of the harvest.

As might be expected, Wilson was disappointed to find his professional problems no closer to solution than they were before his last trip. When he asked Sargent for a higher salary to cover his herbarium work, Sargent replied that any increase would only generate ill feelings among Arboretum staff members, who worked for less. Dissatisfied though he was, Wilson had no better alternatives, so in September he packed up his wife and daughter and sailed for the United States to settle down in the herbarium for a while.

Since the arrangements for the fourth expedition were made on the spot in Jamaica Plain, there is no illuminating correspondence to reveal Wilson's attitude. Sargent's earlier letters expose his eagerness to send Wilson out again as well as the supposition that the collector would not agree to a new venture for another year or two. Mrs. Wilson probably opposed another long separation from her husband. China was dangerous, and she feared for Wilson's safety. Yet given the opportunity, Wilson could not bring himself to turn it down.

Just a year earlier, Wilson was almost glad to be leaving China, fearful of political chaos. By now his predictions were coming true, and restlessness dominated the country. Traveling mostly in the wilderness as he did, he would have to worry less about large-scale riots and battles than about general lawlessness of the kind that nearly cost Purdom his life. Even knowing this, Wilson returned. In February 1910, he set off, via Europe, Russia, and the trans-Siberian railroad to Peiping.

This time he had instructions to find seeds of conifers in general and of species of the Abietineae (Fir trees) in particular to compensate for the poor showing during his last attempt. He also planned to try again to send lily bulbs to Farquhar to replace the shipments that had spoiled. Since his trust in Wilson was complete, Sargent made his orders

E. H. Wilson

purposefully brief and vague, leaving the collector to make his own decisions. Having journeyed by the long overland route, leaving his wife and daughter in England and presumably hoping to collect northern conifers along the way (which he did not), it took Wilson until May to reach China and until June 1 to reach I-ch'ang. His men were out in the country and had to be summoned. As soon as he settled necessary business, Wilson made off for a long excursion to Ch'eng-tu through the rugged hills of Hupeh and westward into Szechwan. The journey took the party fifty-five days, because of rough terrain and hot weather. Wilson's achievements were not proportional to the time he expended. Pickings were very poor indeed. In Hupeh, rich in species though it was, Wilson saw little that was new to him; in Szechwan he found the flora generally unexciting and much of the land under cultivation.[33]

From Ch'eng-tu he headed in the direction of his beloved Sung-p'an near the Tibetan border. This time, to Sargent's delight, he reported good collections of seed from *Abies recurvata* and other conifers from the Sung-p'an region. Satisfied with these results, he turned back to Ch'eng-tu. On September 3, in the Min River valley, he had almost completed the round trip when he sighted the Regal Lily. He dug thousands of bulbs of the lovely species, its large white flowers flecked reddish-purple outside, golden throated within. The bulbs, as well as those of *Lilium sargentiae* and *L. davidii,* survived all the way to Boston.*

Customarily when he was out in the wilds on one of his long journeys, Wilson did not write letters, so it was not until

---

* Without seeing it in flower, Wilson had collected the Regal Lily under the name *L. myriaphyllum* for Veitch in 1903, but it had not reached the United States. In 1908 he had returned to the locality in June and found the species in flower. The bulbs he dug then were packed in the ill-fated shipment of that expedition. Since it was one of his favorite and most famous introductions, it seems worth noting that in 1913 he had a change of heart and, comparing his lily with a fragment of Franchet's original *L. myriaphyllum,* he described his collection as a new species under the name of "*L. regale* Wilson."

The Treasure Hunt

he returned to Ch'eng-tu, more or less a center of civilization, that he informed Sargent of the latest developments.

> I returned to Chengtu on the 6th [September] from a round trip to Sung P'an. The trip was highly successful up to within a few days of the finish, when it ended in catastrophe. Three days' journey from Chengtu, whilst descending the lower reaches of the Min valley by the main highway we were overtaken by a landslide, and I escaped only with a badly broken leg. Both bones are broken about a foot above the ankle, and there is a nasty wound on the outside of the calf. We improvised some crude splints, and I was carried to Chengtu, spending two nights at Chinese inns on the way. Eight miles before reaching Chengtu I overtook some missionaries who very kindly escorted me to the house of Dr. Davidson of the Friends' Mission in Chengtu. Dr. Davidson and his wife, assisted by other friends, immediately took me in hand and rendered every possible assistance . . . As over sixty hours had elapsed since the accident, the leg was much swollen, and the operation was therefore a long one, requiring more than an hour under chloroform. If only the leg makes normal progress towards recovery, there is no fear but that the expedition will come through all right.[34]

Wilson's leg got worse instead of better. At the end of October he wrote the depressing news to Sargent:

> The fracture of the leg was compound, and it became septic, which necessitated rather drastic surgical treatment. For some little time it was a question whether the leg could be saved or not, and the doctors warn me that even yet I am not actually out of the wood.[35]

Sargent, upset by the accident, told Wilson to stop worrying about plants and not to force himself into any premature activity. But there was no danger of that. The damaged leg

E. H. Wilson

dominated Wilson's life for months, stubbornly refusing to heal. In December he wrote again to Sargent:

> Since writing last I have been through a rough & critical time & have had no heart to write anyone. The doctors have managed to save my leg but it is crooked & an inch short. They advise me on reaching civilization to have the limb re-broken and re-set. I have suffered so much that I do not know whether I shall have the necessary courage to undergo another operation . . . Two or three days after writing you last, the leg went all to pieces again & signs of gangrene appeared; another surgical operation was decided upon & in the event of this latter failing it was thought that nothing remained but to amputate at the knee. I had had enough of chloroform & the last operation was done under a heavy dose of morphia & a strong local anaesthetic. I did not feel the cutting very much but the dressing afterwards was nearly the "limit." [36]

Wilson at this time was much weakened, wearied, and frustrated, sapped of confidence and courage. As his health improved, however, his spirits revived. For the moment, he knew only that he could not continue with the expedition, so he organized his departure for the spring of 1911. Efficient to the end, he shipped off all his collections of the previous spring.

Wilson's Chinese adventures reached an unhappy conclusion, but his work was something of which he could be proud. Even on his last expedition he had nearly fulfilled his mission; during that limited time he sent back 1,285 packets of seeds to Sargent. In an equal period Purdom sent only 304.[37]

As he left I-ch'ang for the last time, Wilson reflected with finality: "I have enjoyed my work in China & am proud in the knowledge that I have been privileged to achieve success in worthy employ & am certainly not going to pull a long face because the Fates have given me a parting kick." [38]

The Treasure Hunt

10

Wilson in Japan, Rock in Tibet

In view of the hardships Wilson had sustained on behalf of the Arnold Arboretum, Sargent felt conscience-bound to provide for him professionally when he limped back from China. It was not yet feasible to appoint him to the Arboretum staff in a permanent capacity, so after allowing him a three-month stay in England where he rejoined his family and took a rest, Sargent encouraged him to return and work over his herbarium with a view to publishing an account of his collections. Wilson as a collector was one thing; as a taxonomist he turned out to be quite another. For him, the intellectual adventure of painstaking research with dried specimens and books could neither replace nor equal the thrill of finding living plants in the open field. Moreover, it had been a long time since he had done any serious work in classification. The project evolved into a six-year task, resulting in the volumes called *Plantae Wilsonianae,* a taxonomic treatment of the ligneous species Wilson collected in China. Sargent acted as editor, and other people, Alfred Rehder in particular, collaborated in the effort. Even a casual glance through *Plantae Wilsonianae* reveals that Rehder did a great share of the work, and that Wilson's contribution was correspondingly small. Rehder wrote forty-four articles to Wilson's twelve, and they did forty-seven more together. Evidently Wilson was quite willing to let Rehder assume the burden of preparing the nomenclature, and the two men established a friendly dialogue in the early years of their partnership.

The Wilson family tried to adapt to the United States while living in a modest apartment in Jamaica Plain near the Arboretum. Wilson could not make up his mind about the United States; Ellen Wilson, for her part, liked neither America nor Americans. Wilson soon became accustomed to his new environment and began to enjoy the benefits of his reputation. Before Wilson arrived in Boston, accounts of his adventures made good material for journalists, especially the story of his accident. He had not been at the Arboretum long before he was in popular demand as a speaker for horticultural societies and garden clubs. He excelled at this chore. People began to call him "Chinese" Wilson as the English had done with General Gordon, and the name stuck to the end of his life. Newspaper photographers contrived to take pictures of him so that he even looked somewhat Chinese. Some of his friends said he disliked the epithet and found it embarrassing; others said he secretly—even vainly—enjoyed it. The truth of the matter is that Wilson in his later years was a difficult man to know well.

Quite naturally, he capitalized upon his Chinese experiences. More interesting to the layman than the technical *Plantae Wilsonianae*, and by far more readable, was his account *A Naturalist in Western China*, which appeared in 1913; he compiled it while working on his herbarium. Assembled from notes and diaries he made in China and from letters originally published in *Gardeners' Chronicle*, the two volumes are a fascinating collection of personal observations although they frustrate anyone who tries to trace the routes of his expeditions with any precision. Wilson acknowledged that similar books had been published before, but he felt that a different outlook was a refreshing as well as useful addition to the little available information on China. On the whole, *A Naturalist in Western China* is an unpretentious and often charming book, more so because its author did not feel compelled to be objective but truthfully set down his prejudices.

The Treasure Hunt

Before his first journey to China, Wilson had thought to concentrate on botany rather than horticulture, but he had never had enough time to practice the relevant scientific disciplines. His Chinese experience led him back to ornamental plants. With Rehder handling so much of the taxo-

Ernest Wilson amidst his lilies after receiving an honorary doctorate from Trinity College in Hartford, Connecticut, 1930

nomic work and doing it much better than Wilson could, he was freed to a great extent to put together his Chinese tales and supervise the growing of his introductions. Sargent, for whom the interest of the Arboretum came first, quickly observed Wilson's value in creating publicity for the institution and encouraged him to write popular articles and give lectures. Whatever Wilson did, however, it was certain that he excelled as a collector and, bad leg or not, Sargent determined to use that ability. There was no ques-

Wilson in Japan, Rock in Tibet

tion of sending Wilson back to China; he had a fatalistic attitude and considered himself in no condition to undertake another expedition of that type; had Wilson suggested it himself, however, Sargent would have been the first to cheer him on. On the other hand, there was no good reason why Wilson could not do splendid things in tamer fields. In 1914, Sargent decided to send him to Japan. This time Mrs. Wilson had no grounds for feeling neglected; Wilson arranged for her and Muriel to accompany him. The Wilsons arrived in Japan on February 3, 1914.

Wilson had visited Japanese ports before. It was a considerably more civilized field than he was accustomed to, presenting rather different problems than he had met in China. Sargent had been able to give some practical advice, but it was based on experience already more than twenty years old. Wilson had become very good at dealing with bad roads, primitive lodgings, and local quirks. In Japan, communications and shelter were more apt to be comfortable than not, and, like the "sophisticated" western nations it strove to emulate, it was a very expensive place to get around. Labor there was also costly by contrast with China. Within a few months Wilson realized that he and Sargent had badly underestimated the expenses of the expedition, and he applied for and received a larger account. Although finances were not a serious problem, there were other things that irritated Wilson. Japanese botanists, obligingly courteous, at first pleased but later annoyed him when he began to suspect that they were spying on him, fearful that he would discover something that had eluded them.[1] For a variety of reasons, Wilson never enjoyed Japan the way he had China with all of its hardships.

Wilson viewed Japan as a small and insufficient replica of China. "Japan," he noted, "has drawn freely on the civilization of her ancient neighbour—China. Her written language, art and culture are borrowed and modelled on those of China. The love for flowers is, today, more universal in Japan than in China, yet in all probability it was in emula-

The Treasure Hunt

tion of the Chinese that flowers began to enter so largely into the life of the Japanese people."[2] Despite his notion of the derivative nature of Japanese culture and his reservations about the people, he enjoyed the plant hunting even though it differed so much from collecting in China. There was no very remote country, no groping one's way along treacherous roads or shooting rapids on a river. Instead there were visits to nurseries and garden sites, a closer observation of plants in cultivation, and uneventful collecting in tame forests, sometimes in the company of his daughter. Accordingly, the results of Wilson's Japanese expedition were of a different character.

Most of the plants which Wilson sent back from Japan were already in cultivation there though new to this country; this was seldom true of the species he collected in China or, later, in Korea and Formosa. Since the Japanese, crowded on their small islands, cultivated as much of the land as they could, only patches of wilderness remained. Few ornamental species escaped the attention of Japan's own horticulturists. Moreover, since its opening in the 1850's, Japan had become a favorite hunting ground for botanists and horticulturists. The Veitches, for example, sent several collectors there. Sargent and other Americans had already established Japanese plants in American gardens, and Japanese botanists and nurserymen sent plants regularly to the States. Sargent kept up a lively exchange program with his friend, Dr. Miyabe; Fairchild at the Department of Agriculture had an agreement with H. Suzuki, a leading Japanese nurseryman. Instead of introducing dozens of new species from the field, Wilson brought back horticultural forms. It has been estimated that he made herbarium specimens of between 92 and 95 per cent of the species of Japanese trees and shrubs, including 67 named forms of cherries, of which he also sent cuttings for propagation, and he photographed every known Japanese conifer in its native habitat. Near the end of the expedition, Wilson sent Sargent an appraisal of it:

Wilson in Japan, Rock in Tibet

[It] has been totally different in character to those under-taken in China & it has caused me much anxiety. The country is big & to obtain results commensurate with out-lay has at times seemed hopeless. However, confidence has never quite forsaken me ... I feel now that on the scientific side success will crown our efforts & that the practical side will, in the shape of seeds of rare plants, re-ceive a greater fillip than I had imagined possible. At the outset with your [Sargent's] knowledge of the country & its flora, you doubtless foresaw all these things but much time & anxious thought have been necessary to bring them clearly within my comprehension.[3]

Wilson spent nearly a full year in Japan. In February and March 1914, he was in the southern regions; from April to June he collected in central areas. He probably did not notice, or paid little attention to, news of the assassination on June 28 in Bosnia of the Archduke Francis Ferdinand. Few people in Europe dreamed of the consequences of that act, and there was little reason why an Englishman search-ing for Japanese plants should endow it with any extraordi-nary significance. Wilson headed north in July for Hondo and Saghalin. Meanwhile, Sargent back in Boston was much better informed about the international situation; he always kept abreast of world politics. Yet he did not sense any dan-ger to European peace as he crossed the Atlantic in mid-July in search of plants and, perhaps, a man to collect in Korea.

When war broke out, Sargent was in England. He canceled plans for a week in France and suffered only minor incon-veniences in obtaining return passage. He used an extra week in England to visit Oxford, Cambridge, and London nurseries. The solidarity he witnessed in England moved him.

Every one is very much in earnest, very much united, and apparently efficient in war work and preparations. Horticultural Hall in London is turned over for a hospital

The Treasure Hunt

and there will be nothing doing horticulturally for a long time to come ... Every man under forty will soon be under arms, and of course we have lost all touch with France, Germany and Austria.[4]

He interpreted the large-scale disorders in terms of his own microcosm of trees and shrubs. Although the United States had not committed itself to a position, Sargent immediately realized that international chaos would have nothing but bad effects on the Arboretum. He worried that the institution would suffer financially; wealthy Bostonians would be inclined to hold on to their money if the economic situation became serious. There was also the likelihood that collecting activities would be curtailed. Sargent knew, for example, that the Austrian botanist, Camillo Schneider, was collecting in Western Szechwan and Yunnan and, because Austria was a belligerent, was in danger of being interned by British authorities in China. In an effort to prevent this, Sargent made a trip to Washington and urged Fairchild to employ Schneider under Department of Agriculture auspices and keep him in China, immune from British authority, for the duration of the war. Fairchild regretfully replied that he could not help. Schneider, meanwhile, in the company of Handel Mazzetti, encountered George Forrest, and all three were working the Li-chiang range when news of the war reached them in September. Forrest and Handel-Mazzetti crossed the Himalayas to India, but Schneider headed for Shanghai where, as Sargent feared, he was promptly arrested. The sequel to the story is that Schneider, unable to reach his homeland, eventually arrived in the United States just as this country was about to declare war on Austria; he was nearly interned again, but Sargent came to his rescue by putting him to work identifying Chinese collections in the herbarium at the Arboretum until after the war.[5]

Sargent, worried about Wilson, wrote him to complete his work in Japan but to abandon the original plan of extending his efforts to the Ryukyu Islands and Formosa.[6] Japan seemed a safe enough place, isolated from the main arena.

Wilson in Japan, Rock in Tibet

Wilson had no inkling of danger. He was so busy with his collecting that Europe had already been at war for two weeks before he heard anything about it. He was shocked by the news, but as long as Japan stayed quiet and his movements were in no way restricted, he was eager to proceed with his work. He agreed with Sargent's advice to limit his field to Japan and to finish his task within a few months so he could return to the United States before the war got much worse. Sargent wanted him to sail on the first of December, but Wilson did not manage to get away until January. Nevertheless, he returned to the Arboretum in February 1915, without incident or injury.

Wilson's injured leg gave him no trouble on the expedition; on the contrary, he had been pleasantly surprised to find it was hardly a handicap at all. In Boston, however, he discovered cause to build up resentment about that accident. It was one thing to hear war rumors in Japan, but another to read the American newspapers. The Central Powers were gaining in Europe, the fighting had spread to the high seas, and the *Lusitania* had been sunk by a German submarine. Wilson wanted to join his countrymen-at-arms. But though he had hiked over miles of Japan, the condition of his leg automatically disqualified him from active military service. Wilson felt useless and bitter. He seldom spoke about the war, but every now and then something caustic slipped out. Edward Farrington, his biographer and friend, tells of an incident "during the war. As they [Wilson and a companion] entered the hall, a large group of Regal Lilies was shown, but badly marred in transit and not well arranged. 'Look there,' exclaimed Dr. Wilson to his friend, 'was it for that that I broke this leg and prevented my fighting for my country?' He slapped the offending member as he spoke." [7] The war was bound to produce tensions. Wilson's patriotism ran deep and frustration blurred his judgment. Before the war Rehder and Wilson had been close friends. Now, although the professional dialogue continued amiably, Wilson —under pressure from his wife—discontinued their social relations. No longer did the Wilsons invite the Rehders to

The Treasure Hunt

dinner or accept invitations from them. Rehder, a scholarly, gentle person, was apolitical, and it was some time before either he or Mrs. Rehder understood why the Wilsons mistrusted them. For some time after the war, Wilson was still sensitive on that point.

Sargent, for his part, surveyed the situation coolly. His sympathies lay firmly with the Allies and he was no more callous or indifferent to the horror across the Atlantic than he had been, let us say, to the death of his father. Now, as then, his life and work went on, and he wasted no emotions on self-indulgent sentimentality. He summed up his attitude right after the *Lusitania* disaster when he wrote to a correspondent in Louisiana, "Pretty bad times these but there is no use thinking about them when there are trees to think of." [8] As the war continued, Sargent became conscious of Wilson's irritability and restlessness, and these influenced his decision to send Wilson on a new collecting expedition even though the fighting was still in progress. Despite rumors of friendship between Germany and Japan, it seemed unlikely that eastern Asia would become involved dangerously in the holocaust, and the journey might help Wilson get his mind off the war. In January 1917, Wilson set off to the Far East again, with orders to collect in Japan, Formosa, and Korea.

Without a doubt his best-known introductions from this expedition were the spectacular Kurume Azaleas from Japan. He had seen some on the last trip and made an effort to investigate them further.

> What I saw in 1914 whetted my appetite and I was hungry to see and learn more about these delightful plants. Opportunity came in 1918, and to my great good fortune my friend, Suzuki [Fairchild's nurseryman], was able to accompany me to the headquarters of the family, the city of Kurume. This city is on the Island of Kyushy, situated some 800 miles south by west of Tokyo and is quite an important place. But the fame of its Azaleas will make it universally known. There we arrived on a fine May morn-

Wilson in Japan, Rock in Tibet

ing to find the Azaleas in the pink of perfection. I went prepared to see a display of blossoms, but the entrancing beauty of myriad delicately colored flowers clothing a multitude of shapely grown plants surpassed my most sanguine expectations. The gardens of two leading specialists were veritable fairy-lands and I gasped with astonishment when I realized that garden-lovers of America and Europe knew virtually nothing of this wealth of beauty.[9]

Wilson brought back fifty forms to the United States. As they were pot Azaleas and not for planting out-of-doors, he deposited them in Sargent's greenhouse at Holm Lea and at the John S. Ames greenhouses—a compensation to Ames for his patronage. Wilson's admiration for the Kurume Azaleas never waned; it became, in fact, something akin to a love affair which he did not blush to publicize:

Her first lover in this part of the world, her sponsor and guardian, I immediately found myself a mere atom in her universe. A crown of gold was by unanimous consent placed on her head and with loud acclamation she was proclaimed mistress royal of her clan. Pleasing speeches were made and nice things said of me, for the part I had played in prevailing upon her to leave her island home of the Rising Sun to grace these western shores. Her conquest was too spontaneous and complete for jealousy to wing dart. Hard-headed nurserymen fell in love with her at first sight even as I had done, and she was surrounded by chaperons intent on providing for her well-being and proper education into western modes of life.[10]

(Princess Kurume had also dealt a blow to Wilson's prose. The account illustrates his unfortunate tendency in later years to allow his writing to be overrun by adjectives and questionable metaphors, often producing some pretty sticky reading material far inferior to his Chinese journals.)

The pilgrimage to the Kurume Azaleas came at the latter

The Treasure Hunt

part of an expedition which was, as one expected from Wilson, a success both botanically and horticulturally. He began early in 1917 by exploring the Ryukyu islands south of Japan "where Pine & Palm meet," spending seventeen days on Okinawa and scanning several islets.[11] In May, he went to Korea and the islands of Dagalet and Quelpaert; he found so much of interest on the Korean peninsula that he returned in the autumn to collect seeds, and again in June 1918. From Korea he introduced a new Rhododendron (*R. weyrichii*) and *Stewartia koreana* along with several other fine plants.

Sargent kept him posted on news at home. Everyone was depressed about the war, of course, though spirits revived a bit in June after American forces finally joined the battle. In the meantime, work proceeded. In December 1917, Liberty Hyde Bailey visited the herbarium to consult Wilson's specimens and compare them with those he had collected in Hupeh and Honan earlier that year. After viewing Bailey's efforts—which included two new species each of *Salix* and *Crataegus*—Sargent suggested that Wilson might pass the summer in Honan to considerable advantage, for Bailey had only passed through hurriedly, and the province was otherwise little known botanically. If Wilson were to cut short his trip to Formosa, he would have time to go into China. Within six weeks, however, Sargent changed his mind and warned Wilson off the trip. Word had reached the United States of political disturbances in Russia, and although it was impossible to make any sense out of the reports, Sargent thought it inadvisable to travel in China anywhere near the Russian border. Wilson, therefore, stayed in Formosa for the early spring, returned to Japan in late April, spent the summer in Korea, went back to Formosa in the fall and returned to Japan again for the winter of 1918–19.

In Formosa, collecting was somewhat as it had been in the old days in China. The island was wilder and less explored botanically than either Japan or Korea, and for local color there were reformed head-hunters who showed some reluctance about retiring from their favorite sport. Knowing that the tribesmen would be most familiar with the savage countryside, Wilson decided to hire them as porters though he did not achieve this without difficulty. "Like many other unsophisticated people," he mused, "the Formosan savage is not partial to manual labor, neither is money an overweening incentive to work. A bribe of Chinese wine is much more potent but even this is not always sufficient." [12] As he soon discovered, the gift of a rifle was often an effective incentive. Accompanied by an escort of wary Japanese officials, Wilson and the natives worked the wildest country he had seen since China. He traveled in the mountains and scaled the 13,000-foot Mount Morrison, Formosa's highest peak, in the midst of a typhoon. Later in 1918, he crossed treacherous cliffs at the northeast end of the island to collect seeds of *Taiwania cryptomerioides*. He relished the adventure of it all; he was older and, this time, slightly handicapped by his leg, but he could still manage rugged country. As usual, his collections surpassed expectations.

If Wilson secretly longed for China during this expedition, Sargent's bulletin in June 1918 may have given him second thoughts. "I hear from Fairchild," Sargent informed him, "that Frank Meyer disappeared one night from a boat between Hankow and Nanking and that nothing further has been heard of him. He may have committed suicide or some of the Chinamen may have thrown him overboard. This is certainly bad news for he was getting to be a useful collector." [13] No one ever determined the circumstances of Meyer's death. Wilson's failure to comment on the report makes one wonder whether he did not suspect that his initial criticisms of Meyer's behavior toward the Chinese natives had been correct and that Meyer had never heeded his warnings.

Wilson, by contrast, survived the head-hunters in good health and was as pleased as Sargent was with the results of his explorations. The only complication they faced was the Department of Agriculture's recent enforcement of a

The Treasure Hunt

1912 law regarding the importation of plant materials from the Orient, which ruled that all seeds and plants must pass through Washington for inspection before they could be released. The government had honorable intentions in its desire to arrest the proliferation of plant pests, but for a professional institution like the Arboretum the law had chiefly nuisance value. Sargent, who became apoplectic every time he thought about the federal regulations, morosely predicted that anything handled in Washington would arrive at Boston in shambles, and he looked for ways to circumvent the rules, gaining some concessions. Since Washington inspectors were not quite so inept as Sargent feared, and Wilson was finally allowed to send much of the material directly to Boston, the expedition proved successful. By the time the explorer set foot on American soil again, the war was over and the world had begun picking up the pieces.

Wilson's sixth trip to the Orient—his fourth under the direction of Sargent for Arnold Arboretum—was his last. In 1916, Harvard paid tribute to him by awarding him an honorary Master of Arts degree; in 1919, upon Sargent's recommendation, the Harvard Corporation appointed him Assistant Director of the Arboretum. Wilson made only one more important journey: in 1920 he began a tour of Australia, New Zealand, Tasmania, India, Kenya, Rhodesia, and South Africa. Because of the plant quarantine regulations, the trip was designed as a public relations effort and was neither planned nor executed with a view to introducing new plants, although Wilson collected a good number of herbarium specimens on the way. The expeditions to the Orient, however, provide his major contributions to horticulture and botany.

There is no way of determining precisely how many different plant forms previously unknown to western horticulture Wilson actually introduced into cultivation in England and the United States. Rehder estimated the number of species at more than a thousand.[14] This enormous number in itself

Wilson in Japan, Rock in Tibet

deserves admiration; considering the hardships Wilson endured to get many of the plants, the total merits reverence. As of 1930, when Rehder made his estimate, he believed that Wilson had "succeeded in collecting and introducing into cultivation a greater number of plants than any other collector." Furthermore, he amassed about 16,000 numbers of herbarium specimens, always with several duplicate sets. Wilson's contemporary, George Forrest, made seven expeditions to Yunnan, collecting vast amounts of plants, particularly Rhododendrons. It is conceivable that he introduced as many or more new forms into cultivation than Wilson, but here, again, it is impossible to count accurately. More recently, perhaps Frank Kingdon Ward has surpassed Wilson's record.

Numbers, obviously, count for less than beauty and usefulness. Not all of Wilson's introductions succeeded in cultivation either in England or the United States. Some like *Meconopsis punicea,* the Red Poppywort, grew at first but eventually died out, unable to thrive in their new environment. Others flourished in England but failed in America. Still others, though collected with the Arboretum in mind, were not hardy in the severe New England climate but proved adaptable to gardens farther south. Accordingly, some of Wilson's plants are no longer in cultivation anywhere, some are only occasionally found in gardens, but many are still in common cultivation. Roughly 300 of Wilson's introductions are currently available in the American nursery trade. During the trips he made for Veitch, Wilson collected both herbaceous and woody species; he made his largest collection of herbs on the second expedition. Under Sargent's direction, he concentrated almost exclusively on ligneous material, making exceptions such as the lilies for Farquhar, orchids for Ames, or anything which struck him as having unusual ornamental value. Within the Arboretum there are more than 200 living taxa representing Wilson introductions, and this is a good index of the woody forms hardy—if not necessarily on the open market—in New

The Treasure Hunt

England. Many of Wilson's plants (such as *Picea asperta,* *Berberis julianae, Kolkwitzia amabilis,* the Kurume Azaleas) are such common sights that people seldom realize that they are not native to this country.

By the 1920's, Wilson could rest on his laurels and the fame of his Kurume Azaleas. Except for his trip to Australia and Africa, he stayed close to his adopted home and devoted his time to research, writing, lecturing, and pampering the plants he had introduced in his youth. He was, without doubt, a model for plant hunters to emulate, but his own exploring days had ended.

Sargent, on the other had, did not intend to abandon China as long as he thought there was something left in the field. Much to his disgust, he could not carry on with his program as he would have liked. As a result of the 1912 federal legislation, there had already been problems with Wilson's shipments from the last two expeditions, but the loose wording and casual implementation made it possible for Sargent to dodge the rules most of the time. By 1919 the regulations were tougher for, in accordance with the 1912 law, the Secretary of Agriculture issued Quarantine Order No. 37 which, in the opinion of its opponents, "in effect acted as an embargo, preventing the importation of any plants or seeds except those permitted by narrow and seemingly arbitrary rulings." [15] The opposition to the new ruling, which Sargent immediately and vociferously joined, was spearheaded by J. Horace McFarland, editor of *The American Rose Annual,* and was supported by nurserymen and horticulturists, who sought special concessions for professional growers. For his part, Sargent professed unwillingness to work within the new system and, hoping to arouse sympathy for his position, he expressed himself strongly in his 1919–20 Report to the Harvard President:

The introduction of new plants from foreign countries which has been carried on successfully by the Arboretum since its earliest days has been stopped by the rulings of

Wilson in Japan, Rock in Tibet

the Federal Horticultural Board. This Board, established by the Secretary of Agriculture of the United States by authority of Congress, prohibits the importation, with few exceptions, of living plants and of the seeds of trees and shrubs unless on arrival in this country they are sent to Washington for inspection and disinfection.

The methods of disinfection adopted by the Federal Board are so crude and unnecessarily severe that a large proportion of the plants and seeds subjected to them are killed. The Arboretum has therefore given up the importation of plants and seeds.[16]

The following year he wrote that the authorities in Washington subjected plants to treatment "which practically insures their death, or if the plants survive the Washington inspection they must be placed under a quarantine which makes it impossible to use them for several years."[17] Sargent's evaluation of the situation seems severe, though he felt it was justified. He flatly refused to recognize the difficulties of the Federal Horticultural Board. How, for instance, was it to distinguish a professional grower from an amateur? And even if it could do that, how could it be certain that the professional acted responsibly to control pests and diseases? Even under carefully controlled circumstances, infections sometimes crept into the greenhouses. In 1921, Sargent grudgingly permitted officials of the Federal Horticultural Board to inspect the Arboretum for plant pests. Their conclusions cannot have pleased him:

The Arboretum under existing conditions [that is, with federal restrictions and inspection] is not apt to cause the introduction or distribution of injurious insects in the United States. On the other hand, the discovery, in the course of an incomplete inspection, of four potentially injurious species of insects not previously known to occur in this country suggests the possibility that the Arboretum may have made such introductions in the past.[18]

The Treasure Hunt

To Sargent, the federal regulations represented a classic case of a law designed to protect the majority interfering with the contributions of a capable minority. As part of that minority, he did what he could to get the rules changed. Not one to attend meetings or make speeches, he used his authority and money to muster support among his colleagues, and his social connections to influence congressmen. The opposition made itself sufficiently irritating to force itself upon the attention of the Washington authorities. In May 1922, the Secretary of Agriculture, Henry C. Wallace, met with representatives of the critics, including delegates from European countries, to defend the government's side of the problem and to listen to objections. The meeting cleared up some misunderstandings shared by the opponents of the legislation while the Secretary, without altering the regulations, conceded that certain changes might be made in the regulations and procedures to favor incoming plants.[19] This left little for Sargent and his allies to do except abide by the rules and hope that Washington inspectors would handle plant materials with care. As a demonstration of contempt, Sargent, by then in his eighties, would occasionally make the trip to Washington to oversee the handling of a particularly important shipment—a habit which did not endear him to the inspectors. Nevertheless, the quarantine regulations did not prove as damaging to introduction efforts as he had originally feared.

Contrary to what he had written in his report in 1920 about giving up the importation of plants and seeds, in that same period Sargent did receive a small seed shipment containing thirty-three species of Chinese plants collected in northern Honan and thus of interest to the Arboretum because of their hardiness.[20] The collector was a Belgian, Joseph Hers. By profession he was a railway engineer who lived in north central China for several years; by hobby he became a dendrologist and collector and, like many amateurs, he was quite skillful.[21] He sent Sargent sets of his herbarium material which helped shed some light on the poorly known flora of Honan. According to the records of the

Wilson in Japan, Rock in Tibet

USDA Office of Foreign Seed and Plant Introduction, however, Hers dispatched the single mailing of seeds and no living plants at all to the Arboretum. Despite the highly publicized ruthless practices of the Washington inspectors, the lot did nicely in Massachusetts. The Hers collection was the only shipment of any significance of either seed or herbarium material which the Arboretum received directly from China since Wilson's 1910 expedition.

With the exception of Hers' seeds, however, Sargent actually did discontinue importing plants for a few years after the war and Wilson's second Japanese trip. As a result introductions from Wilson's Australian-African venture are conspicuously absent. It seems likely that Sargent resented the fact that the Department of Agriculture had taken to plant hunting and introduction on a massive scale while he found his own program crippled by federal legislation. In earlier days the USDA had been keen on introducing economically valuable plants, but lately, under Fairchild's energetic direction, it included a greater proportion of ornamentals. Sargent's facetious quip, in 1911, that Washington botanists only concerned themselves with plants they could eat was no longer true in 1920.[22] Having set the example, Sargent could not relax and observe with equanimity while the organization that had interrupted his introduction proceeded with its own.

At odds with the quarantine laws, he concentrated on amassing specimens for the herbarium. But sooner or later he had to give way to the troublesome regulations which, it appeared, were bound to be permanent whether he liked them or not. He could not afford to abandon the introduction program; otherwise the Arboretum would shrink from its hard-won status of leadership to the lowly role of follower. Much of the Chinese flora still remained unknown, and Sargent, though aged and periodically afflicted with shingles, was as determined as ever to extract what he could from the Orient. In 1924, he hired Joseph Rock, an experienced botanist and explorer who spoke Chinese. Rock became the most important American-based collector of Chinese plants

The Treasure Hunt

since Wilson. The British had George Forrest, Reginald Farrer, and Frank Kingdon Ward working in China during the period of Arnold Arboretum inactivity; each of them made large-scale contributions to horticulture. Though ornamentals arrived in the United States from China all the time, they came in fluctuating quantities from various sources, and there was no single outstanding collector between Wilson and Rock.

Rock, like Wilson, was foreign born; but whereas Wilson spent his youth in the English countryside Rock grew up in the sophisticated environment of Vienna.[23] When Josef Franz Karl—later Americanized to Joseph Francis Charles—Rock was only ten years old, his father took him to Egypt, where he astonished everyone by learning to speak and write Arabic fluently. By the age of sixteen, he taught Arabic at the University in Vienna and studied Chinese secretly at home. Rock's family planned for him to enter the priesthood, but he had different ideas; he was too interested in worldly things. To escape the impending crisis at home, he packed his belongings as soon as he completed his university education, left home, traveled aimlessly in Europe for a short time, and emigrated to the United States in 1905, at the age of twenty-one. Rock's talent and ambition, though much in evidence, as yet had shown itself only in his study of languages.

In the United States, Rock moved west and studied English in Texas. On doctor's orders he went farther west, this time to Hawaii, where he hoped the climate would cure his tuberculosis. In the course of his travels, he developed a curiosity about plants and taught himself botany. In Hawaii, imperfect health kept him out of doors, and he did his first serious botanical work. In 1908, he joined the Division of Forestry for Hawaii as Botanical Collector, spent most of his time in the field, and built up a herbarium.[24] He became an expert on the Hawaiian flora and earned a reputation among American and European botanists. By 1911 he was in charge of the herbarium at the College of Hawaii; later he taught systematic botany and Chinese.[25]

Wilson in Japan, Rock in Tibet

Although he knew a great deal about the flora of Hawaii, Rock won his fame as an explorer of remote places. He made his first expedition in 1913, on behalf of the Bernice P. Bishop Museum, to investigate the vegetation of the tiny island of Palmyra, one of those specks of land in the Pacific, south-southwest of Hawaii, only one and a half miles square. After his return he was given charge of the campus botanic garden at the college and began to think about introducing plants to Hawaiian horticulture. In 1916 he traveled at his own expense to the Philippines, Java, and Singapore; two years later he went to Siam, Malaya, and back again to Java. Between journeys he lectured, wrote, and attended to his curatorial duties. Two books, *The Indigenous Trees of the Hawaiian Islands* (1913) and *The Ornamental Trees of Hawaii* (1917), signaled his interest in dendrology.

Since boyhood, when he had surreptitiously studied Chinese, Rock wanted to visit China. His chance finally came in 1920, when the USDA Office of Foreign Seed and Plant Introduction—Sargent's *bête noire* of the moment—sent him to Indo-China, Siam, Burma, and India to gather seeds of *Hydnocarpus kurzii,* the source of chaulmoogra oil, used in the treatment of leprosy. He succeeded quickly in his appointed task, but instead of returning to the United States he headed for the province of Yunnan, set up headquarters at Li-chiang, and proceeded to explore the territory along the Burma-China border. Hearing of his travels, the National Geographic Society underwrote his wanderings in 1923.

Rock was a master explorer. With his broad interests and aptitude for languages, he took a scholarly approach to the cultural, anthropological, and religious phenomena he found in the remote Chinese villages. He mapped entire regions, and collected birds and mammals along with his plants.[26] Plant collecting was only one among several objectives. Rock was much more Chinese than "Chinese" Wilson ever dreamed of being. He lived among the people, studied their dialects and customs, dressed in their clothes, and for years —in fact, up until the communist upheavals in 1949—he returned again and again to China, seizing every opportunity

The Treasure Hunt

that came his way. His wanderlust and curiosity were free from domestic restraints, for he never married. He was far from being an ordinary person and, predictably, many of his occidental acquaintances considered him eccentric.

In the course of his first journey to the East, Rock collected 80,000 herbarium specimens, seeds of scores of horticultural plants, and 1,600 bird skins. Sargent, keeping himself abreast of botanical activities in China, suspected another Wilson in the making. In Washington with his collections during the summer of 1924, Rock decided to make a trip to Boston to visit the Arboretum, perhaps for scientific purposes or possibly to swap stories with Wilson. As a result of a swift conference, Sargent pinned him down for another expedition to China. Or did Rock pin Sargent down? In either case, Rock's credentials were beyond question, and since he had proved competent in making ornithological collections, Sargent persuaded the Museum of Comparative Zoology at Harvard to take on a small share of the financial burden. Rock's eagerness suited Sargent well; by September Rock was on his way to China.

The agreement was that Rock would explore the Amne Machin [Che-shih shan] and Richthofen [Chi-lien shan-mo] mountain ranges in northwestern China and northern Tibet, respectively. "It is fair to suppose," Sargent explained, "that in the forests which cover these regions are trees and other plants unknown to science, and that all the plants of these extremely cold northern regions can be successfully cultivated in New England." [27] It was thought that the Amne Machin mountains might reach the heights of Mount Everest, but no westerners were on record as having explored them. They were said to be barren, yet huge logs floating down the Yellow River suggested forests of big trees somewhere in the vicinity. [28]

Rock intended to begin his westward trek in Peiping, but China, for so long ravaged by domestic and foreign wars, was again in the throes of civil distress and the capital was inaccessible. If anything, the political situation had deteriorated since Wilson's days. Rock proceeded, therefore,

Wilson in Japan, Rock in Tibet

via Shanghai and Hong Kong, to Haiphong, Hanoi and Yunnanfu [K'un-ming], where he picked up some of his former collectors. Yunnan was in a state of chaos. Brigands constantly molested Rock's party, the soldiers assigned to accompany him were lazy, and delays were the most regular features of his progress. Morosely he confided that he would spend Christmas in a temple in a filthy town with only a portable phonograph and a record of "Stille Nacht, Heilige Nacht!" for consolation.[29] So widespread were the robbers and looters that on January 5, having barely survived a harrowing attack, Rock suffered a nervous collapse.[30] The journey through Szechwan, however, was more placid, and he found Ch'eng-tu a pleasant city until he contracted flu. North of Ch'eng-tu, bandits began to bother him again and he was forced to travel with a large military escort—once he mentioned 140 men and another time 190—which caused further delays. He did not reach Minchow [Min-hsien] in southwest Kansu until mid-April. A month later he arrived in Cho-ni, farther north, and to assure Sargent, who might well have been anxious by this time, Rock reported that there was not a single leaf yet unfurled. His enforced idleness gave him ample time to make friends with the local prince. There was trouble in the region between the Chinese Confucians and Taoists, the Chinese Mohammedans, and the Tibetans, and the Mohammedans had somehow gotten the idea that Rock was a Chinese spy. Another month passed before it seemed safe to strike out. Rock decided to tackle the Amne Machin range first.

The extraordinary thing about Rock's letters to Sargent is that it was June 24, 1925, after more than seven months in China, before he mentioned a single plant by name. The correspondence would be invaluable to a student of Chinese history, detailing as it does the local political intrigues of which the collector was kept well informed by his good friend the Prince of Cho-ni. Doubtless aware that his sponsor might be alarmed by his troubled reports, Rock took pains to reassure him that he could handle the situation; but he felt it necessary to point out that Cho-ni was much less civil-

The Treasure Hunt

Joseph Rock in Tibetan dress, ca. 1926

Wilson in Japan, Rock in Tibet

ized than Wilson country in Szechwan.[31] Sargent, usually understanding and indeed worried about Rock's safety, sent messages of encouragement and confidence.

What had appeared to Rock to be an easing of the local political tensions soon proved to be just a lull in the storm. Within a week of a promising letter to Sargent, the country swarmed with bandits again, and not even Cho-ni was safe. Rock collected what he could in Tebbu country, a locality with a rich flora southeast of Cho-ni, during July and August. He worked quickly, trying to dodge clashes between Upper Tebbu and Lower Tebbu tribesmen. The long-standing hostility between the tribes had put off many collectors before him. (Purdom had made some attempt to travel there but never penetrated beyond the perimeters, so well did the natives defend themselves against intruders.) Rock's success there was a *tour de force*.

He still hoped to reach the Amne Machin range but mistrusted reports that the countryside was settled. By mid-September, when he set off for the Kokonor district [Ch'ing-hai sheng] on the way to the mountains, he had already missed the early flowering species but hoped to catch the late bloomers. To his dismay he discovered that "the scarcest thing in this country [Kokonor] is a tree or a bush, everything is barren and search for such is indeed an undertaking."[32] He did, however, find two species of *Picea* and some Rhododendrons.

Because of the disorder, Rock altered his first plan and decided to head for the Richthofen range. He persuaded some Tibetan nomads to guide his party to the Mongolian border, and worked the southwestern slopes of the mountains. The effort proved frustrating and fruitless. Along with the discomforts of below-freezing weather, snow, and high altitudes, the mountains yielded little in the way of vegetation and disappointed him thoroughly. At the end of the season, even Cho-ni was a welcome sight to him. In all he had collected seed of what he estimated to be some three hundred woody species, mostly from Tebbu country, in-

The Treasure Hunt

cluding forty kinds of conifers, and an additional batch of cuttings. Sargent, for his part, was all admiration and considered the first season's work a success. By March 1926, he reported thousands of Rock seedlings growing at the Arboretum and at Holm Lea; thanks to Rock's careful handling of material the percentage of germination had been remarkably high.[33]

Rock spent the early spring of 1926 trying to find a guiding party to take him to the Amne Machins. In the spirit of diplomacy, he befriended the "Living Buddha of Labrang" [Hsia-ho], a friend of the Prince of Cho-ni, hoping that the Buddha could talk the Prince into providing a large enough escort for the exploring party. The apple-polishing process included presenting the Buddha with a large black horse, a worthwhile expenditure. By mid-April Rock set out for the mountains with escorts, ammunition, yaks, and the blessings of the Labrang Buddha, who also gave him letters of introduction. The latter proved of great value, as when Rock called on the "Living Buddha of Radja," a young man who claimed—much to Rock's amusement—to be the reincarnation of the mother of Tosongkaba. In May the party headed up the Yellow River, the gorges of which Rock described with as much enthusiasm as Henry and Wilson had spoken of the Yangtze gorges near I-ch'ang. From a mountain pass at 13,000 feet, he had his first dazzling view of the Che-shih shan. From a distance he thought that the peaks might indeed be higher than the Himalayas. He traveled through country where no white men had been. Local tribesmen, the Ugoloks, harassed him every step of the way, but at last he reached the mountains. The tallest peak was, after all, only around 28,000 feet, and the range, even in the foothills, was bereft of trees and shrubs. It was even barer than the Richthofen range. Rock mapped the region, but botanically the trip was nearly useless. He found a total of only 250 species along the way, most of them herbaceous. Sargent took the news philosophically. "No one certainly has a better reason not to be disheartened than you," he wrote. "Do not forget

Wilson in Japan, Rock in Tibet

that it is as important to discover that no plants grow in a country as it is to find what grows in it, and for this reason I consider your Tibet journey a great success." [34]

Rock passed most of the fall and winter in Cho-ni packing his seeds, plants, and birds for Harvard, and keeping a watchful eye on the political situation, which continued to get worse. He wrote long, frequent, worried letters to Sargent, betraying his nervousness. In late November a communist-inspired faction of the Kuomintang, China's nationalist party, gained control of the area, and a red flag fluttered over Cho-ni. Rock debated going south to Sungpan, Wilson's old Shangri-La, but the roads were blocked by early snow and the journey would probably be more dangerous than staying the winter in Cho-ni. As tensions mounted, Rock found himself in real danger because the Chinese displayed an anti-foreign, Boxer-like attitude along with their red flag. Under the circumstances, friendship with the Prince did not help much. Sargent, aware of the general situation from the newspapers, became anxious for his collector. On December 2, 1926, he wrote Rock, "It would be all right to return home at once or as soon as possible. You have had a very long and hard journey, and I do not want you to be entirely broken down by it. You are too valuable for that and the sooner we can see you in this country, the better we shall be pleased." [35] Much as he desired to spend another season in Tebbu country, Rock was close to mental exhaustion from the sheer effort of staying alive. Shortly after receiving the signal from Sargent, he began the long, perilous march to Shanghai. On March 22, 1927, Sargent died without knowing whether Rock had reached safety.

Rock returned to the United States in the summer of 1927. As far as his collections for the Arboretum were concerned, while they did not compete with Wilson's for novelties, they did surprisingly well. He did not discover a great number of new species but—and this had been Sargent's principal objective—he sent seeds and cuttings of hardier forms of species which had been originally collected in more southerly stations. Besides having been handicapped by political

The Treasure Hunt

problems he had, like Purdom, run into species which had already been introduced; and there had been little to collect on the two mountain ranges. As for Rock, China had captivated him, and he would return in less than a year to spend the greater part of his remaining life in remote outposts studying Chinese customs, plants, and animals.

Wilson in Japan, Rock in Tibet

Part Four. Last Glances

11

Crataegus: A Thorny Problem

Sargent was a creative administrator, a man with an uncommon sense of the future, a noted dendrologist, a prodigious and exacting worker, but he is also remembered as the man who made a taxonomic disaster out of the genus *Crataegus*. It must be said in his defense that he did not create the havoc singlehandedly, but, as one critic put it, he was a "heavyweight" in the story.[1] To his misfortune, although he is remembered as a great dendrologist, Sargent's taxonomic reputation suffers from his work on one genus.

Taxonomy is the orderly classification of plants and animals according to their presumed natural relationships. It is man's effort to comprehend and organize intellectually his biological environment. Philosophically speaking, taxonomists divide—not necessarily equally—into two schools of thought: Aristotelians ("realists"), who believe that nature is inherently orderly and that man works to define that order; and Platonists ("idealists"), who think that nature is chaotic and that the order is in man's mind. Though the two ways of thinking are far apart, the differences do not ordinarily show up in practical taxonomy except in difficult groups. On one level classification might be considered a cerebral exercise of no practical value; indeed, there are some critics who claim that taxonomists are not real scientists at all but slightly demented people involved in an elaborate game. The criticism indicates a narrow, misinformed concept of science, because the understanding of relationships among organisms is essential to any phase of biology. Furthermore, as they classify, taxonomists create a vocabulary. Ultimately, a plant or animal form is expressed in its Latin binomial. The specific name denotes the individuality of that particular form; the generic name gives the key to the position of the form within the hierarchy of the plant or animal kingdom. Without having been put through the process of systematization, an organism, for all scientific purposes, remains an isolated phenomenon outside a frame of reference. A limited quantity of knowledge may be obtained by studying the individual, but that knowledge has little value until one understands the organism in terms of its relationship to the overall vegetable or animal system. The taxonomist's objective, then, is to comprehend and express biological relationships in an orderly manner. But classification is not an end in itself; it is one of the means to knowledge which, in turn, is a means to control and use which, one hopes, will contribute to the improvement of the human condition.

Though man has been trying to systematize natural phenomena with more or less sophistication since his arrival on earth, modern plant taxonomy, for all practical purposes, dates back to the Swedish botanist Linnaeus, who initiated the use of the binomial trivial name and a rational—and to a certain extent—natural system of classification. Taxonomic botanists after Linnaeus learned progressively more about plants, grappled with new theories such as Darwinism or the rediscovery of Mendel's laws of heredity in 1900, and thus constantly revised and added to the work of their predecessors. This process of reevaluation in terms of new data continues, and will continue as more evidence becomes available. At any given time, taxonomists, being human, have interpreted data known to them in different and sometimes conflicting fashions, with the result that experts often find themselves in violent disagreement with each other.

Last Glances

And so taxonomic decisions, like those other sciences and areas of scholarly pursuit, are constantly being reassessed. The taxonomist works both analytically and synthetically. His analysis rests on detailed morphological observations of the plant in question and includes, perhaps, such refined considerations as its chromosome number and chemistry. He notes, if possible, the characteristics of the subject in its juvenile and adult forms, its ecological situation, and the pattern of its geographic distribution. In other words, the taxonomist—ideally—studies the plant in the field, in the herbarium and laboratory, and in library sources with the intention of reaching a thorough understanding of it. He then synthesizes the fragments of information in order to express how the species resembles or differs from similar species and how, in turn, it fits into the general scheme of classification.

The genus *Crataegus* that gave Sargent so much trouble has been the nemesis of many botanists.[2] Principally North American and European, commonly called the hawthorns, these prickly, sometimes decorative plants in the rose family are a taxonomic trap, and it is now clear that Sargent did not know exactly what he was dealing with when he started to work on them. André Michaux listed only seven species of *Crataegus* in his *Flora Boreali-Americana,* published in 1803. Frederick Pursh's *Flora Americae Septentrionalis* of 1814 includes eleven species. Thomas Nuttall, in 1818, gave the same eleven in his *Genera of North American Plants.* Torrey and Gray increased the number to seventeen, listing sixteen well-defined and one doubtful *Crataegus* species in the *Flora of North America* in 1840.

Sargent became entangled with the genus, somewhat tentatively, in the course of his *Silva.* In the 1880's he exchanged some correspondence with Engelmann on the subject of *C. arborescens,* and both men questioned the apparent extent of variability within the species. Engelmann died perturbed by the thought that he might not have under-

Crataegus

281

stood *Crataegus.* Having already encountered some pre-liminary problems, Sargent knew that working with the genus might prove difficult. Even before he began to study the Rosaceae for Volume IV of the *Silva,* he wrote Thiselton-Dyer that "with Crataegus and Prunus [it] promises to be about the worst of the whole lot." [3] He managed, however, to untangle the genus to his temporary satisfaction, and Volume IV contained descriptions of fourteen species with four varieties. The list included the one species (*C. arbores-cens*) previously named by Sargent and Engelmann, and three forms which Sargent named as new varieties but did not think sufficiently distinct to be elevated to the level of species. In the key he designed to accompany the descrip-tions, he separated the genus into two parts, depending on whether they had "flowers in ample many-flowered corymbs" or "flowers in simple few-flowered corymbs," thereafter distinguishing species on the bases of the char-acteristics of fruits and leaves respectively.[4] This early key contrasts with his later concept, in which minute morpho-logical characters indicated speciation. Volume IV of the *Silva* appeared on July 2, 1892; Volume XIII, the first sup-plementary volume, was published on December 15, 1902. In the latter, Sargent alluded to eighty-four species of *Cra-taegus,* noting ominously that "[t]he fact . . . must be recog-nized that this Silva does not include all arborescent forms of Crataegus which are now known to exist in North Amer-ica," nor did it take into account any of the shrubby species.[5] In the intervening ten years, several botanists had begun the study of *Crataegus,* and, around 1900, Sargent joined them in an effort to understand this perplexing group of thorny plants. Between 1896 and 1900, taxonomists named sixty-three new species. Of these, William Willard Ashe of the United States Forest Service named thirty-one, and Chaun-cey Beadle, the son of a Canadian nurseryman, named seventeen, including one called *C. sargentii* from a species collected by Sargent in Georgia.

Sargent, contemplating a supplement to his *Silva,* had to reckon with the *Crataegus* problem if only to decide whether

Last Glances

all these new species were valid or whether it would be more justifiable to class them as varieties or even as synonyms of names already published. To make these evaluations, he had to take a new look at the plant material. He solicited herbarium specimens from his correspondents and made a special attempt to collect *Crataegus* himself. In March 1900, he was in the Southwest with his friends Canby and the Missouri botanist Benjamin Franklin Bush; in September, he went to Illinois and the Champlain Valley; in October, he searched the midwest with Canby and Bush again. In January 1901, the *Botanical Gazette* printed Sargent's first list of seven new species and one new variety of *Crataegus* in part II of his "New or Little Known North American Trees." The paper marked the beginning of his career as a "crataegologist."[6] In February of the same year, in "Notes on Crataegus in the Champlain Valley," he described another thirteen species from Vermont and surmised that the list was not exhaustive.[7] In this study he divided the genus into thirteen subgroups, basing his distinctions primarily on leaf characteristics.

By the time he got to preparing the *Silva* supplement, Sargent had already named twenty-one more species in the pages of the *Botanical Gazette;* these, plus the first batches, were included in Volume XIII of the *Silva* along with, among others, six of Ashe's species and fourteen of Beadle's, including *C. sargentii.* Faxon had to provide drawings for everything that had not been figured in Volume IV which meant sixty-nine new plates. Jack, although he collected quantities of *Crataegus* for Sargent, stood by as Sargent named species and later reminisced that Faxon had quietly disapproved of the process while producing the drawings strictly out of loyalty. Jack, long under Faxon's wing, was accordingly skeptical.[8]

Sargent devoted Volume XIII almost exclusively to the hawthorns. By way of introduction and forewarning he pointed out that "in addition to [the species here described] are now known several shrubby species which do not necessarily find a place in a work devoted to trees, and a number

Crataegus

of trees are imperfectly known. To study these sufficiently to bring them into this Silva would require several years of additional field work, and an attempt to include them all would delay perhaps indefinitely the appearance of these supplementary volumes." [9] In effect, Sargent left the flood gates open for the proliferation of new names and served notice that he would have more to say on the subject.

"In this study of the genus," he wrote, "particular attention is paid to the number of stamens and the color of the anthers as important characters for distinguishing species." He was using finer and more elaborate criteria for classification than he had in Volume IV, a change which was reflected in his revised key. The emphasis on the number of stamens and anther color—characters also used by Beadle and Ashe—showed a drastic departure from the earlier studies, where they had not even been mentioned in the specific descriptions. In his paper on the Champlain Valley species, Sargent had outlined thirteen subgroups; for the *Silva* supplement he created eighteen and calmly proceeded to subdivide them. His process of defining species became a matter of selecting the smallest common differential.

Gardeners' Chronicle, in a lengthy article celebrating the completion of the task (Volume XIII appeared simultaneously with the final Volume XIV) diplomatically refrained from any qualitative comments on the *Crataegus* study; [10] *The Journal of Botany* cautiously implied its doubts about the new species by praising the "admirable plates and detailed accounts [which] will be of the greatest value in discriminating these nearly allied species." [11] In general the botanical world recognized what was going on with *Crataegus,* and several respected botanists expressed dismay and alarm at the mushrooming number of species. Charles E. Bessey, a former student of Gray's, specializing in plant anatomy, strongly attacked the hawthorn systematists in the May 16, 1902, issue of *Science.* He did not need to mention names; Ashe, Beadle, and Sargent were the obvious targets of his barbed remarks.

Last Glances

As it often happens that the soldier in a different part of the field of battle is able to see more clearly what is taking place than those in the thick of the mêlée, so it may be that botanists just a little outside of the work of descriptive systematic botany are able to measure the real value of some of the work now being done. One can hardly take up a botanical journal without finding that some of the common species of plants have been split into two or more forms called 'species' by their authors. That such work must be done is inevitable, but it is incredible that ten to twenty species should have been able to hide themselves in plants which had been critically studied by such masters as Gray, Torrey and Watson. As long as these leaders were found to have confused only two or three species in one the interested onlooker was ready enough to accept the dictum of present-day specialists in single genera, and to admit that the masters had blundered, but when we are asked to believe that Gray and Torrey were totally blind and incapable of seeing or defining the limits of species, it is evident that these later workers are dealing with something of which their predecessors either knew nothing or cared nothing when they were defining species. In 1878 there were catalogued for North America in Watson's Bibliographical Index 14 species and 10 varieties of hawthorns, of the genus *Crataegus*. In 1899 these numbers had risen to 34 species and 11 varieties. To-day we are asked by several botanists to add to this list 225 new species almost entirely from the eastern United States, where three years ago there were not *one tenth as many!*[12]

Criticism rained down on the *Crataegus* namers. Because of the way he classified the hawthorns, Sargent himself was classified by his colleagues as a "splitter" rather than a "lumper," and that is the way botany remembers him. (Either epithet constitutes an insult when employed by a member of the opposing faction.) Yet, as his friend William

Crataegus

Trelease observed shortly after his death, Sargent was weaned by Gray on conservative views. Before Sargent took up his study of hawthorns, Trelease recalled, "the segregation views of certain continental systematists seemed beneath his contempt, as he once expressed himself." In fact, Trelease argued that Sargent was fundamentally a conservative throughout his career and that *Crataegus* was only a freakish departure from this attitude with no real bearing on his general philosophy.[13]

Once involved in the problem, Sargent became obsessed—the word does not seem too strong—with *Crataegus,* and he soon outstripped both Beadle and Ashe in numbers of new species. Between 1901 and 1905, he named 238 species; between 1906 and 1910, he increased the total to 337. During the latter period Beadle dropped out of the picture altogether, and Ashe named only a few. In his lifetime, Sargent named more than 700 species, and 22 varieties with five forms, compared to Beadle and Ashe, who each named fewer than 200. Inasmuch as no one has undertaken the menacing task of making a thorough revision of the genus, taxonomists are now burdened with more than a thousand specific names for hawthorns.

During what E. J. Palmer liked to call "the period of expansion for the genus,"[14] the first decade of the century, several botanists, only some of whom were taxonomists, expressed alarm less because they had any particular interest in *Crataegus* than because of the theoretical implications for taxonomy as a whole. Bessey warned against the inherent dangers of Sargent's reasoning:

> Of course, this brings up the old question of the limits of species. This cannot be discussed in a short note, but this is certain, that in [*Crataegus*] we are asked to give greater values than formerly to observable variations. This is carried to such an extreme that one is compelled to ask whether this change is warranted . . . The ornithologists have noticed similar minute variations in birds, although they have not regarded them as specific, but rather vari-

Last Glances

etal, or sub-varietal. Yet there are ornithologists who question the wisdom of requiring that all members of a particular sub-variety should have been taken "under the same blackberry bush." Are not the botanists who are making so many species open to a similar criticism? If in *Crataegus* we have species with such slight variations, what are we to do with the varieties of the common apple trees? We shudder at the thought of these species-multipliers getting into our orchards. There must be at least a thousand or so good 'species' hidden in *Pirus malus* of Linnaeus![15]

It is true that at the time Bessey wrote, and also today, there was no rigid set of regulations governing the making of species. The word itself refers to a concept, a convenient unit to which individuals sharing a number of apparent common characters are assigned by an experienced observer. Before Darwin, taxonomists either speculated that minute differences were sufficient reason to name a new species or, for the sake of order, herded the deviant forms under one name without understanding the operative natural laws. With the acceptance of Darwinism, systematists tended to describe species broadly enough to include their ideas of reasonable variation. The nineteenth-century botanists— and Sargent was one of them even in 1910—defined species on the basis of morphological features and the supposition that species, as opposed to hybrids, bred true. Ultimately, a species is a consequence of personal judgments and is, therefore, vulnerable to another critical judgment. But it is one thing to argue whether a particular plant belongs to this species or that, and another to question the validity of hundreds of species where there used to be less than a dozen. The reckless multiplication of species on the basis of subtle differences generated confusion instead of order and subverted the essence of systematization. If all taxonomy were approached in this manner, there would be enough "species" to turn order into chaos.

That Sargent did this work in *Crataegus* is both consistent

Crataegus

and inconsistent with his nature. It should have troubled his strong sense of order—political, social, and scientific. Raised to respect a social hierarchy, he lived his personal life within the accepted boundaries of his social level. He thought of government conservatively, as the maintainer and protector of public order and not as an instrument of social change. Sargent was so dedicated to the principle of order that when European and American taxonomists were quarreling over nomenclatural questions, he pleaded for rapid agreement without really caring which side prevailed; he was far more concerned with uniformity than with rules.[16] Yet if his findings in *Crataegus* were not in accord with his orderly instincts, his stubborn grip on the problem was an instance of his usual tenacity. Having waded into the *Crataegus* quagmire, Sargent got in deeper and deeper, for it was not his style to retreat or, having gone so far, to observe that the specific study might contradict his general principles.

Once he began his study of hawthorns, Sargent methodically sowed seed in the Arboretum of every species he described so that he would have the living plants for observation. For years the Peters' Hill tract supported a great *Crataegus* crop. Between 1899 and 1927, the year of Sargent's death, 4,515 seed lots were planted and, at its peak, the living collection comprised around 1,400 labeled trees and shrubs representing nearly 700 "species" and "varieties." Of these he claimed that over 600 species were new to cultivation.* Beadle raised a substantial *Crataegus* crop at the Biltmore Arboretum from seed collected in the southern Allegheny region,[17] and another collection was started later by the Park Department in Rochester, New York, but the Arnold Arboretum boasted the most extensive hawthorn plantation in the world. In view of the fact that *Crataegus*

---

* After Sargent had been safely dead for twenty years, the Arboretum staff agreed to dispose of the plants, which had become unsightly and neglected, and they were unceremoniously dug up and plowed under, much to the relief of everyone except E. J. Palmer, who, having worked with them for so long, had a sentimental attachment to them.

Last Glances

is not a glamorous ornamental like azaleas or crabapples, or a majestic one like *Pinus* or *Abies,* Sargent was disproportionately proud of the display, featuring it in correspondence with his colleagues and in his various published accounts of the Arboretum. He even went so far as to convince his English friend, Miss Willmott, to accept cuttings of over 550 forms for her garden in France, thereby endowing her with the dubious privilege of tending the most complete collection of American hawthorns in Europe. Miss Willmott received these tokens of friendship and affection with genteel graciousness.

Sargent's solicitation of herbarium specimens was no less ardent than his planting program. Before he was through, there were around 25,000 dried specimens of *Crataegus* in the Administration Building in Jamaica Plain, enough to fill twenty-eight herbarium cases and occupy more than 33,000 cubic feet of space. Sargent begged material from various colleagues, collected much himself, and alerted the Arboretum staff to watch for hawthorns whenever they were out in the field. Men like Jack, Faxon, and, in later years, Palmer, who were suspicious of their master's conclusions, religiously gathered branches for his perusal. Furthermore, along with the mass plantings and herbarium collections went a voluminous correspondence exclusively devoted to *Crataegus;* urgent letters prodding collectors to get this or that species in flower or fruit, to others to confirm morphological observations or to query geographic distribution, to colleagues to send lists of determinations.

Sargent did nearly all his *Crataegus* work between 1899 and 1913, a period when he was occupied with other concerns, including Wilson's Chinese exploits, his own travels, and the writing of his *Manual.* He appears to have worked doggedly, with no real love for the plants but as a captive of the challenge to understand and classify them. The more species he named, the more complicated the task became, because it was impossible to know from memory hundreds of subtly differentiated species. Judging from some of the specific names he employed ("confusa," "cruda," "horri-

Crataegus

dula" "incerta," "obscura," "repulsans") he suffered periodic attacks of frustration and despair. There were times when he simply grew sick and tired of the whole business. On his return from South America in 1906, Sargent commented to a fellow enthusiast, "unless you have tried it, you can form no idea how delightful it is to travel in a country where there is no *Crataegus*." [18] The question arises, finally, as to why Sargent named so many species. He offered his own explanation of his work in the pages of the British Museum's *Journal of Botany* for August 1907. The paper was defensive in tone. Although he showed no inclination to change his position, he took pains to protect his vanity against the critics' darts.

Our interest at the Arboretum in the genus was roused by the fact that plants raised here from seeds collected in various parts of the country differed constantly from any of the described species. [In December 1899, Beadle described a similar circumstance, and it is possible that his experiments inspired Sargent.[19]] It was soon seen that different plants which it had been supposed belonged to one species differed in their time of flowering, in the number of their stamens, in the colour of their anthers, in the time of the ripening of their fruit, and in the nature of the fruit and the form of the nutlets, and that these characters were constant and could be depended on as distinguishing characters.

Following up the investigation, it was found that these seedling plants in the Arboretum were identical in all these characters with the wild plants from whose seeds they had been raised. These facts led to a more careful study of the genus in several States, with the result that about five hundred species have been described in the last eight years. It is not surprising that botanists, looking at the genus through the eyes of Torrey and Gray, or reaching their conclusions from the study of the scanty and generally incomplete material found in herbaria, have regarded the makers of these species with pity, and

Last Glances

have tried to throw ridicule on this investigation and its results. To those persons, however, who examine the plants in the field even casually, the fact is soon apparent that the genus contains many very distinct forms, whether these are to be called species or not. These distinct forms or species fall into twenty natural groups, and the plants of these groups can be recognized at a glance. [Note an increase of two groups over the key in Volume XIII in the *Silva*, which appeared in 1902.] For botanists with broad ideas in regard to the limitation of species the twenty groups may represent twenty species, under each of which can be grouped a number of subspecies and varieties, while other botanists may consider it more *convenient* to treat all distinct forms as species . . . The origin of these many forms I cannot pretend to account for. The theory that they are hybrids of recent origin, however, can hardly be accepted. All the forms are constantly and abundantly prolific, and the seedlings that have been raised at the Arboretum in the last few years show none of the tendencies to variation usually found in the offspring of recent hybrids. Unlike the seedlings of *Malus, Rosa,* and other *Rosaceae,* the seedlings of any of these supposed species of *Crataegus* do not vary, either in foliage, flower, or fruit, and I have never seen what seemed to me to be a hybrid *Crataegus.*[20]

Since constancy of characters was widely accepted as a key factor in the determination of specific rank, Sargent's argument was logical even if his idea of what was "convenient" was debatable. Yet loyal as he was to the memory of The Professor, Jack wrote candidly in 1948 "that probably not one-fourth of the . . . named species of hawthorns would now be accepted by botanists or research students as having distinct specific rank."[21] What he might have added is that if Sargent had had the information and techniques available to later botanists, he most likely would not have recognized the species either.

Using information and techniques which were not avail-

Crataegus

able in Sargent's hawthorn-naming hey-day, and making comparisons with other troublesome genera such as *Rubus*, later botanists deduced that *Crataegus* appeared in numerous, diverse, constant forms because its reproductive processes were not ordinary. Cytological studies and detailed observations of the embryo were especially helpful in arriving at what seems to be a reasonable explanation of the situation.

In thinking of this genus we should bear in mind that the Crataegus-population of North America probably consists of a relatively few basic, sexual, diploid species, on which is superposed an unwieldy and highly complex population of triploids which, although they flower and produce fruits, are really asexual apomicts.[22]

It is now presumed, by analogy with other genera, that a number of *Crataegus* forms reproduce apogamically; that is, they are capable of producing viable seed in the ovary *without* fertilization. Effectively, apogamy is a means of vegetative propagation comparable to the sending out of new shoots. In both cases the offspring are identical with the parent plant of which they are more appropriately extensions than progeny. Any number of plants thus produced existing together in a group is called a clonal population or a clone. Sargent erroneously supposed that forms of *Crataegus* so produced were identical plants produced by normal sexual means. In 1841, J. Smith made the first known observation of seed formation without fertilization as it occurred in female plants of an Australian *Alchornea*, but the phenomenon was not widely explored until the late 1930's, and Åke Gustafsson's revealing discussions of apomixis did not appear until after the Second World War.[23] From the number of species which Sargent noted as "known only in a single locality" it appears that he often described clones. That he chose to call them species rather than varieties or forms is, for the moment, another question.

If the occurrence of apomixis does not sufficiently compli-

Last Glances

cate life for the taxonomist, it is well to remember that hybridization may occur in *Crataegus*. If a hybrid offspring reproduces apogamically, the new crop of plants shows no evidence of its dual ancestry in conformance with Mendelian principles. The same hawthorn plant theoretically may produce apogamous and normal seeds simultaneously, but the indication is that the genus favors the former, vegetative means of reproduction. These factors explain why Sargent's Arboretum seedlings did not vary from the parent plants.[24]

The epidemic of *Crataegus* species between 1896 and 1910—altogether 866 species were described during that period—generated speculation concerning their origins. One enterprising botanist, Harry Brown of Cornell University, decided to take a poll of six hawthorn experts, including Sargent. He sent each man (W. W. Eggleston, Ashe, Beadle, Ezra Brainerd, John Dunbar, and Sargent) a list of five questions. To Question 1, "Why did not the systematic botanists discover the large number of *Crataegus* species years ago?" Sargent replied, "Because they did not use their eyes and were satisfied to take for granted that what had been published about the genus was correct and final." Question 2, "Do you consider the species now being described elementary species?" he evaded by replying, "I do not know what you mean by elementary species." Questions 3 and 4 asked whether species bred true and whether they hybridized; Sargent answered "yes" and "evidently no," respectively. To the fifth question, "Do you consider the numerous species to have arisen as mutations?" he simply stated, "I cannot answer this question." These were the irritated and irritating responses of a stubborn man who was sick and tired of the persistent pressures on him to defend his work. While not substantially different from his explanation in the 1907 *Journal of Botany*, the tone was new and petulant. The snide remark about former systematic botanists—which, of course, included Torrey and Gray—sounded particularly offensive, and the refusal to deal with the question about elementary species revealed a disposition at once arrogant and unscholarly.[25]

Crataegus

Brown's survey showed a wide range of theories among the experts. Ashe, Beadle, Eggleston, and Brainerd thought the species probably hybridized; Dunbar, having seen no proof of it and influenced by Sargent, refused to commit himself to an opinion. Dunbar said the new names were "true species," and Beadle agreed in principle; but Ashe and Brainerd felt that many of the names were unworthy of specific rank. Eggleston, who wrote the *Crataegus* section for the seventh edition of Gray's *Manual* in 1908, favored reducing the number of species and, accordingly, listed only 65 species with 55 varieties in that treatment. The only point on which all five agreed was that the various forms bred true from seed. In answer to the first question, pertaining to earlier botanists, theories were offered and excuses made for the failure of the botanical forefathers to recognize a number of species: they made conservative interpretations of species, the herbarium material was poor, or they simply did not have time to explore the genus intensively. All of these reasons contained particles of truth. Brainerd further observed: "the genus *Crataegus*, I believe, has vastly increased in individuals and in forms in the northeastern U. S. since the forests were cut off; specimens are rarely found in the original forests of this region. But the plants rapidly take possession of neglected pastures, fencerows, and untilled ledges." Subsequent study has supported Brainerd's speculation.

Significantly, all the experts expressed or intimated some perplexity about the reproductive habits of the genus; none of them suspected anything like apomixis, and Brown in his conclusions offered no clues in this direction save that he remarked on the unusual number of local "species."

In the Peters' Hill *Crataegus* collection and out in the field, there was enough difference among forms and none of the customary signs of hybridization to allow Sargent to believe he was dealing with true species or—as he grudgingly conceded in 1907, if one preferred—true varieties or forms. Contemporary botanists do not blame him for not

Last Glances

understanding apomixis, although some, with the advantage of hindsight, say that since he worked so intimately with the genus and grew quantities of plants from seed he should have suspected that *something* peculiar was happening. The real fault found in Sargent's work is that he named so many species based on inconsequential differences. In his 1907 explanation, in which he pleaded "convenience" as his excuse, Sargent left leeway for more conservative interpretations of the genus. As Palmer pointed out, for the sake of simplicity it was easier for the specialist to deal only with the Latin binomials.[26] Sargent might have thought it easier to conceive of almost every form he encountered as a "species," but from the nature and quantity of criticism he attracted, this was obviously not a satisfactory solution for most botanists, who found the multitude of species clumsy and confounding. To make hundreds of species on the grounds of minute characters defied the spirit of taxonomy.

No amount of criticism, no matter how strong, could sway Sargent from his chosen course. He clung to his ideas, and the plants on Peters' Hill provided the substance of his argument by faithfully coming true from seed. As long as no one could explain the occurrence of so many invariable forms in a sensible fashion, he had no particular motive for revising his labors of so many years. Up to the end of his life, Sargent continued to name *Crataegus* species, including some new ones in the 1922 edition of his *Manual of the Trees of North America*, in which he pointed out with resignation that the genus was still imperfectly understood.

Crataegus was not the only genus to suffer from the zealous scrutiny of botanists. Just about the same time as Sargent, Beadle, and Ashe began turning out *Crataegus* species, Europeans took to describing species of their native *Rubus* at approximately the same rate. In the 1920's the *Rubus*-naming fever caught on in the United States where L. H. Bailey, one of the most respected names in American horticulture and botany, took the lead by naming hundreds of species, many of them in the 1940's when

Crataegus

apomixis was already a known phenomenon. Eventually scientists demonstrated that *Rubus* reproduces vegetatively in a process similar to that presumed to occur in *Crataegus*.

Sargent should have had doubts in his last years. In 1916, L. M. Standish demonstrated the frequency of pollen sterility in the genus and deduced a high percentage of hybridization.[27] An even more convincing paper was written in 1923 by Albert E. Longley, a Harvard morphologist who availed himself of the living collection at the Arboretum to make cytological studies on over a hundred named "species." Although Sargent had seen no evidence of hybridization on Peters' Hill, Longley found signs of it in his investigation of cytoplasm and, following Standish, indicated that nearly 80 per cent of the "species" he studied were polyploid forms showing pollen sterility and irregular chromosome distribution.[28] He concluded that the numerous forms in the genus had arisen through hybridization. He could not explain why Sargent's hawthorns bred true from seed, but he came closer to an explanation than he realized when he guessed that "some hybrids ... may mature into organisms vigorous vegetatively," though he was mistaken in his qualification, "but unable to produce flowers and fruit." [29] While neither Standish nor Longley solved the *Crataegus* mystery, their findings ought to have disturbed Sargent, especially the information regarding the high frequency of pollen sterility. It seems unlikely that he could treat these statements with indifference as he had the mere conjectures of Ashe, Beadle, Brainerd, and Eggleston. Unfortunately, Sargent did not leave any record of his last correspondence on *Crataegus*. In some notes on *Crataegus* published in the *Journal of the Arnold Arboretum* more than six months after Longley's paper was in print, Sargent made no reference to the cytological study, though he had ample opportunity to do so, but contributed a few casual corrections to his own work.[30] While he graciously acknowledged errors in practice, he refused to recognize any error in principle.

By the time Sargent was through with *Crataegus*, there were so many barely distinguishable species that most

Last Glances

taxonomists threw up their hands in horror and would have nothing to do with the genus. One man, however, mixed courage with curiosity to continue with the study and went part way toward simplifying the systematic tangle. Ernest Jesse Palmer, for many years a field collector for Sargent and by 1921 a staff member at the Arboretum, had been interested in *Crataegus* since the turn of the century, when he started collecting them in Missouri. He followed the species explosion closely and knew hawthorns in the field, in the Arboretum herbarium, and in the cultivated collections. After he joined the Arboretum staff, he made polite suggestions to Sargent about one form or another, but perhaps in deference to his sponsor, he did not flaunt his private opinions on the fabrication of species. After Sargent's death he began to try to repair some of the damage.

In a paper published in 1932 he confessed that "[i]t has long seemed to the writer that, for practical reasons . . . a conservative treatment in dealing with as large a genus as *Crataegus* is desirable." Even disregarding abnormal reproductive mechanisms, Palmer preferred the "convenience" of a broad species concept. Unlike Sargent, he recognized the significance of Standish's and Longley's investigations, realizing the implications for systematics. He went a step beyond them and cited the work of Karl Sax, a cytologist at the Arboretum, as a further explanation for the puzzling habits of the plants: "The fact that so large a percentage of forms come true to the parent type scarcely seems to lend support to the theory that they are of hibrid origin, and if that is admitted to be the case upon other evidence, it would seem to indicate that triploid forms have developed a type of apogamous reproduction, as pointed out by Sax, and as a consequence do not develop the variations of usual hybrids." [31] Although his hypothesis has never been demonstrated conclusively, it is now commonly considered to explain the numerous true-breeding forms. True to his conservative inclinations and his acceptance of cytological observations, Palmer worked for many years on *Crataegus*. He named some new species, but reduced many more to

Crataegus

synonymy, demoted others to the varietal level, and attempted to determine the hybrid origin of others. He prepared the hawthorn section for the eighth edition of Gray's *Manual* in 1950, listing only 103 species and even then suspecting that several of them were hybrids. Palmer never completed a revision of the genus, and most of the problems initiated by Sargent, Ashe, Beadle, and the others remain.

Last Glances

12

Giving Out Advice

Sargent viewed the Arboretum not only as an end in itself but also as a means of propagating knowledge of trees. The Arboretum became the chief expression of his private ambitions whereas the broader objective was a matter of intellectual principle. The means and end in this case related directly to each other, the one justifying the other, and there was no tortured rationalization. The activities which Sargent and his staff members performed outside the Arboretum satisfied both goals. Extracurricular work was of obvious advantage to the institution, spreading its reputation and sometimes yielding more tangible rewards.

Sargent accepted the invitation to undertake the Census survey with the realization that he could make a mark for the fledgling Arboretum, and he achieved this regardless of his subsequent disappointments in the manner in which federal authorities mistreated his findings. He served the Northern Transcontinental Survey, the Adirondack survey, and the National Academy of Sciences forestry commission in the same spirit. He encouraged his staff to participate in public service, locally and nationally, because he knew that the botanical and horticultural work of the Arboretum would have little significance if they remained locked within the boundaries at Jamaica Plain or in the pages of specialized scientific journals. Far from taking an academic ivory-tower attitude, his goal was to develop an institution which could simultaneously do sophisticated research and express the findings, or the implications of the findings, to a popular audience. The need for endowment funds influenced his thinking, for public effort attracted patrons; but practical though he was, money was not the prevailing reason for his efforts. He assumed what he considered to be his responsibility in educating the public about trees and shrubs. He had little use for knowledge for its own sake, a concept too mystical for him. A practical man, he preferred an active life where cause and effect were clearly related with a minimum amount of time between them.

In the Boston area where the Sargent name carried great weight, the Professor rose quickly as a power in the prominent horticulturally oriented societies after his appointment as Director of the Botanic Garden in Cambridge and the new Arboretum. He became actively involved in the Massachusetts Horticultural Society and particularly in the Massachusetts Society for Promoting Agriculture, reigning as its president for thirty-two years. At the time these groups were made up mainly of patricians: wealthy, influential, informed amateurs. That the Massachusetts Horticultural Society admitted Jackson Dawson indicated its serious intent.

When Sargent joined the Massachusetts Horticultural Society in 1870, he had no Cambridge Botanic Garden or Arboretum endowment to worry him, but membership in the organization was considered necessary for any serious plant lover of social standing. Sargent's father, Francis Parkman, and H. H. Hunnewell were all lifetime members as were several other acquaintances. Lifetime membership required approval of the members and payment of a fee of thirty dollars. Incorporated in 1829, the Society had long been a popular success with its flower shows, and gardeners were proud to win its coveted awards. Through displays and citations, the Society encouraged plant introductions and tasteful horticulture, and provided its members with opportunities for keeping abreast of horticultural developments and for exchanging ideas. Like many organizations of its time,

Last Glances

it was a substitute for the elaborate communications network which today informs people about almost everything. Sargent's relationship with the Massachusetts Horticultural Society was pleasantly symbiotic. For years he served them as a vice-president, chairman of the library committee, and expert adviser in return for the service which the individual members performed for him in the way of financial support for the Arboretum. He stimulated and directed the expansion of the library into one of the most complete horticultural collections in the world; he helped plan the construction of Horticultural Hall on Massachusetts Avenue in Boston. As the author of his final tribute observed, "his advice was always sought whenever any new undertaking was contemplated." [1]

The Massachusetts Society for Promoting Agriculture predated the Horticultural Society by more than a quarter of a century. It went back to 1792, when a group of earnest, wealthy gentlemen of the Commonwealth, including Samuel Adams, successfully petitioned Governor John Hancock for permission to incorporate a society for the purposes of understanding and improving agricultural practices in the state. During the early years, the society interested itself in fundamental questions: soil, manure, animal husbandry, and crop diseases—a program weighted toward farm-related studies. The Society awarded substantial cash prizes for achievement and offered financial aid for agricultural research. Conservation and, therefore, forestry fell within the orbit of the Society's interests, but horticulture as we think of it today received only a small share of its resources. It had, however, been instrumental in the establishment of the Cambridge Botanic Garden and the Fisher Professorship of Natural History.

Sargent became a Trustee of the Society in 1871, when he was still a mere foreman at Holm Lea. The Society formally acknowledged his abilities in 1876, when it voted to finance the reprinting of ten thousand copies of his first publication, *A Few Suggestions on Tree-planting*, which had originally appeared in the 1875 report of the Massachusetts State

Giving Out Advice

301

Board of Agriculture, for free distribution to the public. In 1879, the Trustees elected him Corresponding Secretary, an honor to which was attached the thankless job of letter-writing. He dutifully fulfilled the obligations of his office until 1895, when the Trustees elevated him to the first vice-presidency; he succeeded to the presidency by election following the death of Thomas Motley a month later, and he retained that position for the rest of his life. There is a charming account of the centennial celebration on June 14, 1892, from the pen of Francis H. Appleton, Recording Secretary at that time. Sargent invited the Trustees and their ladies to Holm Lea, sparing nothing for their entertainment:

> When the doors of the dining room were thrown open . . . a beautiful and artistic sight was disclosed. The centre of the oblong dining-table, extending nearly from end to end, was covered with a mass of flowers and appropriate greens, which surrounded a finely proportioned member of the swine family, carved in ice, with a remarkably large litter of well-formed young around her, as only a good farmer could be expected to possess. The latter were represented by lemons . . . These cool and beautiful specimens of the farmers' and horticulturists' skill were a fitting adornment to the feast that followed.[2]

Sargent's membership in the Society paid off well. It is likely that the Arboretum would have received some financial assistance under any circumstances because the Trustees—many of them Harvard men—had a tradition of cooperation with the University, aiding both the Botanic Garden and the Bussey Institution. Sargent's influence from within, however, no doubt affected the amount and direction of the Society's donations. It appears that he was responsible for the Society's annual donation to the Botanic Garden, which paid Sereno Watson's salary during hard times.[3] It donated generously to the Arboretum in its early days. Then in June 1897, a little more than two years after Sargent's election as President, the Trustees voted an annual

Last Glances

$2,500 for the Arboretum for the next five years; they renewed this appropriation for three years in 1901 and every three years thereafter as long as Sargent was alive. After his death, they authorized a $50,000 memorial contribution. Over the years the donations totaled over $125,000. As uninterested as they were in the principles of arboriculture, it does not seem possible that even the enticing combination of Harvard and an arboretum could have inspired the Trustees to such magnanimity without Sargent's presence in their midst. He was not, perhaps, an able public speaker, but he must have had some political skill. It should be noted, furthermore, that contributions to the Botanic Garden and the Bussey Institution fell off during the Sargent regime.

On one occasion Sargent talked the Trustees into voting $1,000 to improve the condition of the trees in Harvard Yard. According to the Society's historian, President Theodore Roosevelt, marching in a Commencement Day procession, "stopped and gazed with alarmed eye and corrugated forehead into the vista of afflicted trees, and exclaimed with characteristic energy, 'What're you going to *do* about it Lowell!'" Although Cambridge folklore has it that the President of Harvard University was ill disposed to taking advice from the President of the United States, the remark either shook Lowell into awareness that the trees were indeed a sorry sight, or Roosevelt's voice was hearty enough to carry back in the line to sensitive ears. Whatever may have transpired on that day, word reached Sargent and the Society; the Trustees put up the money, and Sargent himself reported on the condition of the yard and looked after its improvement.[4]

During the Sargent administration, the Society, aside from expressing avid concern for the Arnold Arboretum, continued in the general course laid down during its first century. The geographical application of funds was regional but always with the idea that local achievements would prove to be of wider usefulness. In the early 1920's, at Sargent's insistence, the Trustees took up the cause of national parks. Since the 1880's, when he first saw the northwestern gla-

Giving Out Advice

ciers, Sargent championed the principle of national parks despite his disapproval of the way they were being handled by the federal authorities. His friendship with Muir, his work in the Adirondacks, and his investigation for the National Academy contributed to his conviction that the United States badly needed a sweeping, strongly enforced conservation program. For many years, however, he maintained a stubborn silence on conservation issues because early disappointments left him frustrated and helpless. When, in 1913, the Federal Government authorized the city of San Francisco to take control of the Hetch Hetchy Valley from Yosemite for a water and power reservoir, Sargent was as angry as other conservationists—the sentimental story was that Muir died of a broken heart over the incident—but he was scarcely surprised, for he had learned to expect little from Washington. The most he could claim was a sour I-told-you-so satisfaction because his old nemesis, Gifford Pinchot, had aided in the "Rape of Hetch Hetchy." While the Sierra Club and other private organizations made desperate efforts to save the canyon, Sargent observed the debacle with passive cynicism; he had already had his share of defeats. However, he became involved accidentally when a similar problem arose with respect to Yellowstone National Park in 1920.

The territorial integrity of Yellowstone came under attack shortly after Sargent engaged in the battle against federal plant quarantine regulations. J. Horace McFarland, Sargent's friend and chairman of the hastily improvised Committee on Horticultural Quarantine, was better known as president of the American Civic Association, a group committed to the defense of park land as wilderness areas. Having received Sargent's enthusiastic support to fight the quarantine, McFarland solicited his aid in this cause too. While Yellowstone had no bearing on the immediate interests of the Arboretum, as did the restrictions on importing plant materials, the proposed legislation violated Sargent's conviction that national parks should be beyond the reach

Last Glances

of Congress. Sargent reserved the better part of his ferocity for the stand against the quarantine but willingly cooperated in defense of Yellowstone. McFarland kept him up to date on the political intricacies of both efforts, writing the details of the first on the white stationery of the Committee on Horticultural Quarantine and of the second on the blue paper of the American Civic Association, thus making it possible for his correspondent to know at a glance which issue he should worry about.

The Yellowstone Park problem began when Addison Smith, Representative from Idaho, encouraged by Senator Nugent of the same state, proposed a bill to permit the damming of the Falls River Basin to create an irrigation reservoir. Since the site in question was marshland, proponents of the bill insisted that the resulting lake would be an aesthetic improvement over existing conditions. McFarland's group and other like-minded organizations were concerned with the danger that approval of the measure would touch off a series of land grabs from the national parks. Still smarting from the Hetch Hetchy steal, the conservationists determined to prevent further encroachments. In view of more recent arguments over similar questions—notably concerning the Everglades and the Grand Canyon—it should be noted that the conservationists debated strictly on the issues of scenic beauty and public interest; unlike contemporary scientists and laymen, they were not concerned with protecting natural ecological environments.

The problem was to see that the Smith bill, or any similar measure that might spring up to replace it, was defeated; but affecting the behavior of Congress was no simple matter. McFarland commuted back and forth between Washington and his headquarters in Harrisburg, Pennsylvania, haggling with politicians and members of the administration on one hand and writing letters to gain public support on the other, leading the harried life of a lobbyist. Meanwhile he appealed to Sargent, less as a forestry expert than as a man of social prominence and influence, to get his friends to put pressure

Giving Out Advice

on Senator Lodge, the Republic floor leader, and urge him to lead a campaign in the Senate against the commercialization of national parks.[5]

Sargent, who considered the matter "a very serious danger to American civilization,"[6] contacted the Garden Club of America and brought it before the Trustees of the Society for Promoting Agriculture with the result that several individuals promptly wrote out hundred-dollar checks to help finance the campaign. The Society as a whole, however, took no official stand.

Sargent could have written letters-to-the-editor by the dozens, but money and moral support of influential persons were more important to McFarland. Nugent's bill was passed by the Senate in April 1920 but successfully headed off in the House Rules Committee the following month. Later in the year, Smith's bill expired quietly without reaching the floor, but Smith promised to introduce new measures to alter the Yellowstone boundaries when Congress convened in March 1921. Alerted to the forthcoming danger, McFarland circulated thousands of notices warning people to protest any legislation Smith might propose on the subject of Yellowstone.

In the meantime the conservationists concentrated their forces against Senator Tom Walsh of Montana, the sponsor of a bill which would authorize damming the Yellowstone River; their positive cause was the Jones-Esch bill asking the exemption of national parks and monuments from the scope of the Federal Water Power Act. McFarland hastily reminded Sargent to see what he could do to win Lodge's sympathy. Apparently Sargent and his allies did their share, for McFarland later thanked them, citing Lodge's role in the victory of the Jones-Esch bill in March 1921. The Walsh bill, despite some cunning maneuverings on the part of its sponsor, failed in a Senate committee in the face of testimony by conservationists, and Smith's threats were not carried out.

In June of the same year, a new crisis appeared. Representative Barbour of California, in an earnest effort to enlarge Sequoia Park in the Sierra Nevada, sponsored a bill

Last Glances

which surrendered part of the park area to the forest service and left a loophole for the development of water-power installations within the suggested boundaries. Conservationists, generally sympathetic to Barbour and his proposal, were anxious to eliminate the offending clauses. Sargent persuaded the Society for Promoting Agriculture to join other organizations in opposing the measure, and the Trustees issued a declaration proposing an amendment "to protect the entire area within the Park . . . this Society favors the creation of such a park if thus protected, and opposes the establishment of any national park without such protection."[7] In December 1923, a rewritten Barbour bill was passed by Congress, falling short of the conservationists' goals in area but, at least, protecting the land included within the park boundaries.

Sargent's role in national park defense in the 1920's was marginal, effective in a small, significant way. He gave of his money and influence with little enthusiasm and less faith that anything good would come of his efforts, for by that time his disillusionment with government was complete. Washington controlled what it should not (plant importation) and did not protect what it should (natural resources). He took no pains to disguise his scorn for the Forestry Service and particularly for the Department of Agriculture's horticultural officials, some of whom he characterized as colossal idiots. His outspoken criticism did not make him popular in Washington, a fact which did not bother him at all, though old friends like Fairchild withstood his abuse with more tolerance than he appreciated.

Local government, beginning with the days when the Boston City Council raised objections to the arboretum proposal, had proved almost as difficult to deal with as Washington. One of Sargent's pet irritations was the situation regarding the trees of Commonwealth Avenue in Boston's Back Bay section. In 1880, Charles Dalton, Chairman of the Board of Park Commissioners in Boston, had asked Sargent and Olmsted for a plan for replanting the central greens along the avenue. This was an elementary problem for a skilled

Giving Out Advice

307

landscape architect and an expert dendrologist, and their reply was correspondingly brief and simple.[8] The objectives of beauty and dignity, they opined, could be achieved best by planting one hundred and eighty trees of a single variety of European elm in single rows ten feet from the street line on each side of the mall from the Boston Common to Massachusetts Avenue. The single variety would insure uniformity, while the widely spaced rows would allow room for the mature development of individual specimens; the existing system of double rows inhibited full, healthy growth. Aside from a few remarks on replenishing the mall's impoverished soil, Sargent and Olmsted made no further recommendations.

Dalton accepted the Sargent-Olmsted proposal and forwarded it with favorable comments to the City Council for approval. The Councilmen rejected it. They argued that double rows of trees would produce a better effect than single rows, a point which was undoubtedly true for the short term. The politicians had some difficulty in seeing beyond their respective terms of office. The conflict of opinion stirred some comment in the local press, and people chose up sides either as two-row or four-row men. Sargent was peeved but could do nothing more after the decision was reached so he dropped the matter altogether. He had more important things to worry about. Heaping insult upon injury, the City proceeded to leave three blocks of the Avenue as before, to plant double rows of American elms on the next block, and double rows of various European elms thereafter. With remarkable obstinacy, the City had succeeded in ignoring the advice of the man whom it hired to design the park system, and its leading tree expert.

Sargent was not at all surprised when, twenty years later, citizens began to complain that the Commonwealth Avenue trees looked crowded, lopsided, and degenerate. Clearly the 1880 plantings had been disastrous; if Commonwealth Avenue was to maintain its reputation for dignity, the calamity must be reversed somehow. As though they thought he could produce some miraculous cure, the Park Commis-

Last Glances

sion appealed to Sargent again—Olmsted no longer practiced. If they expected a new proposal, they were sorely
disappointed, for he advised a gradual transition from existing conditions to two rows of a uniform variety of trees,
exactly what he and Olmsted had originally recommended.
This time, the two-row men prevailed and the City spent
ten thousand dollars undoing its previous work.

The four-row men, however, refused to go down in defeat.
When the subject of planting the three blocks from Arlington to Dartmouth streets (that portion which had not been
touched in 1880) arose about 1907, they succeeded in per-
suading the Park Commission to uproot *all* the trees, including those put in in 1903–04, and beginning all over
again with double rows. They made a mild concession to
Sargent's argument about space for development by proposing to stagger the rows. When Sargent realized that the Commission was taking the proposal seriously, he was furious.
With very little encouragement from three sympathetic,
rich friends, he composed a biting essay which they had
printed for general circulation.

> There is no question that four rows of trees in Common-
> wealth Avenue would produce a better effect than two
> rows, and that by the four-row plan the central walk and
> the two roadways would be more quickly shaded than by
> the trees in two rows. It is probable, moreover, that eight
> rows of trees would produce a better effect than four rows,
> but, unfortunately, certain conditions are fixed in the
> Avenue . . . trees even in two rows must become cramped
> and injured by the trees opposite them long before they
> can attain half their size.
>
> . . .
>
> In 1903–4 . . . the City spent ten thousand dollars in
> planting the two rows of trees on Commonwealth Ave-
> nue . . . The Commission now recommends a further
> expenditure of about twenty-four thousand dollars to
> undo its work of six years ago. This is something more
> than a waste of public money, for it destroys a good plan

Giving Out Advice

in the attempt to adopt one which it is impossible, under existing conditions, to carry out.[9]

Sargent's words dropped like rain on an ocean. The people with power ignored them. On Commonwealth Avenue, one may still see the double rows of lopsided trees, crammed together by their neighbors and afflicted with Dutch Elm disease.

As a Park Commissioner in the Town of Brookline for over forty years, Sargent succeeded better in imposing his views, with the consequence that the Brookline plantings are, on the whole, far superior to those of Boston, the latter excelling only where Olmsted was permitted to have his way. To be sure, Brookline was a wealthier community and its citizens were willing to spend money on parks and street trees; the politicians were less intimidated and the results correspondingly better.

Throughout his professional life, Sargent found it difficult to understand why people who asked his advice as an expert so often refused to take it or took it unwillingly. Dealing with governments was frustrating enough, but when he faced the thirty matronly ladies of the Mount Vernon Ladies' Association, Sargent confronted a real challenge.

Since 1853, when the Association was founded, the Mount Vernon Ladies dedicated their energies to the restoration and preservation of the George Washington homestead in a form approximating the original. Sargent's Mount Vernon entanglement began in 1901, when Mrs. Howard Townsend, Regent of the Association, invited him to make suggestions on the trees. Intrigued by the idea, Sargent went to visit Mount Vernon, cast a baleful eye over the plantings, and accepted the invitation on the condition that he be allowed to carry out his work without interference. The ladies, accustomed to having their own way, could not accept his terms and decided, on second thought, that a less important man might be easier to manipulate. Sargent retreated from the scene more than a bit annoyed with feminine stubbornness against which he had proved defenseless. The fact that

Last Glances

the ladies refused to accept him officially did not prevent them from addressing him with numerous questions which their less eminent, more malleable tree-man seemed unable to answer. Sargent offered such flippant replies as "Certainly Box-trees sometimes grow in limestone soil, but if the plants at Mount Vernon are doing well, why fool with them at all?" [10]
The lesser tree-expert had lesser results than might have been expected from a Sargent. Mrs. Townsend retired in 1909, and Miss Harriet Clayton Comegys succeeded her as Regent. It was Miss Comegys, willful in her own right, who managed to reverse the earlier Council decision and to bring Sargent back to Mount Vernon, she assured him, on his own terms. But even with the redoubtable Regent as his ally, Sargent's professional freedom was limited. With the ladies, however, his peculiar charm proved more effective than it had with government officials; sarcasm and obstinacy won the day for him. He complained to Miss Comegys, no doubt intending his remarks for all the ladies,

of course it is a very difficult matter to keep Mount Vernon trees in good condition if the removal of every worthless tree has to be passed on by a Committee of the Council, the members of which cannot be expected to have technical knowledge about trees and their requirements and prospects of long life. Some expert has got to be trusted in such matters. So far as the trees are concerned, the most important thing is the removal of the wreck of the Ash tree on the right hand side of the garden gate, which I have recommended for years, and the planting in its place of a young Ash tree and Holly. I hope to live long enough to see this Ash tree removed, but I confess some discouragement. [11]

In 1922, he was still bemoaning the fact that, after more than ten years, the Council persisted in disrupting his planting schemes. Discussing some particular point, he resorted to desperate arguments: "The thing which I feel sure about

Giving Out Advice

in this matter is that if Washington were here himself he would be on my side." [12]

Partly out of pique and partly out of interest, Sargent badgered them with extraneous advice unrelated to his proper work, thus indulging himself in the same luxury of expressing opinions as the amateurs who annoyed him. He said the sundial was anachronistic, complained about the iron rails near the kitchen entrance arguing that Washington would never have had them, and pointed out the sloppiness of the waste-disposal system.

Besides the alterations which he managed to bulldoze through the Council, in 1917 Sargent directed the plotting of all Mount Vernon trees on a map to serve as a record for any future work; he revised the diagrams in 1926 in part because some Washington diaries had recently been published and in part because there had been a severe storm. The ladies approved of the report; it was useful and did not make any changes. Furthermore, Sargent organized the return of what was presumed to be Washington's original Sago Palm. Inherited by Martha Washington and given away by her, the palm had come into the possession of Henry Winthrop Sargent at Wodenethe; through his family connections, Sargent secured the precious tree for Mount Vernon. On the whole, despite the sharp exchanges, Sargent usually managed to get his own way and achieved a good deal for the sake of the plantings.

Whether they took advantage of them or not, people demanded Sargent's talents for widely varied reasons, from amateurs who sought psychological reassurance and status in his approval to earnest plantsmen calling on his experience. As a consultant he was consistently—sometimes tactlessly—truthful, uttering opinions as though they were facts and facts as though they were axioms, thereby leaving his listeners with few alternatives. One gentleman, having transplanted a birch from the roadside to his estate, boasted of his accomplishment to Sargent who predicted, mercilessly, that the tree would die. Rising to the challenge, the gentleman nursed the birch along and showed it off, quite

Last Glances

alive, to Sargent a few years later. The Professor is said to have glanced at the tree and muttered, "there are things worse than death." [13]

Sargent gave assistance generously unless he detected hostility, stupidity, or treachery as he did with Pinchot and forestry legislation or with the Park Commissioners and the Commonwealth Avenue trees. In those circumstances he shifted abruptly to the role of critic, and the sting of his criticism knew no moderation. He was as loyal to his enemies as to his friends. Inevitably, his uncompromising, officious manner and his sharp tongue were as much a part of his reputation as his experience and ability, a fact which did not trouble him for a moment. Had he stopped to consider the situation, he probably would have reflected that a conservative blend of terror and respect worked, after all, in his favor.

Giving Out Advice

13

Looking Backward and Forward

The front hall of the Sargent house was high of stud, darkly paneled and immensely forbidding. It was of the kind to have been ornamented with bronze statues or suits of armor or battle shields. In the large drawing room that looked out onto a terrace at the rear, several people already sat and we stood at the entrance trying not to seem shy. The professor must have been watching for us and he came forward to greet us almost at once. He seemed less formidable than in his Arboretum office, his eyes more friendly, his handshake of the kind that expresses good will. He led us to a sofa corner where Mrs. Sargent was established. She was a large broad woman with a pale face and upswept chestnut hair pinned on top of her head, and she looked as though a deep chair or sofa corner filled with cushions would fit her better than anything upright and unyielding... We took our places, presently, ten or twelve of us, around a table in a dining room which I have remembered because of the conservatory upon which it opened at the far end, the end looking out over the grounds wherein were the magnificent trees and shrubs ... It was difficult at first to be aware of the human beings at the table— even though next me sat the professor's son Robeson, who was very nice to me—when so much that was more perfect than any person stood just beyond my shoulder.

Here in the conservatory, against a background of tall ferns and flowering mimosa, were azalea plants in white and pink, giant plants and ancient. Here too were white lilies and tall amaryllis striped more wonderfully than the zebra, and fine primulas from China by way of Kew in England. This bit of information about the primulas was given me by Robeson Sargent, himself a landscape gardener with a fondness for greenhouse plants ... I managed to turn away at last, to fix my eyes on the center of the table where the silver cock pheasants spread their tails between silver bonbon dishes, and to listen as my neighbor on either side carried along the conversation of a Sunday lunch party while eating the delicious food which was, in its way, as perfect as were the conservatory plants.[1]

These are the giddy reminiscences of Gladys Brooks, née Rice, recalling herself as an impressionable twenty-year-old when she and her bosom companion, Elizabeth Hoyt, passed part of a year studying landscape gardening at the Arboretum. Miss Rice and Miss Hoyt came from well-to-do, socially prominent families; otherwise, being females, they would never have been accepted as "students," much less invited to dinner, by Sargent. A recommendation from Beatrix Jones Farrand helped them. (The girls repaid Sargent handsomely for his favor; Gladys especially was a generous benefactor of the institution for years after.) The Sargent who confronted them at the Arboretum was the intimidating man figured in most portraits, his stern features fringed by a neat white beard and the proverbial gleam in his eye so well disguised that only the most imaginative people perceived it. The girls heard society gossip suggesting that Sargent had once been quite a man with the ladies but they found the rumors difficult to reconcile with the presence before them. Boston society, meanwhile, though liberal with romantic speculations was stingy with supporting data—if, indeed, there were any—and the rumors remained rumors.

At home Sargent lived in the English baronial style, with

all the pomp and circumstance of a titled Briton. A few miles from the city, Holm Lea had the ingredients of a country manor: land, lakes, plantings, stables, outbuildings, liveried servants, gardeners, stable boys, and, commanding all, a skilled, gracious mistress and an inflexible master. Sargent expended his interest and money on the development of the grounds and greenhouses, fussed over the care and labeling of his plants in Brookline as enthusiastically as he did at the Arboretum, and worried lest they come by any foul play. He trusted his longtime chief gardener Charles Sander, winner of more than one Massachusetts Horticultural Society award, with precious propagating material and general management, but he checked every plant regularly. With a gesture of noblesse oblige, he permitted the neighborhood children to bicycle through the property—every parent warned his child against transgressions—provided they stayed along the pathways and did not pick the flowers. In Sargent's lifetime, Holm Lea became a horticultural show-case, and for several years on Sundays in May and June when the lilacs, wisterias, rhododendrons, and azaleas blossomed, the Sargents opened the grounds and glass houses to the public, which reciprocated by arriving in throngs. On these occasions Sargent stood around looking aristocratic and trying not to betray his nervousness over the well-being of the plants.

Inside the main house, however, Sargent did not care for crowds and loathed large—from his point of view, purpose-less—parties. He attended them as infrequently as possible, leaving unobtrusively at the earliest possible moment, and he gave them only in cases of urgency, such as his daughters' debuts, or in deference to his wife. Small, elegant, frequent dinner parties suited him better; the men could retire after dinner for brandy, cigars, discussions of the stock market and politics, and, more often than not, a few words concern-ing the financial condition of the Arnold Arboretum. Dinner at Holm Lea was a ceremony which most guests appreciated, for the Sargents served fine food and superb wines in an elegant setting. Sargent was so insistent on good form that

Last Glances

316

a cousin recalled a dinner at Holm Lea in the 1920's during Prohibition with a butler behind each chair and seven crystal wine glasses at every place setting. The wine glasses remained empty throughout the meal.

Sargent's professional orderliness carried over into his domestic life. In the early days when he was still working a good part of the time at Holm Lea, he did not tolerate interruptions from his family and inspired his children with "fear rather than love," according to his middle daughter Molly (Mary).[2] When they were youngsters, he appeared to them much less as a man than as a myth, visiting them at brief, appointed times; an inquisitor, judge, authority, and dispenser of formal affection. Most of the time he was busy with the Arboretum or some botanical pursuit, and when he was so occupied in the house, the children were forbidden to distract him. They tiptoed by, whispering, awed by the thought of their father and his mysteriously important work, and impressed by the presence of a Great Man.

Soft, ample Mary Sargent balanced the severe patriarch, lavishing her affection upon her children. "She took care of us when we were well and when we were ill, she attended to our education, she loved us and was inordinately loved in return, she defended us against our sterner parent, she stood by us when we made mistakes, was always on the lookout for a troubled or sad expression, drew our friends about her and judged accurately and independently any issue connected with our lives."[3] A romantic woman, brimming with warmth, she indulged her children with the unrestrained love which she could not permit herself to display to her husband.

As his children matured, Sargent became more involved in their lives, for he distinguished between "people" and children, the latter being little more than lovable objects to his mind, scarcely worthy of serious consideration. By the time he showed genuine interest in them, the effects of their upbringing were etched on their characters and, thanks to Mary Sargent's devotion, they laughed and relaxed more easily than their father. Henrietta and Molly, the elder girls,

Looking Backward and Forward

grew into stately beauties, tall, stunning young women. Eminently marriageable, they enjoyed amusing social lives. In 1898 at the age of twenty-three, Henrietta wed Guy Lowell, an architect with an ornamental family tree, and the couple moved to a nearby home in Brookline. The Lowells had no children. Henrietta, a gay and intelligent creature, managed Lowell's office during the War while he was in Italy. Molly, much admired by her relative John Singer Sargent,* was almost thirty before she married Dr. Nathaniel Bowditch Potter, a clinical specialist in the study of metabolic diseases. Potter was attached to Columbia University, so the couple lived in New York, making frequent trips to Boston. In 1909, Molly provided Sargent with his first grandchild, Nathalie, who delighted him greatly.

Sargent's youngest daughter, Alice, was most like her father and grandfather. She possessed the strong Sargent will and, unfortunately, she also resembled her father in appearance. She draped her large, rawboned frame in heavy tweeds, perched a mannish hat on her head, smoked cigarettes in public, drove recklessly, ran around with what was considered in Boston society as a "fast"—but acceptable— crowd, and spent the warmer days sailing at Marblehead. Alice remained single and lived at Holm Lea.

Sargent favored his older son, Robeson. As a young man, Robeson resembled his father physically but had his mother's gentle good nature. It is conceivable that Sargent hoped to name his son as his successor as Director of the Arboretum, for he guided Robeson into the world of plants, taking him on collecting trips in the Southwest and on travels to South America and around the world. The boy's flair for landscape design and success in the profession delighted him. About 1909, Robeson fell in love with an exceptionally pretty girl of Spanish origin, Maria Cecilia de Acosta, and decided to marry; this proved to be one of the rare occasions when the father defended a child against his mother. Mary Sargent

---

* John Singer Sargent painted an oil of Henrietta and Molly on board Herbert Mason Sears' yacht *Constellation*.

Last Glances

opposed the marriage violently because the girl was a Roman Catholic. As a devout Episcopalian, the idea that her son might wed a Catholic repelled her, and she suffered an unusual outburst of tearful protests over the matter until Sargent interceded with the declaration that the boy should be allowed to do as he wished. The second son, Charles, marked by his father for a financial career, married another beautiful woman from New York, Dagmar Wetmore, a direct descendant of Richard Mather, father of Increase and Cotton Mather. The Charles Sprague Sargents VII lived in New York, where Charles rose to partnership in a banking firm.

By 1912, then, all the children had married except Alice. Henrietta and Robeson lived close by and paid their parents frequent visits. Mrs. Sargent's health was bad, and her doctor often confined her to bed. Sargent was over seventy and, having disregarded George Englemann's advice against rich foods over the last forty odd years, he continued to be plagued by gout. He limped severely, leaning heavily on a sturdy cane. His secretary noticed with amusement that when he arrived at his office desk he always landed in his chair with a thud, necessitating frequent repairs to the caned seat. Yielding to the pressures of mechanization, he traveled now more often by motor car than by horse and carriage. His automobile was a great Rolls Royce fitted with polished brass headlights and a brass rubber bulb horn, and driven either by a chauffeur (whose seat was exposed to the capricious elements) or, if he was free, by Robeson. On a sunny day it was a special treat to drive up to visit his cousin Winthrop Sargent VII at his vacation home at Bass Rocks in Gloucester and to sit with Winthrop rocking on the porch, looking out over the moody Atlantic. Except for a barely perceptible loss of momentum, Sargent lived by the rules which he had followed for half a century, subscribing to the same moral standards and the same scientific theory. He was living proof of his own observation that "it is always a good plan to leave well enough alone, especially in the case of old plants and old people." [4]

Around 1916, Sargent met a "new" Sargent, the most

Looking Backward and Forward

319

celebrated Sargent of them all, John Singer: the current rage of Europe, the artist for whom every fashionable woman longed to pose, the painter of the widely discussed portrait of Isabella Gardner. Charles Sargent had followed his younger cousin's rising career with something more than casual interest, for he was fond of painting and curious about the distant blood relationship. He did not, however, presume to contact the painter on his earlier trips to Boston. John, for his part, knew nothing of his botanist cousin, for he spent most of his life in Europe, devoted to his art, and felt little concern for Sargent genealogy and even less for botany. Molly brought the two men together. She met John in Paris and he was so taken by her beauty that he invited her to the London opening of Sir Philip Sassoon's ballroom. Molly introduced her father to the artist when he came to the United States in 1916. The Boston Sargent felt himself in the presence not only of a superlative artist ("for more than thirty years . . . the greatest living figure in the world of art") but also, despite his European upbringing, a veritable Sargent with "the robust rectitude, modesty, industry and power of sustained concentration which have been found in other descendants of Epes Sargent." [5] John and Charles were only third cousins once removed and separated in age by fifteen years, yet they looked enough alike to elicit the comment that "[t]hey are plainly chips from the same block." [6] The two men, so disparate in background and profession, so uncannily alike in character and appearance, settled into a comfortable undemanding relationship.

John was in Boston to work on the murals for the Boston Public Library and for the rotunda dome at the Museum of Fine Arts. He was also much in demand to do charcoal portraits at four hundred dollars apiece. He kept a studio in the Pope Building on Columbus Avenue while living at the Hotel Vendome; in 1919, he took rooms in the new Copley Plaza. He visited Holm Lea frequently, and sometimes accompanied his cousin out to Winthrop's place at Bass Rocks to join them in rocking on the front porch. Boston society welcomed him with open arms, and he needed no introductions from his resident cousins; both Harvard and Yale bestowed doctorates on him.

Charles Sargent advanced into old age with majesty; encounters with his grandchildren, upon whom he doted, contributed to softening the sharp contours of his character, tempting him now and then to indulge in some alien gesture of affectionate mischief. But years of habitual severity and restraint were already engraved on his face too deeply to be erased in late life. John Singer Sargent captured his cousin's stern, haughty essence in a charcoal sketch drawn in 1919. Charles suffered no indication of intellectual weakening. Only his adherence to nineteenth-century ideas and forms betrayed his static spirit, and he became, more and more, the "intellectual mastodon" to which Muir had likened him: a creature of awesome dignity verging on obsolescence. He moved through his days with the deliberate, assured pace that had served him all his adult years, toward death, which neither attracted nor frightened him.

In 1917, the Sargent family circle began to disintegrate. Sargent's brother-in-law, James Macmaster Codman, died in January of that year. On March 19, 1918, Robeson, who was on a trip in the Midwest, went to bed perfectly well in the evening and died in his sleep, presumably of heart failure. The body was shipped back to Brookline for burial in the family plot in Walnut Hill. At his funeral, Mary Sargent, her own strength sapped by illness, wept pitifully and, sensing her husband's hidden distress, turned to him and murmured, "Well, Father, your little boy has come home." Sargent, in careful control of himself, ignored the remark and turned away to comment to his daughter-in-law Dagmar that the spring flower show at Horticultural Hall had never been better, leaving her with the indelible impression that he was incapable of feeling emotion, much less of expressing it. He had stood stolidly at his father's grave; now he stood at his best-loved son's. Words, which had been of little use to him all his life, failed him again, and the tender-

Looking Backward and Forward

est he could muster came a week later in a letter to his colleague in New Orleans, Reginald Cocks: "We have been so often together," he wrote, "in different and often remote parts of the world that the bond between us was a very close one."[7] Later when he prepared Robeson's biographical sketch for the Sargent genealogy, he wrote only one clinical sentence.

In March 1919, young Charles Sargent and his wife Dagmar lost their third child, a boy only a year and a half old. In July, Molly's husband Nathaniel Potter died of an incurable disease in Santa Barbara, California, where the Potters had moved for the sake of his health. Sargent was fond of his son-in-law, proud of the work he was doing, and saddened by his death. The bereaved Molly returned to Brookline to help care for her mother, whose health suddenly declined rapidly.

A month after Potter's death, Mary Sargent died of diabetes, at the age of sixty-six. It was as if her last reserves had been spent in grief over her children's tragedies. Mrs. Potter noted that her mother's last conscious act was to go to her husband's bedroom to make sure he was comfortable. Bishop Lawrence wrote of her: "Whenever she entered a room, be it a drawing-room filled with guests, a bedroom with one solitary invalid, or an institution filled with forlorn and wayward girls, the atmosphere was immediately charged with vitality, sympathy, and cheer. She did not have to do or even say anything in order to be felt; her presence was enough; and her voice and deeds were the unconscious expression of a very warm heart and a very friendly spirit."[8] Her death created a vacuum, for she had been the soul of Holm Lea, and no one knew that better than her husband. Two days after she died he wrote a friend: "The glory and the true meaning of Holm have gone forever, but I have the Arboretum to work for, and enough work laid out to occupy every day of my remaining years."[9] Appropriately, he closed Holm Lea to the public for the next six years. With its promise of indefinite life, the Arboretum served him as a refuge. Eight days after Mary Sargent's death, he sat at his desk in

Last Glances

Jamaica Plain dictating instructions for packaging seeds to Joseph Hers in China and requesting seeds of *Cupressus guadalupensis* from Alice Eastwood in San Francisco.[10]

The Arboretum did not fail Sargent. It matured and improved despite the war and, as he had promised, it filled up his time; like its director, as it aged it lost some of its family. Jackson Dawson died during the summer of 1916, and Faxon died in 1918. Though no human being can replace another, one man can do someone else's work. Sargent put the propagating department in the hands of William Judd, a Kew-trained Englishman who had worked as Dawson's understudy since Sargent brought him from England in 1913. Judd, meticulous and self-conscious, kept detailed diaries of his life. With Dawson gone, he happily put the propagating area in order; though they had been friendly, Dawson's mess had always annoyed him. Judd was an excellent, efficient plantsman and a popular public speaker despite his grammatical lapses. When Faxon died, Sargent elevated Rehder to the rank of curator of the herbarium, but there was no one to take Faxon's place as an artist. He had published 1,920 plates during his thirty-six years at the Arboretum. Sargent found an artist named Mary Gill, of Washington, D.C., to finish the drawings for a new edition of his *Manual*. The work of the Arboretum continued without a pause.

The war should have had some effect on normal operations, but Sargent determined that the repercussions would be minimal. When the United States entered the war, the University found itself confronted with new problems: decreased student enrollment, drain on funds, shortage of faculty and administrative officers, questions of military education as a temporary part of the curriculum. Moreover, Harvard administrators grappled with abstract questions, for the war had brought into focus new social, moral, and intellectual values of profound bearing on the philosophy of higher education. The University committed itself to the war effort, providing military programs for officer training.

Looking Backward and Forward

Dormitories were converted to barracks; outside the classroom students were subject to military discipline and, in effect, Harvard became a military school. Simultaneously, financial gifts to the University fell off drastically. A 1916–17 projected Alumni program to raise ten million dollars for the general endowment fund was postponed; the proceeds for 1917–18 were only half of what they had been the year before.

None of Sargent's professional staff was drafted, and since the Arboretum did not participate in the regular University teaching program, it was not involved with the student population. As a result, Sargent steered the Arboretum through the hostilities with negligible deviations in routine and no introspective meditations, although some individuals, like Wilson and Judd, had strong personal feelings. It is curious to discover in the Report of the President and Treasurer for the year 1916–17 that thirty-three of thirty-eight reporting departments of the University noted that the war had in some way affected their work. The five which made absolutely no references to the conflict were the Fogg Museum, the Museum of Comparative Zoology, Radcliffe College, the Gray Herbarium, and the Arboretum. By the following year, the MCZ, Radcliffe, and the Gray Herbarium found cause to mention the war, leaving the Fogg and the Arboretum as the only departments which gave it no official recognition.

As a botanist or horticulturist, Sargent might have ignored the international situation altogether, but as an administrator and businessman he was concerned for the disturbance threatened his ambitions for building up the endowment fund. In 1916, he convinced Henry S. Hunnewell (Trustee of the Massachusetts Society for Promoting Agriculture, banker, son of H. H. Hunnewell, and lover of horticulture) and William C. Endicott of the Board of Overseers, of the necessity for raising money, and they spearheaded a campaign which grossed $219,950 for the endowment for a fiscal year when most of the University reported a falling off of income. By the war's end Sargent could rely on an annual income of at least $38,547.30, not counting gifts for

Last Glances

immediate use. If this was not financial security, it was surely an improvement over former years.

Instead of complaining about the war, Sargent worried about the weather. The summer of 1917 was dry enough to cause plant damage; then in November a sudden freeze followed heavy rains, and Boston began its coldest winter in recorded weather history. Many species perished or suffered from the cold, though not as many as the staff feared. The most encouraging sign was that Wilson's Chinese introductions fared relatively well over the winter. Between 1914 and 1918, the exchange program of plants and seeds continued as usual with the exception that nothing was received from or sent to Germany, Austria-Hungary, or Italy. In 1917–18 the propagating department was shifted from its old location on land leased from the Adams Nervine Asylum to a plot at the corner of Centre and Orchard streets, where improved facilities were constructed. In June of 1918, the Arboretum published the final volume of the *Bradley Bibliography*. From start to finish, Rehder had spent the better part of eighteen years of largely tedious effort to complete the task, the costs had exceeded the original estimates and the income on the Bradley contribution so the funds had been supplemented by further donations from Miss Bradley and others. The five volumes ran to almost four thousand pages. Wilson was off collecting in Korea and Formosa, and Thomas Grant Harbison and E. J. Palmer made headway with their botanical investigations of the flora of the southern United States under Sargent's direction. While men slaughtered each other in Europe, the Arnold Arboretum successfully maintained its course of vigorous growth. After all, the Arboretum was Sargent's business; the war was not. Consistently, when the war ended there was still no change of tempo.

The policy which Sargent had set for the Arboretum emerged clearly by the postwar years. Given the absence of precedence, Sargent's lack of formal training or experience, and the loosely worded instructions of the 1872 indenture, the statement of institutional goals and range of activities

Looking Backward and Forward

Alfred Rehder, 1917

had been defined slowly, sometimes haphazardly, according to the Director's inclinations. Over the years the program evolved into a thorough investigation within a limited scope. With the exception of Wilson's publications on lilies, the

Last Glances

Arboretum staff was exclusively concerned with woody plants. They investigated ligneous species in their scientific context and in their practical application. Within this framework, Sargent set priorities. For practical purposes, the appearance of the grounds topped his list, closely followed by carefully cultivated relationships with patrons. The approach aimed shamelessly and expediently at harvesting the funds essential to the effectiveness of the Arboretum on all levels and, very likely, to its permanence. In this situation, priority was not confused with values. Sargent did not judge horticulture to be either more or less important than botanical research; he simply knew that, for all practical purposes, the support of botanical research depended upon the support of horticulture. Yet he did not like to draw a fine line between applied and theoretical science because he was as much concerned with the economic or artistic merits of a species as he was with its taxonomic status or its geographic distribution. His own bibliography, including the Census report on forestry, the *Silva*, and popular writings about the Arboretum, suggests the range of his appreciation.

In keeping with his notion, he engaged men versed in both botany and horticulture, a relatively rare combination. In general—L. H. Bailey is the outstanding exception—the rule was that botanists worked with wild plants, horticulturists with cultivated species, and the two seldom met. Men like Torrey, Engelmann, and Gray had no serious interest in garden plants; and horticulturists did not bother their heads with botanical literature. But the backbone of the Arboretum staff—Sargent, Rehder, Wilson, and Jack—dealt with both. They were all experienced field botanists; they knew taxonomic techniques; they were familiar with popular and scientific literature; they knew cultivated plants. Within the restricted world of ligneous flora, they were versatile scholars. They divided their working hours between the field, the herbarium and the library and visits to gardens, private estates, and nurseries. They kept themselves informed of the decisions of botanical societies, forestry associations,

Looking Backward and Forwards

conservation lobbies, and horticultural clubs. In its combined publications, its plant exploration and introduction program, and its physical presence, the Arboretum had developed into a uniquely authoritative institution not in spite of but because of the limitations which Sargent had set for it. Since the demise of *Garden and Forest* in 1897, Sargent was skeptical about publishing periodicals. Having tried and failed once with a broad format, he had no desire to fail again, yet he needed some kind of regular outlet for information about the plants in the Arboretum. In 1911, therefore, the Arboretum began publishing the modest "Bulletin of Popular Information" consisting of two or three page articles at regular intervals in spring, summer, and fall, about plants of immediate interest in the Arboretum, similar to Jack's old "Notes from the Arnold Arboretum" which used to appear in *Garden and Forest*. Sargent wrote most of the crusty little articles in his usual style: direct, manicured, and full of information for curious amateurs. For some reason, he never signed the papers.[11] In 1919, in a more ambitious effort, the Arboretum began to publish its own scientific journal on a quarterly basis, a step which contributed to its reputation in botanical circles and had the advantage of combining the scientific research of staff members under a single cover. Sargent listed himself as editor of the *Journal of the Arnold Arboretum*, but from the beginning it was Rehder who did the bulk of the work under the Director's ever-watchful eye. Wilson and Rehder were busy with their monograph on azaleas, for which Wilson wrote up the Old World species while Rehder worked out the New World representatives. Meanwhile Wilson—since 1919 Assistant Director—plotted the course of his new journey to Australia, India, and Africa and in July 1920 left the United States for two years.

The longer Sargent worked in taxonomy, the more apparent it was to him that the study involved an indefinite number of revisions, that a text was only complete by relative standards. During the postwar years he concentrated on updating his *Manual*, which had gone through two printings in 1905. The work resulted in a second edition in 1922 and some miscellaneous shorter articles under the heading of "Notes on North American Trees," produced as by-products of his investigations along the way. He neither forgot nor abandoned *Crataegus* and its haunting perplexities; if he had not quite made peace with the thorns, he had, he thought, finished most of the work. Since 1905, however, he had accumulated enough new material to feel the necessity for a new *Manual*. He had prepared the first edition quickly, largely by distilling the *Silva* for compact packaging. The second edition involved a good deal of fresh field work, a little of which he did himself in the southern states, but most of which he had grown too old and lame to accomplish effectively. For the field work, he had five principal collectors: Alfred Rehder made several trips south and eventually helped prepare the new keys; Alice Eastwood, the first great lady botanist and Curator and Head of the Department of Botany of the California Academy of Sciences, collected in California and made special trips to Alaska and New Mexico for Sargent; R. S. Cocks at Tulane tramped the Louisiana forests; E. J. Palmer and T. G. Harbison explored the southeastern states and the Missouri-Texas region respectively. These areas, with emphasis on the South, were the ones Sargent singled out for intensive investigation.

The collectors worked hard, as people who worked for Sargent usually did, but none worked harder than Palmer and Harbison.[12] Following complicated itineraries and directives set by Sargent's needs, they roamed the southern forests, striving to be somewhere in time for the flowering of one species and somewhere else to pick fruits of another. Sargent deluged them with requests, for more specimens, seeds, new collections at old localities, and more detailed descriptions—what, for example, was the anther color on that *Crataegus* specimen from Texas? His demands were seemingly endless, his letters never friendly, though not exactly unfriendly, but intensely businesslike. With monumental patience, Harbison and Palmer filled Sargent's orders as well as they could, dutifully replied to his letters, and carefully worked over their collections in winter and between field trips. Cocks and Miss Eastwood came in for their share of correspondence, sometimes receiving two letters in one day, as Sargent resumed his old ritual of "100 questions" from the days of Engelmann and the Census report. Rehder, mercifully, was on hand to receive most of his orders orally.

Sargent completed the second edition of the *Manual* by September 1921. He added eighty-nine species and many new varieties of trees to his original count; he included only twenty-one new species of *Crataegus*, indicating a fair amount of self-restraint. He demoted *Amelanchier obovalis* and *Cercocarpus parvifolius* from trees to shrubs. The last sentences of the new Preface were not characteristic. "The new edition of the *Manual*," Sargent wrote, "contains the results of forty-four years of my continuous study of the trees of North America carried on in every part of the United States and in many foreign countries. If these studies in any way serve to increase the knowledge and the love of trees I shall feel that these years have not been misspent." It was a simple testimony and, for a man who seldom used the word "love," a moving one.

Considering the agreement between Harvard University and the trustees of James Arnold's will as its beginning, the Arnold Arboretum reached its fiftieth birthday in 1922, in the eighty-first year of the life of its director, who paused to reflect upon that half century and to measure the cumulative achievements of his institutional offspring. By the process of accretion, the Arboretum had nearly doubled its original size of one hundred twenty-five acres, the most recent additions being sixteen acres purchased by patrons from the Bussey Institution in 1919 and a fourteen-acre plot purchased in 1922. Sargent estimated that there were anywhere between five and six thousand species of woody trees and shrubs growing on the grounds (including, of course, the hundreds of "species" of *Crataegus*) representing 324 genera in 87 families, labeled and mapped although

Last Glances

Sargent in the Arboretum, ca. 1904

Looking Backward and Forward

not, it seems, in any way that made it practical to count them to the nearest hundred. The figures take on real meaning when measured against the 123 species that Sargent counted on the original land area before he began systematic planting.[13] In a paper written for the *Journal* in commemoration of the first fifty years, Sargent went on for nineteen pages listing introductions by the Arboretum: 1,932 species and varieties introduced into cultivation in the United States, of which 778 came into cultivation for the first time anywhere, and that does not include the 601 species of *Crataegus*.* Wilson, of course, was the great instrument of Arboretum introductions.

The herbarium, once only a thousand sheets in Dwight House on Sargent's Brookline estate, had increased its size two hundred times. The library, beginning with the few books that Sargent had bought for his own use, had grown to 35,500 bound volumes and 8,000 pamphlets which the librarian, Ethelyn Tucker, had arranged systematically and listed in a catalogue. In addition there was a collection of almost ten thousand photographs of trees and shrubs, types of vegetation, gardens, and scenery, including 2,800 pictures which Wilson had taken on his numerous journeys, all mounted on cardboard and arranged in drawers.

Sargent, with all the advantages of hindsight, offered in his retrospective report the best definition of what the institution did and did not aim to do:

> The Arnold Arboretum is not a School of Forestry or of Landscape Gardening. It is a station for the study of trees as individuals in their scientific relations, economic properties and cultural requirements and possibilities.

---

* The publication of the list of introductions was rather daring because, particularly in later years, it was difficult to keep track of every new plant which came into the United States; doubtless there were some people who found reason to quarrel with Sargent's enumeration. In fact, his own files reveal that more than forty of the plants he listed came to the Arboretum from United States nurseries. Although there may be room for argument over details, the general picture is no less impressive.

Last Glances

On the information gathered in museums like the Arnold Arboretum successful silviculture and landscape gardening are dependent, for silviculture is the cultivation on a large scale of the trees most valuable in a particular locality, and landscape gardening demands a knowledge of the individual plants which can be naturally associated for the decoration of parks and gardens.

... [I]t has been managed not merely as a New England museum but as a national and international institution working to increase knowledge of trees in all parts of the world and as anxious to help a student in Tasmania or New Caledonia as in Massachusetts. An institution with such ambitions must be equipped to answer any question about any tree growing in any part of the world which may be addressed to it. During the first fifty years of the Arnold Arboretum only the foundations of such an establishment have been laid.[14]

But laid well enough, he might have added, that students journeyed from China and Japan to study their native trees in Jamaica Plain.

The role which Sargent outlined for the Arboretum went far beyond anything conceived by Arnold's trustees or Harvard, to say nothing of the City of Boston. His global program, however, posed complications. As long as the Arboretum confined its activities to the North Temperate Zone, it could base its research upon living specimens, a condition which under the existing circumstances could not be applied to tropical trees and shrubs. The ideal solution to the problem would be some kind of national arboretum, a central organization with various substations in different climatic zones of the United States—an American version of Kew. When he wrote the section on arboreta for Bailey's *Cyclopedia of Horticulture* in 1914, Sargent scorned the idea that the government should take charge of such an operation on the basis that "political association is not conducive to the best scientific research" and hinted broadly at a network with himself and the Arnold Arboretum in control—

Looking Backward and Forward

333

"conditions of permanence and freedom in this country will best be obtained in connection with one of the great endowed universities." [15] While Sargent was strongly attached to this scheme in theory, he saw little hope of putting it into practice during his lifetime. In his fifty-year report he proposed only that the Arboretum should broaden the scope of its activities to secure photographs and herbarium specimens of every kind of tree in the world with an immediate emphasis on tropical trees.

Even as he described his objectives, Sargent was closer to token fulfillment of his scheme than he realized, for in 1926, when Mr. Edward F. Atkins died, his will provided that the heirs lease his estate of over 200 acres in Soledad, Cuba, to Harvard; the University, in turn, placed the Atkins garden under the administration of the Arboretum. Goodale, who died in April 1922, and Oakes Ames had been friendly with Atkins since the beginning of the century and had advised him on his sugar cane production; Atkins, in return, allowed them to use his estate as an informal biological research station. Sargent, on the other hand, had never visited Cuba and evidenced no particular interest in the Soledad garden until the early spring of 1926, when he appears to have heard of Atkins' intention to leave the estate to Harvard. In February, he sent Jack down to collect and study the plant material; in March, he discussed the possibilities with Henry Hunnewell of the Arnold Arboretum Visiting Committee, who acted as liaison with the University administrators; in May, Atkins died.[16] Sargent himself did not live long enough to administer the Cuban station, where he had hoped to establish an arboretum of native Cuban trees. In the long run, his dream was but a dream, and his more modest hope of building complete records of the world's trees did not effectively survive his administration.

The plea for widely expanded field work was the first of five areas of growth described by Sargent in the fifty-year report. The other four projects were: a department to study tree diseases; a department to investigate tree-damaging insects; a plant breeding station; rose and rock gardens,

Last Glances

projects which had not been launched in the past because small plants were considered easy targets for vandals. Sargent squeezed his most significant comment on his grand design into one terse terminal sentence: "Only a larger endowment is needed to make possible these Arboretum activities and extensions." [17]

Even taking into account the limitations mentioned in the fifty-year report, the Arboretum had no rivals as a dendrological station in the United States, and there were very few comparable institutions throughout the world. The arboretum at Kew contained the only living collection which Sargent admitted was superior to his own, and he praised the Arboretum National des Barres near Paris, but otherwise there was scarcely a place which was comparable. In the United States, there were only two competing gardens: the New York Botanical Garden, north of Manhattan in Bronx Park, and the Missouri Botanical Garden in St. Louis. Neither institution restricted its displays or studies to woody plants. Missouri, or "Shaw's Garden" as it was sometimes known, claimed to be older than the Arboretum, a detail which Sargent found annoying because the establishment was dated from 1859, when the grounds were part of Henry Shaw's private estate instead of from 1889, when Shaw died and willed the garden to the public. Before his death Shaw had consulted Engelmann and Gray on proposals for a public garden, and Gray had chosen William Trelease as first director. Trelease resigned in 1912 and was succeeded by George Moore. The existing plantings, Engelmann's herbarium—including 57,000 specimens which Engelmann had persuaded Shaw to purchase from the German botanist John Jacob Bernhardi in 1858—a library, and Shaw's generous endowment provided a strong nucleus for development. In New York, Nathaniel Lord Britton, half-jokingly called "Great Britton" or, "Nathaniel, Lord Britton," by some of his colleagues, reigned as Director-in-Chief over 230 acres of garden, conservatories, and woodlands, and carefully built a large herbarium particularly rich in neotropical species. Relations between Sargent and Britton were cool

Looking Backward and Forward

at best, dating back to the 1890's, when Britton had unceremoniously dismissed Sargent's recommendations regarding the layout of the New York garden.[18] Despite Sargent's feelings about Britton, however, he could not fail to acknowledge the stunning growth of the New York complex as a new focus of botanical activity. Still, neither New York nor Missouri challenged the Arboretum as the American authority on woody plants.

During the fifty years of the Arboretum's existence, other smaller, less complex gardens, sometimes with and sometimes without associated research functions, opened to the public throughout the country: Henry E. Huntington's showy botanical garden in San Marino, California, the Highland Park Arboretum in Rochester, New York, the thirteen-acre Eloise Butler Wild Flower Garden in Minneapolis. "It is a noteworthy fact that the United States is beginning to appreciate botanic gardens," mused John Merle Coulter in 1917. "This appreciation may be relatively superficial as yet, but the superficial is usually the preliminary step that leads to the fundamental. The desirability of botanic gardens was not obvious when large areas in a state of nature were available to almost every one; but when we developed congested populations in cities and made artificial most of our open areas, the thought of botanic gardens began to take form." [19] Congress eventually reflected the public's new interest in 1927, when it passed a bill authorizing the Department of Agriculture to establish a national arboretum, but it took the legislators several years to appropriate sufficient funds for the purpose.

If Coulter was right and the swelling number of botanic gardens could be read as a measure of public interest, he was observing only a part of a complicated pattern, for the war had forced changes of greater consequence than the temporary accommodations of wartime. True, city populations had increased rapidly, and city dwellers found reason to become grateful for natural spaces whether they were ordinary parks or bona fide botanic gardens. But the changes in the complexion and attitudes of the public were slower to

Last Glances

register than statistical evidence of migration. Sargent's idea of "public" went back to an older era and fixed on a tiny, mighty fragment of the total population; he neither needed nor knew the rest; it was rumored that he threw checks amounting to less than ten dollars into the wastepaper basket without sending any acknowledgement. The "public" he so avidly desired to educate on the subject of trees and shrubs was a respectable, cultured, influential, and preferably a rich one, composed largely of people like himself. There was an understandable, if obsolete, basis for his narrow outlook, for in the Victorian heyday, serious horticulture had been a rich man's hobby, like sailing and tennis. To Sargent's mind, there was an obvious link between patronage, participation, and power.

World War I acted as a great equalizer; the rich man's psychological defenses proved no stronger than those of the middle-income or poor man; when the killing was finally over, the mood of the country was cynical regardless of income bracket. The voters exchanged their visionary president for a hard-headed conservative, who promised a return to "normalcy." The 1918 income tax law weighed heavily—beginning at 6 per cent over $2,000—on the rich man. The postwar decade produced a new permissiveness in manners and morals for which the prohibition amendment was but a shabby disguise.

Sargent had no sense about social change, for age had only petrified his nineteenth-century attitudes. He had outlived most of his contemporaries, professional colleagues, and friends—even his favorite son—and wanted, finally, to be left alone. He was too old and too rigid to cope with a changing order. He had invested a lifetime in his Arboretum; he concentrated the effort of his last years in protecting that investment, for one thing was clear to him; the Arboretum must continue to earn its right to exist, a task which would be more difficult in the future than it had been in the past. Coulter's cheerful vision of city folk flocking to the neighborhood botanic garden in search of education and spiritual regeneration omitted the complementary problem: as the

Looking Backward and Forward

population density in urban areas increased, mounting pressures would be brought to bear on parkland for building roads, housing, schools, and business facilities. The most effective weapon against invasion was a beautiful garden with a vital research program. Every line of reasoning led Sargent back to the inescapable conclusion that the Arboretum must have a larger endowment.

In fiscal 1922–23, the Arboretum endowment reached nearly one million dollars, yielding slightly over $51,000 in available income. Expenditures were particularly heavy that year because of the construction of three brick residences for Arboretum staff members, the total expenditures exceeding the income by $66,518.80. As usual, Sargent tried to compensate for the difference by soliciting gifts for immediate use. More often than not he succeeded in balancing the budget with some to spare for addition to the endowment, but in 1922–23 he fell short of meeting his needs by $30,000, a failure which did nothing to encourage his sense of financial security.[20] In his report to President Lowell for that year, he pointed out that most of the staff members had come to him with justified requests for higher wages and that the expense of general maintenance had risen sharply since the war because of the increased cost of labor.[21] Enlightened about the financial problems, the Visiting Committee seized upon the half-century anniversary as the occasion for an intensive fund-raising campaign and prepared a circular describing the situation in precise terms: "to meet the deficits of income the Director has been obliged for a long time personally to raise every year from forty to fifty thousand dollars, which have been given usually by not over one hundred and twenty [an average of around $375] persons chiefly living in greater Boston." Soliciting donations of ten dollars or more, the circulars were mailed to a screened list of 22,000 plant amateurs on a nationwide basis. The approach was new for the Arboretum and foreign to Sargent's method of acquiring funds. The members of the Visiting Committee evidently sensed what Sargent failed to recognize, that the days of great patrons were drawing to

Last Glances

depend on a few gifts of one,
___ars. The time had arrived to seek a
smaller contributions and broadly based
___ort. Skeptical though he was of the idea, Sar-
___ighted in its success. Within a few months the drive
___ned almost $16,000 from 778 people (an average of around $20) in all but five states; the following year 800 donors contributed an even larger amount. The total was far less than Sargent needed, but it was a boost to his morale. Personally, he kept his faith in the old ways. Mailing half a dozen copies of his fifty-year report to C. L. Hutchinson, a Chicago banker and member of the Visiting Committee, he wrote:

> I am anxious to make possible through this publication a greater publicity for the Arboretum and I venture to hope that you may send some of these copies to the Chicago papers and to individuals who might become interested in it. I should like to think that one of them might fall into the hands of John D. Rockefeller, Jr. or his wife.[22]

The thought that plagued Sargent in his last years was that he might be indispensable to the financial existence of the Arboretum. Since he had no illusions of immortality, his final efforts aimed to eliminate that possibility, for only a selfish man could find comfort in the idea that he is irreplaceable.

When he reached his eighties, the rigid reserve which used to make him appear fierce and austere gave him a dignified, eccentric old-worldliness. The scientific world had heaped honors on him. Botanists, horticulturists, and foresters in Britain, France, Belgium, Germany, Austria, and Finland paid tribute to his work as did a dozen American societies. The Woman's National Farm and Garden Association of America voted him an honorary membership. He arrived at an age that placed him beyond criticism, when all was temporarily forgiven, including his *Crataegus* efforts.

Looking Backward and Forward

The profession referred to him as a patriarch. His secretaries lost their fear of him and observed his gruff ways with tender amusement. His appearance changed little from the beginning of the century, but inside he softened. Sargent's nurse reported that when his secretary, Miss Carter, died unexpectedly after a brief illness, he actually cried. Katherine Anderson, who had been Wilson's secretary for seven years, replaced Miss Carter. Having scarcely acknowledged her existence before, he called her into his office and said, "You're afraid of me, aren't you? You know, I'm not as bad as I may seem to be. I'm sure we're going to get along fine." They did.[23]

Many people who knew Sargent only in his last years remembered him with warm affection. Susan Delano McKelvey was forever grateful to him for having rescued her from the misery and loneliness of the fresh memory of the deaths of her husband and fifteen-year-old daughter. In 1922 Sargent put her to work at the Arboretum, offering her a distraction from her losses. He had met her socially, and her obvious distress had touched him deeply; perhaps she could find solace as he had found not so many years before. To challenge and test her, he set her to work scrubbing clay pots in the greenhouse, a strange occupation for a woman of social distinction and independent means. Sargent's remedy worked its charm, and Mrs. McKelvey throve under its influence. In 1925 the Arboretum published her first taxonomic description in the *Journal*. After Sargent's death she went on to write the monograph of lilacs which is still accepted as the standard and the enormous *Botanical Exploration of the Trans-Mississippi West*.

Sargent was fortunate enough in his old age not to have any serious ailments besides his chronic gout. But as his body wore out, his resistance to disease lessened; his health was in no way aided by his stubborn insistence on going to the Administration Building daily unless he was uncomfortably ill. Sargent customarily left the Arboretum each day

Last Glances

at four o'clock to return to his empty home, possibly dinner with Alice, a bit more work in his study and early to bed. Because Alice was not always at home and Molly had moved back to New York, he retained a full-time nurse, who managed to keep him in bed now and then. Evenings she would often read mystery stories out loud to him—he liked the Nick Carter series best—until he dropped off to sleep though she might lie awake in terror for the rest of the night. When he was ill and she won the battle of the day, he lay in bed reading, writing, and throwing stale muffins out the window for his pheasants. He played this little game as much to amuse the grandchildren who visited him as for his own pleasure. What was left of his family grew suddenly dear to him, all the more because Holm Lea seemed so deserted since Mary Sargent's death. Alice was usually out evenings at a bridge party. The Lowells paid frequent visits,[24] but there were fewer and fewer dinner guests. Sargent anticipated with special pleasure the arrival of Charles and Dagmar from New York or of Molly because they brought grandchildren and temporary relief from the emptiness of Holm Lea. He knew, at last, a loneliness that the Arboretum could not fill, a need quite apart from the satisfaction of intellect or pride or ambition which had sustained him for years while he had taken his family for granted. He wrote lonesome, loving letters to his favorite granddaughter, young Nathalie Potter, in a practically illegible, increasingly tremulous hand, wishing she would visit her old Grandpa and go coasting in the cow pasture with the neighborhood children, scolding her for a low grade, indulging her with all the attention he had been too busy and too withdrawn to give his own children.

During his last year, Sargent went to the Arboretum whenever he thought himself physically fit, which was most of the time. He read the mail, dictated answers, spoke with some of the many visitors to the building. At noon his chauffeur, George Page, came to fetch him for lunch. They returned at 1:30, and Page would drive him around the grounds

Looking Backward and Forward

in a Ford station wagon. Rock was embroiled in Chinese feudal politics, and Sargent read his adventures half in envy, half in fear, always with the hope that he would repeat Wilson's botanical exploits. Too old, lame, and feeble for field work, Sargent limited his travels to neighborhood estates and gardens.

He grew weak, lonely, and mellow but never pitiful; he was spared the humiliation of senility, but his mental stamina did ebb. His last scientific publication appeared in the January 1926 issue of the *Journal* and consisted of corrections and emendations to the second edition of the *Manual;* much of the work was Rehder's. More and more routine responsibilities fell to Wilson and Rehder while Sargent played the dignitary-in-residence. In June 1926, Sargent turned in his last annual report to the University; there was no hint of a swan song in it. That year, incidentally, he achieved seniority in the Harvard catalogue and the academic procession.

In March 1927, Sargent came down with a variety of intestinal flu. This time he did not recover. Warned by the nurse, Alice summoned the family to his bedside. Molly related that his final vision was of "locust and honey," which she took to mean that "[h]e was already botanizing . . . in the fields of Paradise."[25] He died Tuesday evening, March 22, a month before his eighty-sixth birthday. His death made news throughout the country: there were lengthy obituaries—in Boston they ran a full page—eulogizing editorials. No one, however, felt more deserted than did the staff at the Arnold Arboretum. The old order was gone, and there was no clue as to what the new one would be. Wilson, as Assistant Director, took charge. He wrote to Rock in the Chinese wilderness.

So far as I know, Professor Sargent suffered little physical pain and passed away as if entering sleep. His death was really due to old age . . . It comes to few men to lay down a life so well spent and rich in accomplishment. That he is missed goes without saying . . . Having in view the

Last Glances

altered financial condition of the Arnold Arboretum it is my duty to ask you to leave China and return here with the best possible speed.[26]

Sargent was buried Friday afternoon in the family plot in the Walnut Hill cemetery. A simple gravestone, consonant with his taste, marked his plot. Saturday's *Transcript* wrote of him: "In the 'Large composition of this man' there seemed to be no weakness, no impatience, no conceit, no triviality, as there was no unkindness." The quick were being indulgent of the freshly dead. Of the many verbal portraits of Sargent, the one presented by William Trelease to the National Academy of Sciences came closest to the truth. Trelease, like many others of the Academy, had known Sargent too well to gild the lily. In his honesty he touched, for a moment, the essence of the man.

Professor Sargent was a tall man, a little ponderous to those who knew him in his later life, quiet, never hurried, but always forging ahead with irresistible momentum; conservative and rather hard to swerve from his course or to retard or accelerate in it. He had the reputation of being bluff and a little overpositive; but those who knew him well saw a sympathetic kindliness as underlying any superficial reactions.[27]

Looking Backward and Forward

14

Epilogue

Charles Sprague Sargent was buried, memorialized, praised, and mourned in a fashion befitting his social station and professional accomplishments. At the reading of his will, the Harvard community learned—with a mixture of appreciation and dismay—that he left $30,000 to the Arboretum, directing the income of $20,000 to be used for the purchase of books for the library and the remaining $10,000 to accumulate for 100 years, after which it was to be divided into two funds: one for the maintenance of the Arboretum and the second to accumulate for another hundred years. Journalists estimated that the bequest would amount to nearly $100,000,000 an incredible sum of insurance for the future, but in no way helpful in filling the vacuum which the donor's death created.

Because his direction of the Arboretum had been so intensely personal, Sargent's disappearance from the scene threw the surviving staff into confusion, for he had not prepared anyone to take his place. Wilson, formerly Assistant Director, assumed control pending a decision of the Harvard Corporation. While he dealt efficiently with small crises, such as the dismissal of a wayward superintendent, he clearly lacked the knowledge and experience for coping with the large-scale administration. Until then, Wilson had had only a vague notion of the Arboretum's fiscal affairs. When he discovered that Sargent had regularly committed

himself far beyond the income from endowments, he was baffled, for he had neither personal resources nor the confidence that he could raise subscriptions from others to make up the difference. Fearing financial disaster, he recalled Rock from China with the comment: "what the immediate future of the Arnold Arboretum will be no one can tell."[1] Another expedition which Sargent had planned for making collections in New Guinea had to be canceled.[2]

Rehder and Jack found themselves as much at a loss as Wilson; they had no idea of what the future would bring and both heard many pessimistic rumors. Rehder worried over tales that some officials at Harvard thought the Arboretum should abandon its research functions, remain only as a park, and transfer the library and herbarium to some other department in the University. In early May 1927, he expressed his anxieties in a letter to Sir Arthur Hill, Director at Kew, who was alarmed enough to write President Lowell.[3] The latter, piqued to find out that such unauthorized stories were circulating, acted quickly to dispel any doubts concerning the University's intentions and advised Hill that the Arboretum would definitely not be reduced to park level.[4] Meanwhile the Corporation, searching for a successor to Sargent, found none and settled upon a new scheme which Lowell outlined in his annual report:

Among the most isolated departments of the University have been those of botany; and we may fairly use the plural, for the botanical laboratories and collections, living and dead, have been distinct entities, working each in its own province, often with little cooperation . . . The death of Professor Sargent, who by his personal efforts created at the Arboretum the magnificent collection of living trees and shrubs and herbaria from all temperate zones, brought to the front the question of the future relation of that work to the rest of the University. After careful consideration and consultation with the people most interested, a council for all the botanical collections was created, consisting of the directors or curators in

Epilogue

charge, with Professor Oakes Ames as chairman. At the same time he was appointed Supervisor of the Botanical Museum—of which he had been Curator—of the tropical garden at Soledad in Cuba, and of the Arnold Arboretum; Mr. Wilson, the former Assistant Director, being made Keeper of the Arboretum.[5]

The new arrangement, linking operations in Jamaica Plain with the Botanical Museum in Cambridge, aimed to prevent a continuation of the unilateral administration of Sargent's tenure. It was the first of a series of decisions of the Corporation over a number of years with the object of unifying Harvard botany's separate parts. For the time being, however, the change in policy was a subtle one, re-defining the scope of executive authority; it did not alter either the facilities or the essential character of the Arboretum and its work, and so the worst fears of the staff subsided. The choice of Ames, moreover, seemed financially expedient because, like Sargent, Ames belonged to a powerful local family with influential connections. The drawback was that he had to seek funds for separately endowed institutions.

Inasmuch as the peaceful pursuit of research projects and the operation of the Arboretum proceeded without interruption, the staff, on the whole, was agreeable to the new system though some of them missed Sargent's dynamism. Wilson, however, did not immediately view Ames' appointment with unreserved approval. Having carried the title of Assistant Director, he had had hopes of becoming Director. The hopes reflected a naive understanding of Arboretum financing; had he been more enlightened on that subject, he might have been less disappointed. After a while, he bore the situation in a gentlemanly manner and was soon pleased with Ames, for while handling the big administrative burdens, he did not interfere with Wilson's supervision at Jamaica Plain and he did listen to his requests with a sympathetic ear. In June, Wilson wrote a letter to Rock indicating a pacified, if ambivalent, opinion of the new order:

Last Glances

346

Great changes have taken place. The President and Fellows of Harvard College have taken a firm hold of the Arboretum. They have abolished the Directorship. Placed us along with other departments under a supervisor. I have been given charge under the title of "Keeper of the Arnold Arboretum." Our supervisor is Professor Oakes Ames, a charming gentleman whom it is a pleasure to serve with. If the idea of the President and Fellows of Harvard College to bring about co-operation and co-ordination among the different departments of Harvard interested in botany can be brought to pass, the right man has been chosen to do it. The task, however, is almost superhuman.[6]

Wilson consoled himself with the thought that while he was virtually in charge of the operation of the Arboretum he did not bear the ultimate responsibility for its finances and political problems. He continued, with the title of Keeper, which he had requested for himself—it was the English equivalent of Curator and not used anywhere else within the University—to manage the institution, consulting Ames on appropriate questions. Wilson enjoyed a good deal of public prestige, for his Chinese explorations had made him famous, but as an administrator he was no replacement for Sargent.

When administrative order reasserted itself, the Arboretum picked up where it had left off. It sponsored, wholly or partly, collecting expeditions in several parts of the world with an emphasis on building up the herbarium rather than the living collections; in cooperation with the Bussey Institution a new staff member, Professor J. H. Faull, studied the diseases of trees and shrubs; Karl Sax carried on with his cytological research, begun toward the end of Sargent's career. During the first few years following Sargent's death, the old and new overlapped without conflict, and the Arboretum showed signs of vitality in its research programs and in the gratifying success of a fund-raising campaign which, under the heading of a Sargent Memorial Fund, proved that patrons cared about perpetuating the life and usefulness of

Epilogue

the institution. Wilson's death in an automobile accident, in 1930, further tested its durability, and the new administration succeeded in continuing the Arboretum's work. Sargent had build his "one-man" operation strong enough to survive new leadership and elastic enough to admit new programs.

Last Glances

Notes   Index

Abbreviations

AA	Arnold Arboretum, Jamaica Plain, Massachusetts
AMNH	American Museum of Natural History, New York City
GH	Library of the Gray Herbarium of Harvard University, Cambridge, Massachusetts
HU Archives	Widener Library, Harvard University, Cambridge, Massachusetts
KEW	Library, Royal Botanic Gardens, Kew, Richmond, Surrey, England
MBG	Missouri Botanical Garden, St. Louis, Missouri
Pringle Herbarium	University of Vermont, Burlington, Vermont

Notes

1. The Importance of Being Sargent

1. Emma Worcester Sargent, *Epes Sargent of Gloucester and His Descendants*, with biographical notes by Charles Sprague Sargent (Boston: Houghton Mifflin, 1923). References to Sargent genealogy come from this source unless otherwise noted.

2. W. T. Councilman, "Charles Sprague Sargent," *Later Years of the Saturday Club, 1870–1920*, ed. M. A. DeWolfe Howe (Boston: Houghton Mifflin, 1927), p. 286.

3. James Bowditch, *Herald* (Boston), March 27, 1927.

4. Ignatius Sargent to Charles S. Sargent, February 15, 1846, AA.

5. This somewhat eccentric Sargent was named after his maternal uncle, Horace Binney, lawyer and naturalist, also first president of the Pennsylvania Horticultural Society.

6. Winthrop Sargent, *Early Sargents of New England* (Philadelphia: privately printed, 1922).

7. Ernest H. Wilson, "Charles Sprague Sargent," *Harvard Graduate Magazine*, vol. 35, no. 140, p. 606 (June 1927).

8. *Records of the College Faculty*, vols. 15, 16 (1855–1860), HU Archives.

9. Councilman, "Charles Sprague Sargent," p. 287.

10. Andrew J. Downing, *A Treatise on the Theory and Practice of Landscape Gardening*, 6th ed. (New York, 1859), p. 51. This edition includes a supplement, pp. 427–572, by Henry W. Sargent.

11. *Ibid.*, pp. 438–442.

12. *Ibid.*, p. 34.

13. Charles S. Sargent, "The Weeping Pinus ponderosa," *Garden and Forest*, 1:392 (October 10, 1888).

14. Downing, *Landscape Gardening*, p. 427.

15. Horatio H. Hunnewell, ed., *Life, Letters and Diary of Ho-*

ratio Hollis Hunnewell (Boston: privately printed, 1906), 3:167–178. (The editor is the subject's grandson.) When Sargent checked the Pinetum in 1905, three years after Hunnewell's death, he counted 115 species and varieties of conifers and taxads.

16. Downing, *Landscape Gardening*, p. 40.

17. *Ibid.*, p. 51.

18. Asa Gray to Joseph Dalton Hooker, November 12, 1873, KEW.

2. The Shadow of Asa Gray

1. A. Hunter Dupree, *Asa Gray* (Cambridge, Mass.: Harvard University Press, Belknap Press, 1959). Professor Dupree has written the only full-length biography of Asa Gray. This account is an invaluable reference for any student of the development of the biological sciences in the nineteenth century.

2. Asa Gray to Charles Eliot, December 15, 1871, *Letters of Asa Gray*, ed. Jane Loring Gray (Boston, 1893), 2:620–622 (hereafter cited as *Letters*).

3. Asa Gray to Joseph Dalton Hooker, December 27, 1871, KEW.

4. Asa Gray to Charles Eliot, 1871, HU Archives.

5. Horatio Hollis Hunnewell to Asa Gray, March 21, 1871, GH.

6. Andrew J. Downing, *A Treatise on the Theory and Practice of Landscape Gardening*, 6th ed. (New York, 1859), p. 41.

7. "The Bulletin," Old Dartmouth Historical Society and Whaling Museum, Winter 1964, pp. 1–4.

8. "Last Will and Testament of James Arnold," p. 7, AA (printed copy).

9. Local botanists still find *Trees and Shrubs Growing Naturally in the Forests of Massachusetts* (Boston, 1846) a convenient reference. The volume contains handsome plates from many sources, including the hand of Isaac Sprague.

10. Emma Worcester Sargent, *Epes Sargent of Gloucester and His Descendants*, with biographical notes by Charles Sprague Sargent (Boston: Houghton Mifflin, 1923), p. 14.

11. Hugh M. Raup, "The Genesis of the Arnold Arboretum," *Arnoldia*, ser. 4, vol. 8, no. 1, pp. 4, 7 (April 26, 1940).

12. *Ibid.*, p. 7.

13. *Ibid.*, p. 9.

14. Samuel E. Morison, ed., *The Development of Harvard University since the Inauguration of President Eliot 1869–1929* (Cambridge: Harvard University Press, 1930), pp. 508–509.

15. Dupree, *Asa Gray*, p. 343.

16. *Ibid.*, p. 344.

17. Raup, "The Genesis of the Arnold Arboretum," p. 8.

18. Charles S. Sargent, "The First Fifty Years of the Arnold Arboretum," *Journal of the Arnold Arboretum*, vol. 3, no. 3, pp. 127-171 (1922).

19. *Ibid.*, pp. 129-130.

20. Asa Gray to Joseph Dalton Hooker, May 6, 1872, KEW.

21. Dupree, *Asa Gray*, pp. 353-354.

22. Andrew Denny Rodgers III, *Liberty Hyde Bailey* (Princeton: Princeton University Press, 1949).

23. Charles Sprague Sargent, "Botanic Garden," *Annual Reports of the President and Treasurer of Harvard College, 1878-79* (Cambridge, Mass., 1880), pp. 98-99. Reports in this series are hereafter referred to as *Annual Reports . . . (date)*.

24. Sargent to Hooker, July 29, 1879, KEW.

25. Sargent, *Annual Reports . . . 1878-79*, pp. 98-99.

26. Sargent to Hooker, July 29, 1879, KEW.

27. Asa Gray to Alphonse de Candolle, November 26, 1873, *Letters*, 2:645.

28. Asa Gray to Hooker, April 28, 1879, KEW.

29. Gray to Hooker, October 24, 1872, KEW.

30. Gray to Hooker, November 2, 1872, KEW.

31. Sargent to Horatio Hollis Hunnewell, four letters dated March 6 through March 15, 1874, AA.

32. Sargent to Gray, February 6, 1874, GH.

3. *Sargent on His Own*

1. Charles S. Sargent, "The First Fifty Years of the Arnold Arboretum," *Journal of the Arnold Arboretum*, vol. 3, no. 3, p. 130 (1922).

2. Sargent to the President and Fellows of Harvard College, May 10, 1875, HU Archives.

3. Sargent to Frederick Law Olmsted, October 8, 1877, Olmsted Collection, Library of Congress.

4. Sargent to Hooker, December 12, 1877, KEW.

5. Sargent to Olmsted, October 8, 1877, Olmsted Collection, Library of Congress.

6. Sargent to Hooker, April 12, 1878, KEW.

7. Frederick Law Olmsted, Jr., and Theodora Kimball, eds., *Frederick Law Olmsted: Landscape Architect, 1822-1903* (New York: G. P. Putnam, 1922), 1:22.

8. Sargent to Hooker, October 28, 1878, KEW.

9. Charles Eliot to Sargent, November 27, 1878, AA (typed copy).

10. Sargent to Hooker, July 29, 1879, KEW.

Notes to Pages 34-57

11. Sargent to Cyrus G. Pringle, June 29, 1879, Pringle Herbarium.

12. Charles H. Dalton, William Gray, Jr., and Henry Lee, "Petition to the City Council," November 14, 1879 (City of Boston Department of Parks and Recreation).

13. Horace Clapp as quoted in the *Daily Evening Traveller* (Boston), December 2, 1881.

14. Charles S. Sargent, "Fifth Annual Report of the Board of Commissioners of the Department of Parks, for the City of Boston, for the Year 1879" (City of Boston: Document 15, 1880), pp. 21–22.

15. Sargent, *Annual Reports . . . 1880–81.*

16. *Herald* (Boston), December 1, 1881.

17. Mr. Smith as quoted in the *Daily Evening Traveller* (Boston), December 2, 1881.

18. Charles Eliot, *Annual Reports . . . 1899–1900,* p. 24. Accordding to Eliot's calculations, the City had spent $371,768.82 in construction fees by the turn of the century.

19. Sargent to George Engelmann, March 11, 1879, MBG.

20. William Trelease, "A Biographical Memoir of Charles Sprague Sargent," *National Academy of Sciences,* 12:257 (1929).

21. *Horticulture,* August 12, 1916, pp. 201–203. Dawson's mother brought him to the United States from England as a child. As a small boy he spent a good deal of time helping in his uncle's nursery in Andover, Massachusetts, where he learned about plants. He was wounded many times in the Civil War because, it was said, he often strayed far from camp sites to collect plants and seeds. After the war he worked at a Cambridge nursery until 1871, when he accepted a position, at $800 a year, under Parkman at the Bussey Institution.

22. Gladys Brooks, *Boston and Return* (New York: Atheneum, 1962), p. 78.

23. Charles S. Sargent, "Charles Edward Faxon," *Rhodora,* 20:117–122 (July 1918).

24. Sargent to Hooker, January 29, 1876, KEW.

25. Gray to Hooker, December 25, 1881, *Letters,* 2:729.

26. Hugh Raup, "Notes on the Early Uses of Land Now in the Arnold Arboretum," *Arnoldia,* ser. 4, vol. 3, nos. 9–12, pp. 41–77 (December 23, 1935).

27. Harriet M. Whitcomb, *Annals and Reminiscences of Jamaica Plain* (Cambridge, Mass., 1897), pp. 52–53.

28. Hooker, "American Journal," entry for July 10–11, 1877, KEW (original ms.).

29. Sargent, "Fifth Annual Report of the Board of Commissioners of the Department of Parks . . ." pp. 21–22.

30. *Ibid.*

31. Hooker to Sargent, June 28, 1879, AA.

32. Sargent to Olmsted, February 5, 1885, Olmsted Collection, Library of Congress.

33. Sargent, *Annual Reports . . . 1885–86*.

34. Sargent, *Annual Reports . . . 1886–87*.

35. *Garden and Forest*, 2:61 (February 6, 1889).

36. Donald Wyman, *Trees for American Gardens*, 2nd ed. (New York: Macmillan, 1965), pp. 102–103.

4. *In the Nation's Forests*

1. Sargent to R. U. Johnson, November 25, 1908, AA (typed copy).

2. George P. Marsh, *The Earth as Modified by Human Action* (New York: Charles Scribner's, 1907), p. 38.

3. *Ibid.*, pp. 154–156.

4. David Lowenthal, *George Perkins Marsh, Versatile Vermonter* (New York: Columbia University Press, 1958); S. G. Brown, "A discourse commemorative of the Hon. George Perkins Marsh," delivered before the faculty and students of Dartmouth College, June 5, 1883 (Free Press Association, 1883).

5. B. E. Fernow, "Report on the Forestry Investigations of the U.S. Department of Agriculture, 1877–1898" (Washington, D.C., 1899), 55th Congress, 3rd Session, House of Representatives Document no. 181.

Related statistics for this period are hard to come by. In this report, Fernow based his observation on the 1890 Forest Census:

Until the present century, in fact until nearly the last half of it, the activity of man on this continent has practically been confined to the eastern portion, which . . . was originally covered with a dense or at least continuous forest. The substructure of the entire civilization of the United States was hewn out of these primeval woodlands. Out of the vast virgin forest area of the eastern half of the country there have been cleared for farm use during this time 250,000,000 acres, or 400,000 square miles, leaving about 961,330 square miles covered actually or nominally with forest growth or waste.

Timber being a great obstacle to the settlement of the land, and the market for it until recently being confined and limited, a large amount had to be wasted and disposed of in the log pile, where the flames made quick work of the scrub as well as of the finest walnut trees.

H. R. Josephson and R. C. Wilson in "After a Hundred Years," *The Yearbook of Agriculture* 1962 (Washington, D.C.: U.S. Government Printing Office, 1963), pp. 229–232, give estimates for the whole of the continental United States, suggesting that an original forest area of a billion acres was reduced by one-third between 1620 and 1900. The 1962 report claims a forest area of ca. 1,200,000 sq. miles.

6. A. Hunter Dupree, *Asa Gray* (Cambridge, Mass.: Harvard University Press, Belknap Press, 1959), p. 189.

7. William H. Brewer, *Statistical Atlas of the United States Based on the Results of the Ninth Census, 1870*, Francis A. Walker, compiler, part I (1874).

8. Shirley W. Allen, *An Introduction to American Forestry* (New York: McGraw-Hill, 1938), pp. 239–257.

9. Franklin B. Hough, *Report upon Forestry, Prepared under the Direction of the Commissioner of Agriculture, in Pursuance of an Act of Congress, approved August 15, 1876* (Washington, D.C., 1878), 1:8–9.

10. Sargent to R. U. Johnson, November 25, 1908, AA (carbon copy).

11. Sargent to Hooker, October 13, 1879, KEW.

12. Sargent to Engelmann, November 29, 1879, MBG.

13. Engelmann to Sargent, December 3, 1879, AA.

14. Sargent to Engelmann, December 18, 1879, MBG.

15. Engelmann to Sargent, December 23, 1879, AA.

16. Sargent to Engelmann, March 7, 1880, MBG.

17. *Ibid.*

18. William Canby to Asa Gray, April 10, 1880, GH.

19. Sargent to Hooker, November 15, 1879, KEW.

20. Engelmann to Asa Gray, August 8, 1880, GH.

21. Sargent to Gray, August 8, 1880, KEW. Gray sent this letter on to Hooker, thinking he might enjoy the account.

22. Charles A. White, "A Memoir of George Engelmann" read before the National Academy of Sciences, April 1896 (Washington, D.C., 1896), p. 17.

23. Andrew D. Rodgers III, *American Botany 1873–1892* (Princeton: Princeton University Press, 1944), p. 137.

24. Sargent to Hooker, October 25, 1880, KEW.

25. Sargent to Engelmann, October 23, 1880, MBG.

26. Rodgers, *American Botany*, p. 140.

27. Brewer, *Statistical Atlas of the United States . . . Ninth Census, 1870*. Brewer presumed little and readily acknowledged the gaps in his information. His apologetic statement that "it is probable that, as a whole, the amount of woodlands as exhibited on the maps is underrated east of the Mississippi and overrated west of it" underscores his awareness of the short comings of his work.

28. Sargent to Hooker, November 25, 1883, KEW.
29. Charles S. Sargent, *Nation*, 37:201 (September 6, 1883).
30. *Forestry and Irrigation*, 9:203 (April 4, 1903).
31. Raphael Pumpelly, *My Reminiscences* (New York: Henry Holt, 1918), 2:624.
32. Sargent to Engelmann, June 7, 1883, MBG.
33. Pumpelly, *Reminiscences*, 2:644–645.
34. Sargent to Hooker, October 3, 1883, KEW.
35. Sargent, *Nation*, 37:201 (September 6, 1883).
36. Pumpelly, *Reminiscences*, 2:646.
37. Sargent to Hooker, June 21, 1884, KEW.
38. Sargent to Hooker, November 25, 1883, KEW.
39. Andrew Denny Rodgers III, *Bernhard Eduard Fernow: A Story of North American Forestry* (Princeton: Princeton University Press, 1951), p. 37.
40. Charles S. Sargent *et al.*, "Report of the Forestry Commission Appointed by the Comptroller (New York State)" (Albany, 1885), p. 12.
41. *Ibid.*, p. 1.
42. *Ibid.*, p. 3.
43. *Ibid.*, p. 16.
44. Sargent to Morris K. Jesup, April 14, 1885, AMNH.
45. *Evening Post* (New York), August 26, 1885.
46. *Sun* (New York), August 14, 1885.
47. Sargent to Jesup, May 19, 1885, AMNH.
48. A. S. Bickmore to Sargent, September 2, 1880, AMNH (carbon copy).
49. Sargent to Hooker, May 30, 1884, KEW.
50. Sargent to Jesup, November 11, 1880, KEW.
51. Jesup to Sargent, November 13, 1880, AMNH (carbon copy).
52. Sargent to Jesup, April 25, 1881, AMNH.
53. Jesup to Sargent, April 28, 1881, AMNH (carbon copy).
54. H. C. Bumpus to William H. Hunt, July 18, 1903, AMNH (carbon copy).
55. Sargent to Engelmann, March 24, 1881, MBG.
56. Sargent to Engelmann, February 10, 1881, MBG.
57. Jesup to A. S. Bickmore, memorandum, September 1, 1881, AMNH.
58. Jesup to Sargent, September 1, 1881, AMNH (carbon copy).
59. Sargent to Jesup, November 2, 1885, AMNH.
60. Cyrus G. Pringle to Jesup, December 6, 1882, AMNH.
61. Sargent to Jesup, May 8, 1882, AMNH.
62. Pringle to Jesup, December 6, 1882, AMNH.
63. Sargent to Jesup, November 6, 1882, AMNH.
64. Pringle to Jesup, December 6, 1882, AMNH.

Notes to Pages 91–113

65. Charles C. Parry to Gray, November 10, 1882, GH.
66. Pringle to Gray, November 13, 1882, GH.
67. Sargent to Jesup, December 19, 1882, AMNH.
68. *Sun* (New York), May 17, 1885.
69. Sargent to Jesup, October 1885, AMNH.
70. Sargent to Jesup, October 31, 1894, AMNH.
71. *Garden and Forest*, 5:541–542 (November 16, 1892).
72. Sargent to Jesup, January 2, 1895, AMNH.
73. Jesup to Sargent, January 17, 1895, AMNH (original draft).
74. Jesup to Sargent, January 19, 1895, AMNH (carbon copy).
75. Sargent to Jesup, January 30, 1895, AMNH.
76. Sargent to Jesup, February 9, 1895, AMNH.
77. Sargent to Jesup, August 1895, AMNH.
78. Sargent to Jesup, June 1899, AMNH.
79. Sargent to Mary C. Dickerson, July 1911, AMNH.

5. *Changing of the Guard*

1. Sargent to Engelmann, February 13, 1883, MBG.
2. Sargent to Engelmann, February 22, 1883, MBG.
3. Sargent to Engelmann, June 7, 1883, MBG.
4. Engelmann to Sargent, June 12, 1883, AA.
5. Sargent to Hooker, October 3, 1883, KEW.
6. Engelmann to Sargent, November 11, 1883, AA.
7. Sargent to Engelmann, November 25, 1883, MBG.
8. Sargent to Engelmann, December 14, 1883, MBG.
9. Engelmann to Sargent, December 23, 1883, AA.
10. Engelmann to Sargent, January 27, 1884, AA.
11. Charles A. White, "A Memoir of George Engelmann," read before the National Academy of Sciences, April 1896 (Washington, D.C., 1896), p. 17.
12. Gray to Hooker, March 9, 1886, KEW. One copy of the article in the AA library has corrections in Gray's agitated hand.
13. Sargent to Gray, January 20, 1886, GH.
14. George L. Goodale to Hooker, January 2, 1888, KEW.
15. Charles S. Sargent, "Asa Gray," *Garden and Forest*, 1:1 (February 29, 1888).
16. Charles S. Sargent, *Garden and Forest*, 6:539 (December 27, 1893).
17. Sargent to Thiselton-Dyer, February 1, 1894, KEW.
18. Thiselton-Dyer to Sargent, April 28, 1894, AA.
19. Hooker to Sargent, January 4 and April 18, 1889, AA.
20. James Dwight Dana to Sargent, 1889, AA.
21. Hooker to Sargent, February 12, 1889, AA.

22. Sargent to Thiselton-Dyer, March 15, 1892, KEW.
23. "William A. Stiles," *Garden and Forest,* 10:399 (October 13, 1897).
24. Horatio H. Hunnewell, ed., *Life, Letters and Diary of Horatio Hollis Hunnewell* (Boston: privately printed, 1906), 1:222–223. Hunnewell had signaled Sargent about Blake. "Bye the bye," he wrote, "don't you know my neighbor Bell Telephone Blake? I have seen but very little of him recently, exchanging visits occasionally without his taking any interest at all in the place. But all of a sudden he has become very enthusiastic in conifers, makes a great many inquiries about them, and talks of making a pinetum, etc. He is a bright, clever fellow with money, and, when he goes into anything, does it very thoroughly on a large scale."
25. Charles Eliot, *Annual Reports . . . 1892–93,* p. 38.
26. Sargent, *Annual Reports . . . 1890–91,* p. 165.
27. Sargent to Thiselton-Dyer, August 21, 1891, KEW.
28. Emma Worcester Sargent, *Epes Sargent of Gloucester and His Descendants,* with biographical notes by Charles Sprague Sargent (Boston: Houghton Mifflin, 1923), p. 151.
29. *Garden and Forest,* 6:341 (August 16, 1893).
30. Sargent to Thiselton-Dyer, November 17, 1893, KEW.
31. Sargent to Jane Loring Gray, November 28, 1893, GH.
32. Sargent to Thiselton-Dyer, October 13, 1893, KEW.
33. Sargent to Thiselton-Dyer, December 13, 1893, KEW.
34. Sargent to Thiselton-Dyer, December 20, 1893, KEW.
35. Thiselton-Dyer to Sargent, April 28, 1894, AA.

6. One Success and One Failure

1. Charles S. Sargent, *The Silva of North America* (Boston: Houghton Mifflin, 1891–1902), 1:vi.
2. Charles S. Sargent, "Charles Edward Faxon," *Rhodora,* 20:119 (July 1918).
3. Sargent, *Silva,* 1:v.
4. Sargent to Hooker, April 15, 1885, KEW.
5. Sargent to Jesup, September 11, 1885, AMNH.
6. Gray to Hooker, March 19, 1886, KEW.
7. Sargent to Jesup, May 12, 1886, AMNH.
8. Sargent to Jesup, February 18, 1887, AMNH.
9. Sargent, *Annual Reports . . . 1886–87,* p. 128.
10. Sargent to Thiselton-Dyer, May 12, 1887, KEW.
11. Nathaniel L. Britton, *Garden and Forest,* 3:590 (December 3, 1890).

12. *Botanical Gazette,* 16:31 (January 1891).

13. *Gardeners' Chronicle,* 9:12 (January 3, 1891).

14. John Muir, *Atlantic,* 92:9–10 (July 1903).

15. *Garden and Forest,* 4:181 (April 22, 1891). The lead editorial reflects Sargent's opinion of federal action:

The repeal of this law, was, no doubt, proper, although it may be questioned whether the Government should not have offered to settlers some other stimulus to plant groves and forests . . . On the same day when this act was passed an amendment to it was made which permits timber to be cut and removed from the forest-lands of the public domain for mining, manufacturing or domestic purposes under regulations prescribed by the Secretary of the Interior. This, so far as we can see, practically opens the whole timber domain of the country to the axes of trespassers, with no restraint beyond what the Secretary of the Interior may choose to exercise.

16. *Ibid.*

17. "The National Forest-question," *Garden and Forest,* 4:13 (January 14, 1891).

18. A. Hunter Dupree, *Asa Gray* (Cambridge: Harvard University Press, Belknap Press, 1959), p. 407.

19. Melville B. Anderson, "The Conversation of John Muir," *American Museum Journal,* 15:19 (March 1915). Curiously enough, this article does not mention Sargent by name, but refers to an "eastern naturalist." One of Muir's biographers, Linnie Marsh Wolfe (*Son of the Wilderness: The Life of John Muir* [New York: Knopf, 1945], pp. 277–278) concluded that Muir must have been speaking of Sargent, but there is no documentation for her statement.

20. John Muir to Sargent, January 31, 1898, AA.

21. William F. Bade, *The Life and Letters of John Muir* (Boston: Houghton Mifflin, 1924), 2:269–270.

22. George Perkins Marsh to Sargent, July 20, 1882, AA (typed copy courtesy of David Lowenthal).

23. Charles S. Sargent, *et al., Report of the committee appointed by the National Academy of Sciences upon the inauguration of a forestry policy for the forested lands of the United States to the Secretary of the Interior, May 1, 1897* (Washington, D.C., 1897), p. 5.

24. Andrew Denny Rodgers III, *Bernhard Eduard Fernow: A Story of North American Forestry* (Princeton: Princeton University Press, 1951), pp. 220–221.

25. Sargent to Thiselton-Dyer, March 30, 1896, KEW.

26. M. Nelson McGeary, *Gifford Pinchot: Forester, Politician* (Princeton: Princeton University Press, 1960), pp. 37–44.

Notes to Pages 151–161

27. Bade, *Life and Letters of John Muir*, pp. 299–300.

28. *Ibid.*, pp. 301–302.

29. McGeary, *Gifford Pinchot*, p. 39.

30. Sargent to Thiselton-Dyer, October 23 (28?), 1896, KEW.

31. Sargent, *et. al.*, "Report of the committee appointed by the National Academy..." p. 37.

32. Rodgers, *Bernhard Eduard Fernow*, pp. 222–224.

33. Muir to Sargent, February 24, 1897, AA.

34. Mr. Mondell, Wyoming, *Congressional Record: the Proceedings and Debates of the 54th Congress, 2nd Session*, vol. 29, part 3, p. 2973, (1897).

35. Rodgers, *Bernhard Eduard Fernow*, pp. 223–224.

36. Margaret Leech, *In the Days of McKinley* (New York: Harper, 1959), pp. 116–118.

37. Sargent to R. U. Johnson, November 25, 1908, AA (carbon copy).

38. Sargent to Thiselton-Dyer, April 6, 1897, KEW.

39. Sargent, *et al.*, "Report of the committee appointed by the National Academy..." pp. 43–47.

40. Sargent to R. U. Johnson, November 25, 1908, AA (carbon copy).

41. McGeary, *Gifford Pinchot*, pp. 40–44.

42. Muir to Sargent, October 16, 1897, AA.

43. Abbot to Sargent, July 29, 1897, AA.

44. *Garden and Forest*, 10:291 (July 28, 1897).

7. The Arboretum Grows Up

1. Samuel E. Morison, ed., *The Development of Harvard University since the Inauguration of President Eliot 1869–1929* (Cambridge: Harvard University Press, 1930), p. 338.

2. Sargent to Jane Loring Gray, April 12, 1897, GH.

3. Samuel E. Morison, *Three Centuries of Harvard, 1636–1936* (Cambridge: Harvard University Press, 1936), p. 356. The Arboretum, of course, did not compete for students.

4. F. H. Storer, *Annual Reports . . . 1893–94*, pp. 151–152.

5. Morison, *Development of Harvard University*, pp. 508–517.

6. "Report of the Treasurer," *Annual Reports . . . 1901–02*, pp. 11–13.

7. Charles Eliot, *Annual Reports . . . 1899–1900*, pp. 24–25.

8. Charles Eliot, *Charles Eliot, Landscape Architect* (Boston: Houghton Mifflin, 1902), pp. 44–45.

9. There is no record of an evaluation of Sargent's library at the time, but he was certainly a botanical bibliophile. In addition to

acquiring collector's items and individual volumes of great value, he built the core of a working library by purchasing standard works and periodicals.

10. Sargent to Thiselton-Dyer, December 24, 1897, KEW.

11. "Report of the Treasurer," *Annual Reports ... 1899–1900,* p. 89; "Report of the Treasurer," *Annual Reports ... 1900–01,* p. 87.

12. Clarence E. Kobuski, "Alfred Rehder," *Journal of the Arnold Arboretum,* vol. 31, no. 1, pp. 1–38 (1950).

13. Lucius Beebe, *Boston and the Boston Legend* (New York: D. Appleton-Century, 1935), pp. 234–235.

14. Charles S. Sargent, *A Guide to the Arnold Arboretum* (Boston: Houghton Mifflin, 1912), p. 11.

15. John G. Jack, "The Arnold Arboretum: Some Personal Notes," *Biologia II, An International Year-Book,* Chronica Botanica, vol. 12, no. 4/6, p. 190 (1951).

16. Susan D. McKelvey, "The Arnold Arboretum," *Harvard Alumni Bulletin* 38:464–465.

17. Jack, "The Arnold Arboretum: Some Personal Notes," p. 196.

18. Gladys Brooks, *Boston and Return* (New York: Atheneum, 1962), pp. 74–75.

19. Sargent to Thiselton-Dyer, February 21, 1898, KEW.

20. Sargent to Thiselton-Dyer, January 13, 1899, KEW.

8. Journeys to the East

1. Colonel Sir Henry Yule, ed., *The Book of Ser Marco Polo* (New York: Charles Scribner's, 1903), 2:202.

2. Emil Bretschneider, *History of European Botanical Discoveries in China* (London, 1898), p. 2. Botanists and historians owe a debt to Dr. Bretschneider's work, which remains the uncontested authority on this subject. I have gratefully and frequently used this volume to check historical details.

3. Charles S. Sargent, "Asa Gray," *Garden and Forest,* 1:1 (February 29, 1888).

4. M. L. Fernald, "Specific segregations and identities in some floras of eastern North America and the Old World,"*Rhodora,* 33:25–63 (January 1931).

5. A. Hunter Dupree, ed., *Darwiniana; Essays and Reviews Pertaining to Darwinism by Asa Gray* (Cambridge: Harvard University Press, Belknap Press, 1963), p. 181.

6. For a scholarly discussion of pre-Linnaean collectors in China, see William T. Stearn, "Botanical Exploration to the Time

of Linnaeus," *Proceedings of the Linnean Society,* 164:173–196 (December 15, 1958).

7. E. H. M. Cox, *Plant Hunting in China* (London: Collins Press, 1945), pp. 80–81.

8. James M. Howe, "George Rogers Hall, Lover of Plants," *Journal of the Arnold Arboretum,* vol. 4, no. 2, pp. 91–98 (April 1923). (Howe was Hall's grandson.) An appendix lists species that Hall is presumed to have introduced to the United States.

9. Cox, *Plant Hunting in China,* p. 88.

10. Bretschneider, *History of European Botanical Discoveries in China,* p. 1049.

11. Charles S. Sargent, *Forest Flora of Japan* (Boston, 1894), p. 54.

12. Sargent, *Forest Flora of Japan,* p. 74.

13. Kingo Miyabe to Sargent, October 25, 1892, AA.

14. James Herbert Veitch, *A Traveller's Notes* (Chelsea, England, 1896), pp. 129–130.

15. Sargent, *Forest Flora of Japan,* p. 83.

16. Sargent, *Annual Reports . . . 1892–93,* p. 188.

17. Sargent, *Forest Flora of Japan,* p. 86.

18. Sheila Pim, *The Wood and the Trees: A Biography of Augustine Henry* (London: MacDonald, 1966).

19. *Ibid.,* p. 14.

20. There is an interesting story connected with Henry's native collectors. One of them fooled a prominent British botanist, Daniel Oliver, into describing a new genus by inserting the inflorescence of a *Viburnum* into the terminal bud of *Aesculus chinensis.* Oliver's description appeared in print in the *Icones Plantarum* of 1888 before he discovered his mistake; the subsequent volume contained his retraction.

21. Henry to Sargent, May 31, 1894, AA.

22. E. I. Farrington, *Ernest H. Wilson, Plant Hunter* (Boston: The Stratford Co., 1931); Alfred Rehder, "Ernest Henry Wilson," *Journal of the Arnold Arboretum,* vol. 11, no. 4, pp. 182–192 (October 1930).

23. Ernest H. Wilson, *Aristocrats of the Garden* (Boston: Stratford, 1926), pp. 275–294.

24. *Ibid.,* pp. 281–282.

25. *Ibid.,* p. 284.

26. Ernest H. Wilson, *Gardeners' Chronicle,* February 23, 1901, p. 127.

27. Henry to Sargent, November 14, 1899, AA.

28. Wilson, *Aristocrats of the Garden,* p. 291.

29. *Gardeners' Chronicle,* June 3, 1905, p. 37.

30. Ernest H. Wilson, *A Naturalist in Western China,* 2 vols.

Notes to Pages 199–216

(London: Methuen, 1913). Since Wilson often neglected to give dates, one must piece together his separate journeys with the aid of other sources. In other respects these volumes are quite detailed.

31. In 1897, a French missionary, Père Farges, sent seeds of a *Davidia* to Maurice L. de Vilmorin, the French nurseryman. Only one plant grew from the seed lot, and the Arnold Arboretum received one of four cuttings made from that tree in 1902. Père Farges's introduction is distinguished from the true *Davidia* by its smooth leaves; it represents the variety *vilmoriniana*. Wilson is credited with introducing the straight species, with hairy leaves; more, important, perhaps, he introduced it in large quantities.

32. Ernest H. Wilson, *Gardeners' Chronicle*, July 25, 1903, pp. 49–50.

33. Wilson, *A Naturalist in Western China*, 1:249.

34. Ernest H. Wilson, *Gardeners' Chronicle*, February 25, 1905, p. 114.

9. E. H. Wilson: Our Man in I-ch'ang

1. Henry to Sargent, November 14, 1899, AA.

2. Joseph Ewan, ed., "Letters from Charles Sprague Sargent to Reginald Somers Cocks; 1908–1926," *Journal of the Arnold Arboretum*, vol. 46, no. 3, p. 349 (October 1965).

3. Andrew Robeson Sargent, *Boston Evening Record*, December 29, 1903.

4. Ridley's work on *Hevea brasiliensis* laid the foundations of the Malayan rubber industry.

5. Sargent to Thiselton-Dyer, December 18, 1903, KEW.

6. Sargent to Wilson, July 16, 1906, AA.

7. Wilson to Sargent, August 3, 1906, AA.

8. Ellen Willmott to Sargent, undated, AA.

9. Sargent to Wilson, August 30, 1906, AA.

10. Wilson to Sargent, September 14, 1906, AA.

11. Sargent to C. F. Adams, February 25, 1907, AA (carbon copy).

12. Sargent to Wilson, December 28, 1906, AA.

13. Wilson to Sargent, February 11, 1907, AA.

14. Wilson to Sargent, March 18, 1907, AA.

15. Wilson to Sargent, June 28, 1907, AA.

16. Frank Meyer to Wilson, May 7, 1907, AA.

17. Wilson to Sargent, August 25, 1907, AA.

18. Sargent to Wilson, October 22, 1907, AA.

19. Wilson to Sargent, October 21, 1907, AA.

20. Wilson to Sargent, December 30, 1907, AA.

21. Sargent to Wilson, December 5, 1907, AA.

22. Wilson to Sargent, August 28, 1908, AA.

23. Sargent to Wilson, July 8, 1908, AA.

24. Wilson, *A Naturalist in Western China*, 1:228, 233.

25. Wilson to Sargent, November 21, 1908, AA.

26. Sargent, *Annual Reports . . . 1908–09*, p. 232.

27. Sargent to Harry Veitch, October 15, 1908, AA (carbon copy).

28. William Purdom, *Gardeners' Chronicle*, October 4, 1913, p. 230.

29. Sargent to Veitch, June 13, 1912, AA (carbon copy).

30. Emil Bretschneider, *History of European Botanical Discoveries in China* (London, 1898), pp. 1024–1034.

31. Purdom returned to China with Reginald Farrar in 1914 and ultimately became an inspector of forests in the Chinese Government, but, according to E. H. M. Cox, "he was always shy and retiring, quite overshadowed by Farrar's personality." Still, Cox rated him as an "excellent traveller" (*Plant Hunting in China* [London: Collins Press, 1945], p. 174.)

32. Sargent to Wilson, May 24, 1909, AA.

33. Wilson to Sargent, July 29, 1910, AA.

34. Wilson to Sargent, September 10, 1910, AA.

35. Wilson to Sargent, October 24, 1910, AA.

36. Wilson to Sargent, December 4, 1910, AA.

37. Sargent, *Annual Reports . . . 1910–11*, p. 188.

38. Wilson to Sargent, January 28, 1911, AA.

10. Wilson in Japan, Rock in Tibet

1. Wilson to Sargent, October 11, 1914, AA.

2. Ernest H. Wilson, *Plant Hunting* (Boston: Stratford, 1927), 2:212.

3. Wilson to Sargent, October 11, 1914, AA.

4. Sargent to Wilson, September 2, 1914, AA.

5. David Fairchild, *The World Was My Garden* (New York: Charles Scribner's, 1938), pp. 426–427; E. H. M. Cox, *Plant Hunting in China* (London: Collins Press, 1945), pp. 206–207.

6. Sargent to Wilson, September 2, 1914, AA.

7. E. I. Farrington, *Ernest H. Wilson, Plant Hunter* (Boston: Stratford, 1931), p. 104.

8. Sargent to Reginald Cocks, May 12, 1915, AA (carbon copy). Professor Joseph Ewan of Tulane University has edited the com-

plete set of letters from Sargent to Cocks. The series was published in successive issues of the *Journal of the Arnold Arboretum* and is now bound in a single volume.

9. Wilson, *Plant Hunting*, 2:235.

10. *Ibid.*, pp. 232–233.

11. Wilson to Sargent, March 21, 1917, AA. Dr. John Creech of the USDA has explored many of Wilson's haunts and reports having met an old man in Okinawa who collected with Wilson.

12. Wilson, *Plant Hunting*, 2:175.

13. Sargent to Wilson, June 19, 1918, AA.

14. Alfred Rehder, "Ernest Henry Wilson," *Journal of the Arnold Arboretum*, vol. 11, no. 4, p. 185 (October 1930).

15. "An Appeal to Every Friend of American Horticulture," published by the Executive Committee appointed at a Conference of the Representatives of Horticulture and other societies, held June 15, 1920, in the American Museum of Natural History, New York City, p. 4.

16. Sargent, *Annual Reports . . . 1919–20*, p. 208.

17. Sargent, *Annual Reports . . . 1920–21*, p. 245.

18. Harold Morrison, "A Report on Inspection Work at the Arnold Arboretum, Jamaica Plain, Boston, Mass., July 1921," typed copy at AA.

19. *United States Department of Agriculture Yearbook, 1922* (Washington, D.C.: Government Printing Office, 1923), pp. 35–36.

20. *United States Department of Agriculture Inventory of Seeds and Plants Imported, April 1–May 31, 1920* (Washington, D.C.: Government Printing Office, 1923), nos. 50403–50435.

21. Cox, *Plant Hunting in China*, p. 208.

22. Fairchild, *The World Was My Garden*, p. 381.

23. Alvin K. Chock, "Joseph Rock," *Taxon*, vol. 12, no. 3, pp. 89–102 (April 1963).

24. Rock was hired in Hawaii by Ralph Sheldon Hosmer (1874–1963), later Professor of Forestry at Cornell University. Hosmer took great credit for Rock's turn to botany.

25. Horace Mann, Jr., produced the first flora of the Hawaiian Islands at the Gray Herbarium. His *Enumeration of Hawaiian Plants* was published in 1867.

26. Other botanists were skilled cartographers. Joseph Hooker, for example, had drawn excellent maps of Himalayan wilderness areas.

27. Sargent, *Annual Reports . . . 1924–25*, p. 217.

28. Cox, *Plant Hunting in China*, p. 197.

29. Joseph Rock to Sargent, December 22, 1924, AA.

30. Rock to Sargent, January 5, 1925, AA.

31. Rock to Sargent, August 20, 1926, AA.

32. Cox, *Plant Hunting in China*, p. 198.

33. Sargent to Rock, March 1, 1926, AA (typed copy).

34. Sargent to Rock, October 27, 1926, AA (typed copy).

35. Sargent to Rock, December 2, 1926, AA (typed copy).

11. Crataegus: A Thorny Problem

1. W. H. Camp, "Ecological Problems and Species Concepts in Crataegus," *Ecology*, 23:368 (July 1942).

2. One botanist, B. Semek, collected branches of *Crataegus* in the belief that he could see evolution from year to year on the same plant.

3. Sargent to Thiselton-Dyer, August 21, 1891, KEW.

4. Charles S. Sargent, *The Silva of North America* (Boston: Houghton Mifflin, 1891–1902), 4:85.

5. Sargent, *Silva*, 13:31.

6. Charles S. Sargent, "New or Little Known North American Trees, II," *Botanical Gazette*, 31:1–16 (January 1901).

7. Charles S. Sargent, "Note on Crataegus in the Champlain Valley," *Rhodora* 3:21–31 (February 1901).

8. John G. Jack, "The Arnold Arboretum: Some Personal Notes," *Biologia II, an International Year-Book*, Chronica Botanica, vol. 12, nos. 4/6 (1951), p. 196.

9. Sargent, *Silva*, 13:31.

10. *Gardeners' Chronicle*, January 17, 1903, p. 40.

11. *Journal of Botany*, 41:110 (1903).

12. Charles E. Bessey, *Science*, 15:795 (May 16, 1902).

13. William Trelease, "A Biographical Memoir of Charles Sprague Sargent," *National Academy of Sciences*, 12:256 (1929).

14. Ernest J. Palmer, "The Crataegus Problem," *Journal of the Arnold Arboretum*, vol. 13, no. 3, p. 343 (October 1932).

15. Bessey, *Science*, p. 795.

16. Sargent to Sir David Prain, January 1, 1917, AA (carbon copy).

17. C. D. Beadle, "Studies in Crataegus," *Botanical Gazette*, 28:405 (December 1899).

18. Sargent to M. S. Baxter, May 1, 1906, AA (carbon copy).

19. Beadle, "Studies in Crataegus," pp. 405–406.

20. Charles S. Sargent, "The Genus *Crataegus* in North America," *Journal of Botany*, 47:289–290 (1907).

21. Jack, "The Arnold Arboretum: Some Personal Notes," p. 196.

22. Camp, "Ecological Problems and Species Concepts," p. 368.

23. Åke Gustafsson, "Apomixis in Higher Plants," Lunds Universitets Årsskrift, N.F. Ard. 2, Bot. 42, Nr. 3, pp. 3–4 (1946).

24. Torrey, Gray, et al., describing Crataegus from dried material, did not have to cope with this perplexing knowledge. Given the same data as Sargent had, complete with misleading limitations, they, too, might have had problems.

25. Harry B. Brown, "The genus Crataegus, with some theories concerning the origin of its species," Bulletin of the Torrey Botanical Club, 37:251–260 (January 1910).

26. Palmer, "The Crataegus Problem," p. 349.

27. L. M. Standish, "What Is Happening to the Hawthorns?" Journal of Heredity, 7:266–278 (1916).

28. Albert E. Longley, "Cytological Studies in the Genus Crataegus," American Journal of Botany, 11:295–317 (1924).

29. Ibid., p. 313.

30. Charles S. Sargent, "Notes on Crataegus," Journal of the Arnold Arboretum, 6:1–5 (1925).

31. Palmer, "The Crataegus Problem," pp. 344, 357.

12. Giving Out Advice

1. Massachusetts Horticultural Society Yearbook, 1927, p. 69.

2. A. E. Benson, History of the Massachusetts Society for Promoting Agriculture, 1892–1942 (Boston: Meador, 1942), 2:9.

3. Sargent to Gray, December 15, 1884, GH.

4. Benson, History of the Massachusetts Society for Promoting Agriculture, 2:45.

5. J. Horace McFarland to Sargent, September 22, 1920, AA.

6. Sargent to Mrs. Francis King, September 18, 1920, AA (Xerox copy).

7. Benson, History of the Massachusetts Society for Promoting Agriculture, 2:64.

8. Charles S. Sargent and F. L. Olmsted, "Letter to Charles H. Dalton, Brookline, Mass., November 29, 1880," (Brookline, 1880).

9. Charles S. Sargent, "The Trees of Commonwealth Avenue, Boston" (Boston, 1909), pp. 6, 8.

10. Elswyth Thane, Mount Vernon: The Legacy (Philadelphia and New York: J. B. Lippincott, 1967), p. 200. I have quoted Sargent's letters from Mount Vernon, but have not seen the originals myself. I must acknowledge my gratitude to Miss Thane for illuminating this segment of Sargent's work for me.

11. Ibid., p. 202.

12. Ibid., p. 208.

13. Margaret Deland to John G. Jack, October 4, 1938, AA.

13. *Looking Backward and Forward*

1. Gladys Brooks, *Boston and Return* (New York: Atheneum, 1962), p. 82–84.
2. Mary S. Potter, "Silhouettes: My Mother—My Father," *Spur Magazine* (undated reprint), p. 3.
3. *Ibid.*, pp. 3–4.
4. Elswyth Thane, *Mount Vernon: The Legacy* (Philadelphia and New York: J. B. Lippincott, 1967), p. 200.
5. Emma Worcester Sargent, *Epes Sargent of Gloucester and His Descendants*, with biographical notes by Charles Sprague Sargent (Boston: Houghton Mifflin, 1923), p. 87.
6. Joseph E. Chamberlin, *Boston Evening Transcript*, Book Section, February 16, 1924.
7. Sargent to Reginald Cocks, March 28, 1918, AA (carbon copy).
8. Bishop Lawrence, *Boston Evening Transcript*, August 16, 1919.
9. Sargent to C. Hutchinson, August 21, 1919, AA.
10. Sargent to Joseph Hers; Sargent to Alice Eastwood, August 17, 1919, AA (carbon copies).
11. The first article of the 1927 volume appeared a few weeks after Sargent's death and bore Wilson's initials.
12. For about six years, Palmer's salary was paid in part by the Arboretum and in part by the Missouri Botanical Garden, and he distributed his collections accordingly. The Missouri institution was then interested in doing a flora of the Southwest, but, about 1919, abandoned the project and Palmer; from that time on the Arboretum paid his entire salary. He joined the Arnold Arboretum as an official staff member in 1921.
13. Sargent, *Annual Reports . . . 1873–74*, Appendix A.
14. Charles S. Sargent, "The First Fifty Years of the Arnold Arboretum," *Journal of the Arnold Arboretum*, vol. 3, no. 3, pp. 168–169 (1922).
15. Charles S. Sargent, "Arboretum," *Standard Cyclopedia of Horticulture*, ed. L. H. Bailey (New York: Macmillan, 1914), 1:352, 356.
16. Jack, "The Arnold Arboretum: Some Personal Notes," pp. 198–199.
17. Sargent, "The First Fifty Years of the Arnold Arboretum," p. 171.
18. Nathaniel Lord Britton to Addison Brown, December 5, 1896, AA.
19. John Merle Coulter, "The Social, Educational and Scientific Value of Botanic Gardens," *Science*, n.s. vol. 14, no. 1174, p. 643 (June 29, 1917).

20. "The Arnold Arboretum and Its Future" (Jamaica Plain, Mass.: Harvard University, 1927), p. 33.

21. Sargent, *Annual Reports . . . 1922–23*, pp. 231–232.

22. Sargent to C. Hutchinson, November 16, 1922, AA.

23. Katherine Bunker to Stephanne Sutton, Demember 8, 1966, AA.

24. Lowell died February 4, 1927, while vacationing in Madiera. Thus Sargent outlived another member of the younger generation.

25. Potter, "Silhouettes," p. 4.

26. Wilson to Rock, April 11, 1927, AA.

27. William Trelease, "A Biographical Memoir of Charles Sprague Sargent," *National Academy of Sciences*, 12:247–248 (1929).

14. Epilogue

1. Wilson to Rock, April 1, 1927, AA.

2. C. T. White to Sir Arthur Hill, March 16, 1928, KEW.

3. Alfred Rehder to Sir Arthur Hill, May 4, 1927, KEW.

4. Lowell to Sir Arthur Hill, May 28, 1927, KEW.

5. *Annual Reports . . . 1926–27*, p. 22.

6. Wilson to Rock, June 15, 1927, AA.

Index

324–325; postwar, 325–328; Sargent surveys in 1922, 330–333; Sargent plans for future, 333–335; after Sargent, 344–348

    plant expeditions in Orient: 197–275 *passim;* Wilson (1907), 232–239; Wilson (1909), 244–248; Purdom (1908), 241–244; Rock (1924), 269–275

    finances: 35, 134, 178–181, 324–325, 338–339; Massachusetts Society for Promoting Agriculture, 302–303

    plantings: 68–73, 263–266; *Crataegus,* 288–289

    herbarium and library: 64, 332; building, 134–136; Jesup woods, 119–120

Asa Gray professorship, 173

Ashe, William W., and *Crataegus,* 282, 283, 284, 286, 293, 294, 295, 296, 298

Atkins, Edward F., wills Cuban gardens to Harvard, 334

Bailey, Liberty H.: Chinese collections, 259; names *Rubus* species, 295–296; mentioned, 133, 327, 333

Baird, Spencer, asks Sargent to prepare *Silva,* 144

Balfour, Sir Isaac Bayley, 240, 245

Banks, Gen. Nathaniel P., 10–11

Bartram, John, garden, 41–42

Bary, Anton de, 28

Beadle, Chauncey, and *Crataegus,* 282, 283, 284, 286, 288, 293, 294, 295, 296, 298

Bebb, Michael, botanizes for Census, 84

Beebe, Lucius, 182

Bell, Robert, botanizes for Census, 84

Bentham, George, 23, 38, 128

Bernhardi, John J., herbarium, 335

Bernice P. Bishop Museum (Hawaii), sponsors Rock, 268

Bessey, Charles E., attacks species namers, 284–285, 286–287

Bickmore, Albert S., 105, 106, 109

Biltmore Arboretum, *Crataegus* at, 288

Birmingham Botanical Gardens, Wilson at, 209

Blake, Arthur, 134

Boston, city of: acquires Arboretum, 62–63; constructs Arboretum roads, 70–71; financial investment in Arboretum, 176–177; and Commonwealth Ave. trees, 307–310

    City Council: and Arboretum, 58–63

    Park Commission: and Arboretum, 58–59; and Commonwealth Ave. trees, 307, 308, 309, 310

    parks: Olmsted's plans for, 53

Boston & Albany Railroad, 4, 136

Botanic Garden, Harvard, *see* Harvard Botanic Garden

Botanic gardens, 41–42, 335–337

Botany: at Harvard, 130, 171–176, 345–346, 347; in U.S., 133–134

Bowditch, James, 5

Boxer Rebellion, troubles Wilson, 210–212, 216

Bradley, Abby A., 181, 325

Bradley, William L., 181

Bradley Bibliography, 181, 325

Brainerd, Ezra, and *Crataegus,* 293, 294, 296

Brandegee, T. S., 48, 93, 101, 102

Bretschneider, Emil, 186, 197, 202, 223–224, 244

Brewer, William H.: 1870 Census, 79, 80, 85; National Academy forestry commission, 159–162; mentioned, 28

Britton, Nathaniel L.: praises *Silva,* 151; and New York Botanical Garden, 335; mentioned, 133

Brooks, Gladys Rice, 315

Brooks, Mary, 4

Brooks, Peter C., 4

Brooks, Peter C., Jr., 4

Brown, Harry, and *Crataegus,* 293

Brown, Robert, 23

Index

Index

Dana, James D., and Gray's reputation, 129
Dana, Paul, 94
Darwin, Charles: *Origin of Species*, 9, 25; Gray and, 23–26; effect of theories on botany, 38–39; mentioned, 128, 198
Darwinism, 9, 23–26, 38–39, 287
David, Père Jean P. A., collects in China, 200, 235
Davidia involucrata, see Dove Tree
Davidson, Dr., 247
Dawson, G. M., botanizes for Census, 84
Dawson, Jackson: propagator at Arboretum, 65–66; low pay, 179, 180; meets Wilson, 210; death, 323; mentioned, 70, 126, 136, 240, 241, 300
Decaisne, Joseph: Sargent meets, 47; mentioned, 23, 128
Delavay, Père Jean M., collects in China, 200
Dill, S. D., and Jesup collection, 111, 114–115, 146
Division of Forestry (U.S. Department of Agriculture): Pinchot heads, 169; mentioned, 153, 155
Dixwell, John J., 30, 31, 34
Dove Tree: discovery, 200; Veitch interest in, 208–209; Henry directs Wilson to, 214; Wilson finds, 215–217; popularity of, 222
Downing, Andrew Jackson: influence on landscaping tastes, 13–15; mentioned, 12, 18, 30, 52, 69
Douglas, David, 86, 87
Douglas, Robert, botanizes for Census, 83
Dunbar, John, and *Crataegus*, 293, 294
Dupree, A. Hunter, 36
Dutch elm disease, 310

Eastwood, Alice, 323, 329, 330
Eaton, Daniel C., 65
Eggleston, W. W., and *Crataegus*, 293, 294, 296
Elgin Botanic Garden, 42
Eliot, Charles: and Arnold legacy, 34; opinion of Sargent, 45; Sargent defies, 51–52; objects to Arboretum alliance with Boston, 53, 55, 56, 57; character, 55; and Boston City Council, 60, 61, 62; achievements of, 175; appeals for Arboretum funds, 176–178, 179; mentioned, 26, 27, 28, 29, 31, 33, 73, 124, 190, 194
Eliot, Charles, Jr., landscape gardener, 178
Elm trees, on Commonwealth Ave. (Boston), 308–310
Elwes, H. J., 225, 226
Emerson, George B.: and Arnold legacy, 31, 32, 33, 34; and forestry, 80; mentioned, 30, 54
Endicott, William C., 324
Engelmann, Dora (Mrs. George), death, 82
Engelmann, George: biographical sketch, 47–48; Sargent enlists aid for Census, 81–83; Census trip, 85–88; character, 87–88; death, 121–123, 125; Sargent saves letters of, 188; and *Crataegus*, 281–282; herbarium, 335; mentioned, 17, 38, 94, 108, 128, 319

Fairchild, David, 233, 253, 255, 257, 260, 266, 307
Farlow, W. G.: relations with Sargent, 44–45; and *Silva*, 152; mentioned, 27, 28, 39, 130, 174, 175
Farquhar Nurseries (Boston), 232, 243, 245
Farrand, Beatrix Jones, 138, 315
Farrer, Reginald, collects in China, 267
Faull, J. H., 347
Faxon, Charles E.: as Arboretum curator and artist, 65–66; drawings for Jesup collection, 111, 115; *Silva* artwork, 145, 148, 150–151; West Indian trip with Sargent, 146–147; loyalty to Sargent, 180, 189; and *Crataegus*, 283, 289; death, 323; mentioned, 70, 136

Index

Index

Hague, Arnold: and National Academy forestry commission, 159, 161, 162
Hall, Dr. George, sends Japanese plants, 199–200
Hancock, John, 301
Harbison, Thomas G., botanizes for Sargent, 325, 329
Harrison, Benjamin, 153
Harvard University: Sargent attends, 8–10; botany, after Gray's death, 130, 171–176, 345–346, 347; Museum of Comparative Zoology, 269; trees in Yard, 303; during World War I, 323–324
  Arboretum: Arnold trust agreement, 34–35; city of Boston agreement, 62–63
  Botanic Garden: Sargent appointed Director, 28–29; genesis, 42; under Sargent, 43–46; under Goodale, 171–173; and Mass. Society for Promoting Agriculture, 301, 302, 303; mentioned, 22, 24, 26, 32, 64, 185
  Botanical Museum: and Goodale, 130, 172–173; and Ames, 346
Hawthorns, see Crataegus
Henry, Augustine: collects in China, 207–209, 210, 211, 223–224; aids Wilson, 213–215; Trees of Great Britain and Ireland, 226; mentioned, 216, 221, 231
Herbarium, Arnold Arboretum, see Arnold Arboretum, herbarium
Hers, Joseph, collects in China, 265–266, 323
Hetch Hetchy Valley, 304, 305
Hill, Sir Arthur, 345
Holm Lea (Sargent estate, Brookline, Mass.): Downing praises neighborhood, 13; Sargent takes charge of, 17; Arboretum offices, 64, 134; described by Muir, 157–158; fire at, 163; Kurume azaleas at, 258; entertaining at, 302, 314–315; domestic life at, 316–317; closed to public, 322; mentioned,

6, 8, 11–12, 18, 19, 21, 29, 70, 122, 123
Hooker, Sir Joseph: Sargent meets, 47; in retirement, 128; protects Gray's reputation, 129–130; Sargent saves letters of, 188; Sargent visits, 226; mentioned, 25, 54, 57, 69, 80, 88, 97, 106, 149, 150
Horticultural Hall (Boston), Sargent advises on, 301
Horticultural Society of London, 199, 224
Horticulture: European, 12, 13; in U.S. gardens, 12; American, in nineteenth century, 17, 40–41; Garden and Forest, 132–133; at World Columbian Exposition, 138–140; at Arboretum, 185–186; at Holm Lea, 316; in early twentieth century, 336–337
Hosack, David, 42
Hough, Franklin B.: and Division of Forestry, 80; and Adirondacks, 97, 98, 99, 103
Hoyt, Elizabeth, 315
Hunnewell, Henry S., 324, 334
Hunnewell, Horatio H.: and horticulture, 12, 14–15; aids Gray, 36; finances Arboretum building, 134–135; mentioned, 17, 19, 29, 46, 54, 124, 141, 300
Hunnewell estate (Wellesley, Mass.), 15–16
Huntington, Collis P., 116, 117
Hutchinson, C. L., 339

Imperial Institute (London), Wilson accepts appointment at, 222

Jack, John G.: on Arboretum staff, 136–137; loyalty to Sargent, 180; trip to Japan, Korea, and China, 228–229; and Crataegus, 283, 289, 291; and Atkins gardens, 334; mentioned, 66, 152, 155, 185, 189, 327, 328, 345
James, William, 175
Japan: Gray studies flora of, 38, 197–198; early plant collecting,

Index

376

Index

Index

Index

United States Government: aid to agriculture, 40; forestry, 78–81, 153–170; Sargent's opinion of, 193, 307; and national parks, 304–307

Department of Agriculture: Division of Forestry, 80, 153, 155, 169; plant quarantine, 260, 261, 263–266; sponsors Rock (1920), 268; mentioned, 233, 235, 253, 255

Sargent's Census survey: 80–92, 106, 107, 108, 143–145, 148, 153, 160, 299

Vanderbilt, Cornelius, 108
Vasey, George, 105, 144, 145
Vaux, Calvert, 52
Veitch, Sir Harry: first Wilson expedition, 208; second Wilson expedition, 218; Sargent visits, 226; shares expedition with Arboretum, 240; disappointed by Purdom, 243–244; mentioned, 206, 234
Veitch, James H.: meets Sargent in Japan, 204–205; volunteers for China, 206; mentioned, 223
Veitch Nurseries, see Royal Exotic Nursery
Villard, Henry, 93, 96

Wallace, Alfred Russel, 24
Wallace, Henry C., 265
Walsh, Sen. Thomas, 306
Ward, Frank K.: plant introductions, 262; mentioned, 267
Washington, George, 312. See also Mount Vernon
Washington, Martha, 312
Watson, Sereno: aids Gray, 27, 28; relations with Sargent, 44, 45; botanizes for Census, 84, 89; death, 130; and Crataegus, 285; salary, 302; mentioned, 39, 128, 202
Welles, Isabella, 14
Whitmore, William, 60–62
Willmott, Ellen, 231, 232, 289

Wilson, Annie, 209
Wilson, Ellen Ganderton (Mrs. Ernest H.), 230–231, 245, 246, 250, 252, 256
Wilson, Ernest H.: biographical sketch, 209; marriage, 217–218; appointed botanical assistant at Imperial Institute, 222; negotiates with Sargent, 229–232; at Arboretum, 249–251; Plantae Wilsonianae, 249, 250; A Naturalist in Western China, 250; troubled by World War I, 256–257; Harvard honors, 261; plant introductions evaluated, 261–263; meets Rock, 269; and Arboretum after Sargent, 244–247; death, 348; mentioned, 6, 8, 180, 181, 185, 186, 189, 324, 325, 327, 328, 342

Expeditions: China (1899), 209–217; troubled by Boxers, 210–212, 216; delayed in Indo-China, 211–213; meets Henry, 213–214; Dove Tree, 214–217; China (1903), 218–222; observes Chinese, 220; China (1907), 232–239; comments on politics, 238–239; instructs Purdom, 241; compared with Purdom, 242–244; China (1909), 244–248; injures leg, 247–248; Japan (1914), 252–254; Japan, Korea, Formosa (1917), 257–261; Africa, India, Australia, etc. (1920), 261
Wilson, Henry, 209
Wilson, Muriel P., 230, 245, 246, 252
Wodenethe (H. W. Sargent estate), 12–15, 16
World Columbian Exposition (1893), 138–140
World War I, and Arboretum, 254–257, 324–325
Wright, Charles, 199

Yellow Poppywort, Wilson seeks, 218–222
Yellowstone National Park, 304–306
Yosemite National Park, 304, 305

Index